T

ogy

THE TREE

by

J. Marvin Spiegelman

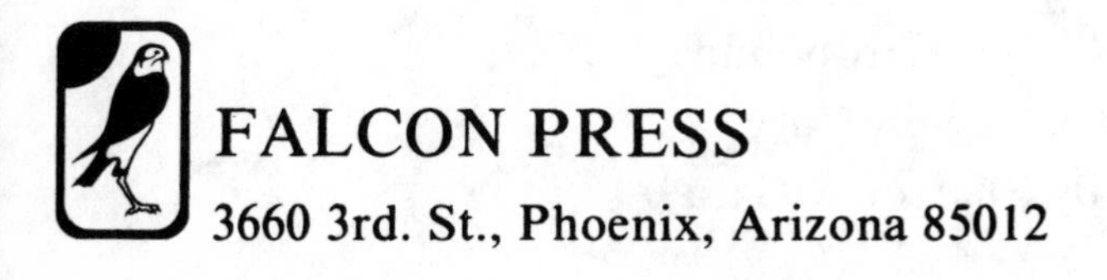
FALCON PRESS
3660 3rd. St., Phoenix, Arizona 85012

THIS BOOK IS DEDICATED TO
THOSE WHO MEET AT THE TREE

First Edition 1974
Second Printing 1982 By Falcon Press

Library Of Congress Card Number 74-81034
Previously Published By Phoenix House
ISBN 0-89031-008-4 Trade
ISBN 0-89031-021-1 Prebound

Printed In The United States Of America
ISBN 0-941404-03-X Hardbound
ISBN 0-941404-04-8 Soft Cover
Cover Design By Sharron & Sara

Contents

Introduction i

1 The Knight 1

2 The Arab 47

3 The "Ronin" 75

4 Julia, The Atheist-Communist 97

5 Sybilla, The Nymphomaniac 151

6 Maria, The Nun 183

7 The African 213

8 Maya, The Yogini 251

9 The Old Chinese Man 313

10 The Medium, Sophie-Sarah 381

11 Psalms 441

PSYCHO-MYTHOLOGY

A New Literary Genre

by

J. Marvin Spiegelman

"Active fantasy being the principal attribute of the artistic mentality, the artist is not merely *representer,* he is also a *creator,* hence essentially an *educator* since his works have the value of symbols that trace out the line of future development. Whether the actual social validity of the symbol is more general or more restricted depends upon the quality or vital capacity of the creative individuality."

C.G. Jung, *Psychological Types* (1, p.580 f)

With the term, "psycho-mythology," I wish to introduce a new literary genre which bears a familial resemblance to both science-fiction and the historical novel. In these forms, there is a peculiar kind of union of the opposites of fact and fiction. Science fiction starts with current scientific knowledge, makes reasonable extrapolations toward future discoveries, and fuses these with fantasy. Historical novels add romance, conjectured conversation and embellishment to what is known of recorded events. In both cases, the structure of "truth" and "reality" is enriched by imagination, which is psychological truth.

"Psycho-mythology" stands for a similar union of fact and imagination, but in this field there is a marriage of psychological knowledge with the type of fantasy that reaches the universal, archetypal, mythological level. I am not referring to the well-known psychological novel, which uses the insights of psychology to probe the depths of a particular personality. That form is closer to the genre of the detective story or the clinical case study, although it can reach heights of artistic excellence as, for example, in Dostoievsky's *Crime and Punishment.*

Rather than concerning itself with the motivations of an individual, psycho-mythology relates to the collective psyche and its' drama. Paradoxically, the perturbations of the modern man, occupied with his struggle for individuation, is both the source and core of it. The reason for this is that the invention or discovery of this genre came out of sixteen years of experience of C.G. Jung's "Active Imagination" (2).

Psycho-mythology is a literature in which an individual's fantasy transcends the personal level, reaching the collective unconscious. In addition, the work is consciously connected with either available religious or mythical material and is clearly intended as a work of art. With this definition, the genre is seen to straddle both what has been customarily called Active Imagination, as taught by Jung, and Art. In active imagination, the intention is a confrontation by the individual with the unconscious, with the aim of expanding his consciousness and fostering individuation and wholeness. In art, the intention is to produce an esthetically satisfying work, which may communicate some quality or experience to others, or may be for itself alone. In art, any development of consciousness or wholeness in the artist is largely incidental. Indeed, there are those who claim that the intrusion of psychological knowledge, aims, or attitude is hurtful to the art of the artist. For psycho-mythology, I shall claim, there is a fusion of the psychological need for growth of consciousness, with the artistic need of esthetics, communication, and for its' own sake.

Before I relate how I came to discover or create this genre, I would like to say a few more words about Jung and active imagination. As is well-known to all who have read Jung's wonderful and remarkable autobiograpy, *Memories, Dreams and Reflections* (3), the great psychologist discovered the method of confrontation with the unconscious after he had broken with Freud. At that time, he was isolated, did not know his direction, and was convinced that he had no personal myth at all. He began to play with his fantasy and with the figures who emerged in that play and from his dreams. He was the first to take the products of that play seriously and to relate to the dwellers of the unconscious as if they were as real as any Swiss Burgher that one might meet strolling the Limat in Zurich. He realized that these figures, though autonomous, were products of his own soul and he undertook a relationship with them.

In this process, Jung changed both the unconscious and himself. Greatly moved by this activity, which lasted several years in his late thirties, he made most of the discoveries which were to be developed during the remainder of his life. The importance of Active Imagination, therefore, was as central for Jung as was the focus upon dreams. Yet he was reluctant to publish very much on this topic. He did produce some work in this area (1,2) and others are now following upon this beginning (6).

Jung's reluctance in publishing on the topic of Active Imagination was strange since he thought this method would ultimately free an individual from dependence upon any analyst at all! He says this beautifully in his Letters (4, pp. 458-461). He recognized that the work of Active Imagination contained both the need for Understanding (which was the effort to raise consciousness) and the Aesthetic (for beautiful and satisfying expression). In his earliest work on the topic (2), he clearly perceived that the method would lead now one way and now the other, yet he was adamant in asserting that this material was surely not art, but had a psychological aim.

The reason for Jung's assertion, in my opinion, comes from his experience of the female personage (whether a fantasy "anima" person or a concrete, living one) mentioned in his autobiography (3). That lady, when shown the beautiful paintings and writings of the artist-poet that Jung was, said that he should be and was an artist. Jung hotly denied this, saying that he was a scientist! I think that Jung, struggling to keep his psychological discoveries in the realm of science, had to lean over backwards and even sacrifice the true artistic value of some of what he produced. Those who have seen some of the paintings of the Red Book in the film of Jung, or read the poetry of his "Sermons to the Dead" (5), already know his artistic capacity. Furthermore, those of us who follow Jung appreciate the scientific value of his discoveries, no longer need to keep the method of Active Imagination strictly in the psychological work-basket, and can allow its' expansion in other ways.

Another hindrance to Active Imagination becoming better known lies not with Jung alone, but also with some of his followers. There are those who are fearful of speaking about it, believing it to be a tool of the second half of life alone, and a dangerous one at that, properly limited to those who are supervised in analysis (6). I am less fearful, having discovered that the technique is difficult for most people to embark upon, quite demanding of discipline and commitment to stay with, thus outside the grasp of the merely dilettante. As for possible danger, the psyche seems to have its' natural protections of boredom, fear, skepticism, or inflation, all of which dissuade the non-devoted. I would add that from the artistic standpoint, probably even fewer of those who embark upon this work will produce material which, as Jung has said, will "communicate with the past and with the future, as well as with contemporaries" (1, pp. 574 f).

A further consideration of Active Imagination can be found in the references. At this point, I wish to tell the story of how I happened upon "psycho-mythology." But, before I do, I feel the necessity of mentioning other available examples of the field. Strictly speaking, there are none, since the method has grown out of Jung's discoveries and his psychology, so that only the future will produce such works of art. Yet there are forerunners, I think, such as Goethe's *Faust,* or Thomas Mann's *Holy Sinner,* to mention only very great ones. These works, one can see, meet the definition of carrying religious-mythological significance, are psychologically insightful, reach the collective psyche, as well as intending artistic expression. They also carry both individual and collective significance simultaneously. Perhaps you can think of other examples.

Now to the story of my stories. On December 28, 1966, I was seated at my desk in my office, reflecting upon the preceding year's events, which had been painful, momentous and shattering for me. During that year, I had found it necessary to resign from my local professional analytic society and to break off some relationships which had proved to be illusory. That day, I was engaged in active imagination, which had been my custom at least twice a week for many years. I had started this process just a few months after beginning my own analysis in 1950 and had continued with it, with only a two year interruption during military service, ever since. It had proved to be especially valuable when I ceased working with any analyst at all some three years previous.

The particular fantasy I had been working on for some months involved being in a cave with an old man, a woman and her daughter, and a young boy with dark eyes who did not speak. I was talking with the group when suddenly a huge Knight, wearing black armor with a golden sun emblazoned on his breastplate, broke in, abducted the mother and daughter, riding away on his horse. I recognized this Knight from a dream I had had some six months earlier. In that dream, which took place after I resigned from the professional society, this Knight appeared and said to me that he had been at my side for a long time, but that now we no longer had a cause to serve. I understood him to mean the collective Jungian cause, as it worked as an institution in the world. I was aware, also, that the Knight was representative of my own inner "hero" figure, going back to early childhood. At the age of three, for example, I had a powerful experience of sitting on my tricycle and feeling the power of God high above and warming me from the sun, and also located inwardly, as an equal power, at my chest.

Now this dream hero appeared in earnest and was carrying off two important feminine figures. I pursued him, continuing my fantasy, and asked him why he did that and what he wanted. The Knight replied that he abducted those ladies in order to get my full attention and that he had some stories to tell. Would I be interested in hearing them, he wondered? He also hinted that there were other people there who had tales to tell, should I be inclined to take the time to hear them and work with them. He suggested that these stories were important for others to hear, as well as for myself. Excitedly, but somewhat skeptically, I agreed to attend to these tales, provided the work could be kept within the periods I had available for such activity. After all, I had patients, family, and other demands upon my time. He agreed, and then began a work which was to take most of two days per week for several years. The Knight's tale was followed by that of a Moslem Arab, a Japanese Buddhist Ronin, and then by three women: Julia, the Atheist-Communist, Sybilla, the Nymphomaniac, and Maria, the Nun. Thereafter came stories by the African, which was alchemical in nature, Maya, the Yogini who performed a kind of Kundalini Yoga, the tale of the Old Chinese Man who struggled with the spirit of the *I Ching,* and finally, the Medium, a woman named Sophie-Sarah who embraced Kaballah.

These ten people each told a story of their own individuation, and each represented a different religion or syncretism, or some meditative, consciousness-seeking activity. Each was rather unorthodox, yet all found themselves at the Tree of Life. Altogether, their tales constituted what came to be called *The Tree.*

This series, some six hundred typewritten pages in length, was barely completed when there appeared another person, who called himself the Son of the Knight. This chap pursued a different series of myths, and this second book took up his quest, and also that of a Mother and Daughter in a cave, a part of the Grail legend involving King Arthur, Lancelot, and Queen Guinevere. That four-hundred page book was called, *The Quest.*

Hardly had that story ended, when another series began, led by the Grandson of the Knight. This time the tales had to do with the problems of love, ending up with a detailed union of Greek mythology with Kundalini Yoga and Kabbalah. This book, some eight hundred pages in length, was called, *The Love.* In all, the trilogy took about six years to complete.

I must add that I was no mere amanuensis to these story-tellers. I often found myself not only relating their tales, but also living them and identifying with them as each of them approached the Gods. I worked and learned with them, although my true ego place seems to be somewhere else, more like the present narrator, but also as multiple and various as all of these, my deep inner friends. It remains for our mutual work to go out to the world and walk among men. "Let each know where the other is," was the message to the Knight, and so say I, too.

REFERENCES

1. Jung, C.G. *Psychological Types.* Routledge and Kegan Paul, London, 1923. Also Collected Works, Vol. 6.
2. Jung, C.G. *The Transcendant Function,* orig. 1916, published in Collected Works, Vol. 8.
3. Jung, C.G. *Memories, Dream, Reflections.* Pantheon Books, New York, 1961.
4. Jung, C.G. *Letters,* Vol. 1: 1906-1950. Princeton University Press, 1973.
5. Jung, C.G. *VII Sermones ad Mortuos.* Stuart and Watkins, London, 1961, Orig. 1925.
6. Weaver, Rix. *The Old Wise Woman, a Study of Active Imagination.* G.P. Putnam's Sons, New York 1973.

THE KNIGHT

ERRATA: TREE

Page Line

ii " 22 Delete apostrophe after "its"
iii " 9 to the art "or" artist.
iii " 12 Delete apostrophe after "its"
iv " 29 Delete apostrophe after "its"
v " 8 Delete apostrophe after "its"
vii " 16 "Kabbalah"
7 " 9 from bottom: on enought delete "t"
18 " 12 "lightning"
49 " 2 "Almighty"
67 " 4 from bottom: "Mahabharata"
84 " 5 close quotes after master?
91 " between line 5 & 6 insert "V"
111 " 20 omit "i" in beneficiently
129 " 4 from bottom: my to "me"
136 " 11 "superficial"
190 " 16 is to "in"
224 " 8 from bottom: "Abbaba"
253 " 22 insert after them, "they gave me their blessing"
271 " 6 "food" instead of good.
314 " 5 from bottom: "helpmate" instead of helpmeet
316 " 8 from bottom: "helpmate" instead of helpmeet
345 " 1 from bottom: "double quotes"
345 " 3 from bottom: "single quotes beginning and end"
346 " 15 "for thou" not thee--"art" instead of are
390 " 7 "and" instead of had
399 " 2 from bottom: reverse single quote
405 " 11 from bottom: single quotes around statute
413 " 1 from bottom: "Kabbalah"
420 " 10 from bottom: "Kabbalah"

THE KNIGHT

I

Once there was a vicious King who lived in a hollow shell in the bottom of the Sea. He was hidden from sight, but because of his evil emanations, he was able to create havoc in the world just by means of his dark thoughts and ill feelings. He had been there for centuries, causing great pain to people, but since no one knew where to find him, they could not understand the cause of their misery and blamed their suffering on "the times", the weather, their leaders, and, of course, their neighbors.

At the time my story begins, I was a young Knight, naive and foolhardy. I had already had adventures aplenty, more with women, perhaps, than battles with other Knights, and I was far from serious. Pleasure was my aim.

One day, however, as I was walking peacefully in the forest, leading my horse to drink at a stream, there appeared before me an Angel of God. It was an astounding thing, and shocking, but just as real as this moment. The Angel was not loving and gentle with me. He was stern and firm.

"Knight," he said, "you have sought after adventure and pleasure. That is all right for a young man, but something more must be made of your life now. It has been decreed that you be sent to the vicious King at the bottom of the Sea, and that you reform him or kill him, as you see fit. There is to be no reward for this. Your only recompense is that you do something more with your life than you have thus far." With that the Angel vanished. He did not ask me if I agreed to take on this task. Nor did he direct me as to how I was to proceed.

I sat down by the stream and stroked the flanks of my horse, wondering at what had happened. I knew that I was no saint, but I did not think that I was so different from other knights as to merit either the particular censure or the special task. As I sat there musing about this event, I noticed that my horse pricked up his ears and started to tremble. I had not noticed how he had reacted to the appearance of the Angel, but now he seemed to know something that I did not. He pranced about impatiently, as if eager to be off. Thinking that perhaps the Angel was sending his messages through my horse to me, I got on my horse's back, let the reins hang loose, and allowed him to go where he would.

At once, he bounded off in a northerly direction, as if he knew exactly where he was going. We rode all day, stopping only for water. Towards evening, we came to the Sea—I know not which—and there the horse halted. I dismounted, tired and wet with perspiration. I sat quietly, apprehensive at what might happen to me. This was no ordinary adventure I knew, and I was no more accustomed to being guided by my horse than I was to the appearance of angels. I looked at my charger and was surprised to see him calm and hardly tired. He grazed peacefully, just as if this were an ordinary day.

I sat and waited. I watched my horse to see if other guidance would be forthcoming, but he behaved just as he had that morning, before the Angel appeared. I looked out over the Sea and saw nothing. Soon it grew dark and cold. I wrapped my blanket around me, with the thought that if the Angel had some desire of me, he would come in his own time and not at my behest. I made a fire and ate what little food I had left. Soon I was lost in dreams—not of adventure, but of a joyous and peaceful life in a pleasant castle with lovely maidens and friends. While enjoying this fantasy, however, I again saw the stern face of the Angel, appearing now in a cloud. He simply shook his head back and forth, as if to say, as he had done that morning, that this life of pleasure and ease was not to be for me. Again, no direction, only a firm "No."

I awakened in the morning, refreshed, though dampened in spirit. I found some fruit and ate thoughtfully. I waited for a sign, but nothing happened. I waited in the heat of the day and the silence of the afternoon. No sign. I was beginning to feel the fool. What a silly fellow I had been, thought I, to let a vision lead me and to put myself under the guidance of a horse! I wondered if it would not be best to quietly retrace my steps and never tell anyone about this peculiar experience. But something made me stay on. Again night fell, and again nothing happened. And so it was the next day and the next. Not until seven days had elapsed, by which time I was tired, irritated, disgruntled, and hungry, did the Angel appear again.

This time, just at sunset, he came walking out of the water and stopped some twenty paces from me. He spoke in a clear, cool voice, not quite as stern as before, but still unloving. "Knight," he said, "you have waited as instructed." (Instructed, thought I, by whom? I waited because I did not know what else to do.) "You are willful and arrogant and I do not know why you have been chosen for this task. But it is not in my province to choose, only to convey. Tomorrow morning you will walk out into the water with your horse. You must trust him to lead you in your task." Thus speaking, the Angel disappeared. I must admit that it was a relief to finally have some indication that my first vision wasn't the last. If this were an aberration, at least it was consistent. I minded madness less than being a fool in those days.

The next morning I awakened early, and made ready to do as the Angel commanded. I mounted my charger and rode into the Sea. It was not so easy, since the waves pushed us back. We clung to the floor of the Sea, however, and I fought against my natural impulse to swim. Following instructions, I gripped the mane and neck of my horse and held my breath as long as I could. I felt my lungs would collapse, was about to gasp for air and drown in water when I lost consciousness.

Some time passed, I know not how long. When I awakened, I was at the bottom of the Sea, inside a hollow shell. I found that I could breath naturally. With me was my horse. The shell was about as large as an ordinary room and had a faint glow in it—a blue light from an unknown source. The shell was barren, like a monk's cell or a cave, but a few paces away was the figure of a man. He was old and bearded. He wore a crown. Here, I thought, was the vicious King that I was sent to reform or kill.

The King looked at me kindly. He waited until I had fully recovered my senses, then spoke to me. His voice was gentle, yet strong.

"I suppose, Knight," he said, "you have been sent here either to kill me or reform me." I was astonished at this and wondered if this creature were so wily as to know all that transpired out on the land. I reflected that since he could cause so much harm, he must, indeed, know a great deal. I felt that I must be wary of him, but his kindness, warmth, and strength disarmed me. Since he knew so much anyway, I concluded, I decided to be open and honest with him. I therefore nodded my head "Yes" in answer to his remark. He sighed at this and seemed to vanish inside himself, lost with his thoughts. I waited respectfully, saying nothing, and soon he began to speak, slowly and sadly.

"It has been so for centuries. Young, brave knights are sent to kill me or reform me. I seek not war, nor violence. I seek only to live in peace. I was once a great King in the world, governed as best I could, and, I think, led a happy kingdom. We tried to live in justice and love. We cared for one another. Each person struggled to develop his own soul, and worked toward the mutuality of being brothers and sisters. Our land flourished. We had pain and sadness, as well as joy, but somehow we grew in understanding and in love. But then it happened that a lasting sadness came over our land. There was bickering and anger. There was dastardy and greed. There was hatred. Of course, we had always had these things, which were painful to us, but now they exceeded our endurance. Worst of all, there was great injustice of each toward each. We could not understand it. We asked our wise men and our wise women, but none could explain.

"Finally, an Angel of the Lord appeared. He appeared before all of us so that all could see, and he spoke sternly. He said that the ravages of the land were all to be laid at my door. He said that I was ambitious and full of pride. He said, even, that I wanted to be God. The people and I were shocked at these accusations and I shook my head in disbelief. The Angel said that the only thing that would remedy the situation would be for me to sacrifice my son, and for me to be banished into a nether world where I would no longer cause havoc to the people. Now, I did not mind being banished, since I was, by nature, a rather retiring man, and I was certainly prepared to give up my rulership if it was the source of such grief and destruction to the people. But my son I loved dearly. He seemed wiser and more full of joy than myself. He seemed to be the natural heir to what I had achieved and would fulfill our hopes more than any of us could. To sacrifice him seemed sore and painful. There seemed no way out, however. The Angel was stern and implacable.

"My son was taken from me and crucified and I have been banished here, at the bottom of the Sea. I can neither die nor live, but remain here, alone with my thoughts and my speculations. The sorrow of my son's sacrifice had diminished with the years—it is many centuries now. But I am not allowed to remain in peace. Every century or so, a Knight like yourself is sent to reform me or kill me. It seems as if the world continues in its grief and agony and inequality, and blame for this is laid at my doorstep. For I, it seems, am the vicious King who is the cause of the darkness. I do not understand it. I have no ill will, desire no power, and certainly do not wish to cause the people trouble, but I am thought to be the Devil, it seems. I am neither God nor Devil, but simply a human King who has been allowed to neither live nor die. Many are the Knights who have been sent to kill me or reform me. They have been of all nations and creeds and temperaments. I have been very willing to die, but none has been able to kill me. Either they have not wanted to, once hearing my story, or their attempts have been in vain. The reforms that they have proposed have all sounded hollow to me—not because I have anything better to offer, but because their plans seemed arrogant and dominating, even when they were seeking the good. I have been unable to see any reform which offers more than we had when I was King: love, justice, mutuality, and a spirit of individual development. I do not assert it, I just fail to see anything better. . . . Well, now, do what you will with me."

I was dumbfounded by this story. Rather than wanting to kill this man, I loved him and wanted to serve him. Perhaps I was in the hands of the Devil, but somehow I preferred this man to anything of God that I had seen up until then.

I began to have strange, disquieting thoughts. Perhaps the Angel of God was the Devil and was leading us all to believe that this wise and kind King was causing the destruction that the Angel himself was causing. But could the Angel do this without the permission of God Himself? No! The next thought was too horrifying for me to consider. . . .

The King looked at me in a strange, lovingly wise, but sad, way. "I know what you are thinking," he continued. "Many other Knights have thought of it before. You are thinking that God, Himself, is the Devil!" I shuddered as he said it, and expected at any moment to be struck dead. "Those who have come to it," he continued, "have either killed themselves, run from me in horror and agony, or quickly returned to their lives, pretending that they have not thought it.

"I do not know the answer myself. But I, too, have concluded that God cannot bear to look at his own darkness and destructiveness. He finds it easier to see it in Man, his loftiest creation on earth."

After thus hearing the King, I sat down, my body becoming a limp, muscleless mass. I had never been a very religious person, but I was sensible enought to know that Man was not the author of creation and that whatever God was, His ways were inexplicable to man and not to be deeply reflected upon. Before the Angel had appeared to me, I had not given it much serious thought. But now, I was forced to confront the issue more deeply. I could not challenge the reality of what I had experienced with the Angel, nor could I disavow what I was experiencing with this most human, and yet divine, King. What was I to do? What was I to follow?

The King sat in silence. He had said his say, and I was not inclined to disturb him. I was certainly not going to kill him, but what was I going to do about the Angel? Indeed, how was I to get back at all? I concluded that I had to go back and face the Angel with what I had experienced. Better to be killed for my failure to do the Angel's will than to outrage this excellent creature. And how was I to get back? The way I came, I supposed: to follow and trust in the horse.

I embraced the King, softly bade him peace and goodbye, took a deep breath from the air in the shell, clasped my horse's neck, and let go of my own will. Again, in the water. Again, the stretched lungs until I fainted.

Some time later, I found myself on land. Not at the point of entrance into the water, but at the place in the forest where I had seen the Angel, many days before. Had I dreamed all this? If so, it was as real as anything that had happened in my life until that time. I was uncertain if the Angel would appear again, but I was prepared to face him.

I sat down and waited. I looked at my horse and found him calm and most ordinary as if he had not, indeed, led me into and out of the depths of the Sea. What was the divine guidance which took him out of himself? What was the meaning of this paradox? I was sent by an Angel to kill a benevolent being, instead learned something profound from him, and was now alive and ready to confront the Angel who sent me on such a horrible mission!

Once more I waited seven long days and seven long nights. This time, however, I looked after the thirst and hunger of my horse and myself. I ate the fruit of the trees, drank the water of the stream, killed and hungrily devoured a deer that mischanced to come near my camp. On the evening of the seventh day, the Angel appeared again. Now he emerged just above the trees, radiant and in a white robe. His beard was white and he continued to look firm, but not so stern as the first time and much more benevolent than the second. This, too, startled me. Where was the evil? Where was the pain? The Angel spoke:

"My son, you have done as you were told. That was not a failure on your part, but a necessary experience which you had to undergo. The King has spoken truly."

"But how can that be, O Angel of God? If the King has spoken truly, then you have lied. And how can the King be right, that God is not aware of his own destructiveness, if you are aware of it?"

"I have not lied, O Knight! Whom you saw at the bottom of the Sea was God, Himself! It is *He* who has forgotten his Godliness. It is *He* who was so ashamed of His power that He cut Himself off from it. It was *He* who so longed after becoming totally human and the brother of His creatures, that He rejected His power. And now it rules as madness in Heaven. The King, our Father, spoke truly of God not knowing of His darkness, and He was speaking of Himself. And I am that link, that piece of Him who is connected with both. But I can only do His bidding. I cannot bring Him to His senses. Were I to do so, His power would kill me, were He to want it or not. It is given to you, O Man, to bring this union about. It is given to you, if you survive, to let each know where the other is."

I sat quietly for a long time. My poor head was almost broken with this paradox. For this is what it was. Nothing less than that God Himself was split up in pieces and somehow needed Man, His creation, to bring Himself together. And this Angel, this divine messenger who linked with Man, he understood, but was powerless. What could Man do, who was far less powerful than an Angel, to bring the pieces together? If an Angel could be destroyed by the power, what would happen to poor Man? He would be burnt to a crisp, or driven mad! But now I saw why there was such confusion in the world: God was split in pieces. Man had to help God pull Himself together somehow. The new task of Creation was to be, indeed, a joint venture: Man and God as brothers and sisters, just as the King of the Sea had wished. But He, poor fellow, hadn't reckoned with His power!

What was I to do? How could I aid in this task? And why was I chosen? The answer came clearly. All and each of us, Everyman, had a piece of the divine spark and this was part of the plan for Salvation that God had spoken of long ago and, it seems, had forgotten. I understood what was meant by the stories of the past, when God walked with Man in peace and friendship. There was still the snake, the Devil-Son of God, who was disrupting and splitting and dividing, and God could not unite with him. So man had to unite himself within himself and, not only that, he had to help God do the same. Perhaps, at the End of Days, as the Ancients said, God would again be One, and Man would be One, too!

And that was the end of my first adventure.

II

Many years passed after I had completed the adventure which I have just described. I meditated about it often, but told no one about it. I was sure that I would either be scoffed at as a fool or madman, for everyone would be sure that all their troubles were a consequence of the vicious King at the bottom of the Sea. And who knows, maybe in a sense they would be right. A god who does not know his own power and quietly retreats from the world, letting that power wreak havoc without love, and without even being conscious of it, is, indeed, vicious in his ignorance. Still, I loved him and cared for him, and wondered how I could best serve him. I wondered too—for I had failed to ask him this question—if any other Knights had come to him, learned from him, and not committed suicide or forgotten their experience. Perhaps, somewhere I had a brother in spirit who was also puzzling about what to do.

The experience, however, changed my life. The issue was so great that all other adventures seemed paltry. I settled down, soon met a lovely woman and, in the course of things, we married and had three fine children—two girls and a boy. I tended my lands and my duties, but knew that one day I would be called upon again to serve in the task of re-uniting God with Himself. I strove to know myself as best I could and to unite the fragments of myself. It was a hard and painful task, but it was rewarding in itself. In time, a certain small fame came to me and I was able to help others come to more self-understanding.

It came to pass in my thirties, however, that I lusted after women once more. I had been a ladies' man in my early twenties, you may recall, but this had subsided after my experience of the Angel and King of the Sea, and I was happily married to a woman of great virtue and love, as well as understanding. This lust proved to be a peculiar one. It was not, as when I was a youth, that I wished to sleep with all the women in the world, but rather it was selective; the lust seemed to seek out just those women of some spirit, just those who were sore troubled in their knowledge and belief, and were pining away, without knowing it, for that God who was also at my back. I was sore troubled in my conscience for all this, for I was concerned lest I violate my marriage or myself. I was able to turn much of the passion to good use in the service of self-knowledge, both for myself and others, but there was always the additional part, which demonically would not be denied nor transformed.

One day, I walked again in the forest where I had had my encounter with the Angel, musing about my wickedness. I came to the spot and looked at it. A few years before, my faithful horse of my youth had died, after spending a peaceful old age, and I had buried him at the place where he had transcended himself and become both more of himself and his greatest self. For I had concluded that it was not just Man who had to aid in the task of divine transformation, but animals and plants, too. For they, too, carried the divine spark, did they not?

I looked at the grave and the simple stone I had erected thereon. It said, "To a faithful friend, from a faithful friend." I wondered about my fidelity, indeed. Had I really been faithful to this creature? Fidelity seemed to be a very questionable virtue with me.

As I looked, a mist collected over the stone. It was as if a certain essence emerged out of the stone itself, a soul-substance that gathered above it. It grew larger and larger, and glowed in the late afternoon dusk. Gradually the mist formed itself into a horse and rider. To my joy and astonishment, I recognized the outlines of my old trusted friend, with the Angel firmly seated upon his back.

"Greetings, O Knight," the Angel said. "It has been long since we have seen each other. But time is an illusion and, in the task of redemption, time is but a mist through which one walks to come to a clearer light. The mist you now see is more clear and real than the light by which you came to it."

I joyously ran forward to embrace both the horse and the Angel, but was stopped in my tracks just several yards away. The Angel spoke again: "Know, O Knight, that horse and rider are one. It was I, long ago, who led you from both above and below."

The Angel paused. I reflected that what he said did, indeed, make sense. I had been led by a heavenly spirit and by an earth spirit and they had, verily, brought me to my understanding in loyalty and safety.

"Yes, Angel," I said, "I now understand. My instinct has been my guide, through you, from above and from below, and I have trusted it—and you. But my instinct has also gotten me into terrible trouble, as you, who walk to and fro in heaven, on earth, and in the sea, must know."

"I know, O Knight," continued the Angel, "for it has been only through that pain and power that you have been able to experience in your bones what you only understood in your head. But now your tortures are coming to an end, and the next phase of your development is about to take place."

With that, the vision vanished. In its place, I saw a yellow flower growing at the base of the stone. I plucked it from the earth and held it tenderly in my hand. I sniffed its fragrance and was so overpowered by its scent that I fell to my knees.

As if intoxicated by the fragrance of that golden flower, I felt myself whirling through smoke and clouds. The next instant found me under the earth, but in a vast place which looked much like above the ground in a volcanic region. Instead of sky, however, there were only the hard walls and ceiling of earth. A suffused light pervaded the place, pale blue in color. As my eyes grew accustomed to the light, I made out the form of a person lying on sand, near a body of water. I walked over to it and saw, clearly, a hag of a woman. She was disheveled, had old and torn clothes, and a face that was marred by ugliness. A stench was about her which was hellish. From all that I saw, I was certain that she was a witch. But then I looked into her eyes. They were dark and abysmal. In them I saw incredible suffering and agony. It was as if there were a continual shriek of pain coming from this being, but her silence was total.

I waited for her to speak, or to recognize my presence. I knew that she was aware that I was there, but I felt paralyzed and unable to initiate any conversation. I waited for a long time, feeling alternately chilled and heated in her presence. She could not or would not speak. I was powerless. Hours, days, weeks passed, or so it seemed. I lost all sense of time. As I sat there, I began to feel a nameless agony. I was reminded of all the pains of my life, physical and mental, and it was as if all of them were continuing for an eternity, without relief. When I thought I might go mad with grief and pain, I found that I could endure still more. I accepted it, not knowing why, just because. I then began to hear a voice, faint at first, but growing louder. I soon recognized the voice as the Angel's and looked around me to see where it was coming from. To my surprise, I could not locate the voice outside myself, and realized that it was coming from within. Somewhere in that shrieking mass of agony within my being, the Angel was speaking to me.

"Know, O Man. You see before you the figure of the woman, scorned. She it is who was the right hand of God. She it is who has been called Witch, Goddess, Mother. She it is who, on that day, long ago, when her son was crucified, took on herself the pain of Hell. And that pain is to suffer what men and God have suffered through eternity. Every hurt, every agony is registered there. She neither lives nor dies. She cannot speak. Indeed, she will not, until men take on their own agonies, and the agony of God as well. Are you prepared to take on her agony?"

Without thought or reflection, I nodded my assent, and I was filled with compassion. The intensity of compassion and of agony were exactly the same. I remembered a story about a boy, locked up in prison, because he was a Jew. He was then hanged for stealing a loaf of bread. I imagined him dangling there and understood the pain that this poor woman must have felt.

I knew, however, that my capacity for the endurance of pain and compassion was terribly limited. I had trouble coping with my own, let alone taking on that of the Goddess. I knelt in reverence.

This was new for me. I had always bowed before the Most High, but to kneel was foreign to me. Now it came naturally. I knelt for a long time.

Though my eyes were half closed, I became aware of a change in the light. The suffused blue was being penetrated by a golden color. I looked up and beheld the figure of the Woman, transformed. She was as bright as the ball of the Sun and cast off a radiance which my poor eyes were less able to contain than my body and soul could contain the suffering. All the same, I felt healed and warmed. I felt, too, that new knowledge had come to me, which was hard to put into words. My lips began to form words of gratitude and devotion, but no sound emerged. Instead, I felt the loving embrace of the Golden Woman and was as overcome with ecstasy as I had been earlier by pain. The joy was less long-lasting, due, no doubt, to my lesser capacity for enduring ecstasy—and I lost consciousness.

When I recovered my senses, I found myself again at the place in the forest where my adventures began. There was the gravestone of my horse, and there, in my hand, was the golden flower I had plucked earlier. Now, I could endure its scent and I sat down to reflect upon my experience.

The witch. The Goddess. The Wife of God and the Mother of God were all One. What did this mean? It meant that agony and ecstasy were one, and that they were endured by both God and Man. Glory and degradation, compassion and coldness, grief, joy, love and sin—all these and more belonged to God and to man, and they come through the Goddess, the right hand of God. Man is asked to endure all the human clash of heaven and hell, and the divine clash as well.

But, I reflected further, here is the Goddess, speechless, rejected by man, but also by God, or has He only forgotten Her? I thought of the King of the Sea and realized that since He has banished

Himself under the Sea, His Wife is banished under the earth. And they are apart. Again the humpty-dumpty of God!

My task remained the same; to recover all those scattered parts of myself and to help God do the same. What had changed? I could feel more intensely. I could also endure the conflict of opposites without running away. Best of all, the Angel seemed to find a home inside me. Could I dare to hope that this Messenger of God would stay?

I quietly wended my way home.

III

Only a few months after my second adventure, I grew restless in my need to bring about a union of the divine figures whom I had encountered. I experienced my own dividedness as a curse, yet I was sore afraid to encounter the Living Power who, in Heaven, was somehow responsible for the suffering I had seen. I did not know if the Angel would continue to guide me or if I was ready to seek out the way to the Power.

Troubled by these thoughts, I went back to the place in the forest where my adventures had begun. I knelt and prayed for a dream to guide me. Very soon, I fell asleep and dreamed that a great bright star, the brightest in the heavens, had fallen from the sky and landed near the top of a mountain. I was wordlessly instructed to find this mountain and this star. I awakened with a start, but knew that this needed to be done, no matter what the cost. I proceeded back to my home, told my wife of my dream and my task. She painfully and quietly accepted it, though I knew that she feared for me. All the same, I lovingly bade farewell to my family and friends and, with the simplest provisions, set out to find mountain and star.

Many days I walked. And weeks. The weeks stretched into

months. I walked through pale cities and hot deserts. I walked in the light of the moon and the heat of the sun. East, I walked. Often I was weary and hungry. Sometimes people helped me and were generous with what they had. At other times, I was kicked like a cur, and laughed at as a wandering fool. But most often people tended to shrink from me, seemingly in fear. I asked a wise man I met why this was so. He said only that I had "fierce, fierce eyes, with a fire in them, and people were sore afraid." I accepted what he said and, when I looked into a stream, found it to be true. Were these the eyes of the Goddess peering through me, I wondered, or a militant spirit which seemed excessive? I did not know.

The months passed and I sometimes lost track of why I was wandering. Forty months I wandered, until one day, after many days without food and many hours without water, in a trackless desert, I fell down in despair. I cursed myself and my fate, but my mouth could not even form the words. Dryness, cracked lips, and a grunt from my belly were all that stayed in my consciousness. Water, I wanted, and nothing else. I looked around me and, in a distance loomed a mountain, far away. Instantly I knew that it was *the* mountain. Again, as I had when confronted with the agony of the Goddess, I summoned up new resources and dragged myself along. After a time, when I walked only from memory, I nearly fell into an oasis. I drank deeply from the water and fell into a deep, dreamless sleep from exhaustion.

I do not know how long I slept, but I awakened refreshed. I ate fruit of the trees, replenished my supply of water, and continued on toward the mountain. As I walked onward, I noticed that the mountain was almost perfectly triangular in shape, and indeed not high at all. It looked grand and overpowering because it was unique in this desert, and compared to the flatness of the desert, was monarch.

At last I reached the base of the mountain and looked up. The face of it was sheer granite, unrelieved by crevices, except near the top, where a large slit strangely presented itself. As I wondered if I should attempt to climb this unclimbable thing—and, if so, how—the slit widened and I was confronted with a huge Eye. I quivered and trembled, but did not flinch from the encounter with this Eye of God.

The Eye looked at me coldly and fiercely and I knew, in an instant, that here was the greater Fierceness, of which the glint in my eye was but a paltry spark.

"Why do you come, O man?" The Eye spoke; how, I do not know, but it was as if thunder and lightening were all around me. The Voice was everywhere and nowhere.

Shaken and awed, I held my ground, and said, "Because you sent for me."

The Eye grew even fiercer. A rumbling took place within the mountain, which made me realize that it was a volcano. There came a crackling of the Voice, saying, "I did not! I go to and fro as I wish; I need no one and send for no one and surely not a mere Man, who is the author of such stupidity and viciousness in a world I regret that I created. Man, the crown of my creation, is lower than dust to me, and I do not know why I have not already obliterated him with a holocaust."

I was silent. What could I say? Could I tell this demon-God that He was the author of the stupidity and viciousness—at least the worst of it—and that He had already delivered so many holocausts that man was despairing of when the next and final one was to occur? I was reminded of what the Angel had said, that if he were to bring the darkness of God to His senses, the result would be the destruction of the Angel, were God to want it or not. For a mere mortal to suggest it would be to ask to be burned to a cinder.

"Speak!" said the Voice.

I continued to be silent. Whatever I might do would be wrong. If I spoke, I would be destroyed, and if I failed to speak I would be destroyed. Why, then, did the Angel tell me that it was up to Man to confront God with Himself? The Angel's words were burned into my soul: "It is given to you, if you survive, to let each know where the other is." I must risk it, I thought.

At that moment, I understood. The Angel, indeed, was an aspect of God Himself, and that God was ready to destroy Himself, or a part at least, but had not, as yet, utterly destroyed men. I had to trust that I would not be destroyed, or, even if I were, other men would take up the task. Surely other Knights had seen what I had seen, and other Brothers would be summoned to the task.

With that realization, I looked up at the Eye once again, for I had been with my own eyes downcast during my reflections.

To my astonishment, the Eye seemed softer and filled with an infinite sadness. The sadness was not like the agony of the Goddess, who felt within herself all the pain and suffering of all creatures, human and divine, everywhere and of all time. Hers was the suffering that had been inflicted. His, however, seemed to bear the marks of one who is racked with guilt for having caused pain and agony. There was no self-pity and no flinching. In His silence, I knew, without words, that God was indeed aware of all the suffering He had caused, and that with his One Eye, he saw all that happened. I knew that He was aware of the whole course of history, and of His creations, but that He knew all of the future—of this I had doubt. I began to feel respectful compassion for this knowledge and suffering and for the Being who bore it, yet I was puzzled. This did not agree with what I learned from the King of the Sea, nor from the Angel. I was now confronted with something unexpected. God was aware of His darkness. How could I reconcile what I had learned from these three emanations of

God?

I gazed in wonder at the Eye of God, openly, without embarrassment, and in tense anticipation. I felt that, despite His protest, He wanted me to know. I waited patiently, knowing that I would get an answer to my unspoken questions.

I did not have long to wait. The Voice began to speak, not in wrath and thunder, but in a tone of quiet despair, much as a loving and wise father would speak to a younger friend about his children. He said:

"Long ago, I dwelt in peace with my creations. Man was my favorite and I lavished my bounty upon him, while he lavished his love upon me. We dwelt in happiness and mutuality. We lived in a garden, with all manner of good things to eat and all the pleasures of love and companionship. I saw my creation and that it was good, but I reckoned without my Son."

Here I was gripped with a deep nausea. It was a sickness that I could not account for. Was I reacting to the anticipated horrors of the old story of the snake? Or was I reacting to a kind of sentimentality in God Himself? I knew that on the human level brutal men lavish sentimental love on animals and plants, while condoning unspeakable tortures to other men.

"Your sickness is my sickness," God continued. "For then I was, indeed, unaware of my own destructiveness. I was a foolish father, who allowed poor mortal man to be tempted. And yet, I wanted it—I wanted them tested. I wanted my sons and daughters to grow and become partners with Me in the work of creation. With all my omniscience I could not entirely grasp the future, since I, too, was developing. And so, I shut my Eye, and allowed my Son to tempt man with knowledge. Man had everything but consciousness of himself, and this my Son gave to him. He is, indeed, cold and hard, and reaches into the depths of the earth and the height of the stars. He wants consciousness above all, and at any price. My Son is surely a part of me, and inherits My lust to know. But His coldness and hardness is also passionate and even I am in awe of Him.

"His lust to know is also My lust. I have everything but knowledge of Myself–or, did so, until My Son gave man a light which is destined to make mankind My partner. *In the very act of giving light to man, my Son also gave light to Me.* That was a miracle I had not anticipated, having no real knowledge of Myself. My wrath was boundless, or nearly so. I would have destroyed Man altogether, if I did not realize that I needed him and that without the help of the divine spark I had given him, as well as the divine spark that my Son had given him, I would, indeed, be alone and that the task of creation would simply end. I was tempted, indeed, to start afresh, and make a new breed of man, yet I knew that I had made man in my own image and this was the best possible partner for the work.

"It took me long to fully grasp what had happened, and what I had done. When I saw the wickedness of men, from beginning to end, I was frequently tempted to start afresh. For, you see, My Son tempts me, too, and my consciousness was fitful. I caused much devastation, but always kept the race of men alive.

"In time, more men came to see the nature of my Son, and to both loathe it and adore it. Only a few saw that it was also my own Nature. As I grew in consciousness in my encounters with men, I came to loathe my Son and Myself. He was my firstborn and I needed Him most, but the price in suffering was too high. What you perceived as my wife was in ever greater agony. It was as if man's self-understanding and my Self-understanding were continually increasing, but it was becoming unbearable to Me.

"I began to see my own injustice, and how I was failing to live by the commandments that I had given man. I decided that with all my suffering, I did not really know how man suffers and that I must undergo that. But I could not undergo that totally, since the totality of my love and of my power would surely destroy man, at the stage of his development at that time. I decided to embrace my humanity and walk among men again, as a loving King. And I did, although I was not fully visible to them. I joined with a mortal woman (as I had done in the past with many heroes, but this time more consciously and resolutely) for the sake of creating my second Son, who was both God and Man, and would repair, in loving-kindness, what my First Son had destroyed with power. And it came to be. But, again, I had reckoned without my Power. Cut off from it, as I was, it began to act autonomously, and had its own aims. Again destruction, and I was forced to experience the greatest of all sacrifices a father can make: the sacrifice of his son. And He, the embodiment of Love, was crucified. I tasted what it meant to be man.

"With that, and in time, the sacrifice was of no avail, and wickedness, pain, grief, agony held sway. My Power banished my Humanity under the Sea, where you saw him as King of the Sea, and my own agony and suffering was banished under the earth, where you saw her as the Goddess.

"I have come back to my Power. Now, my First Son is more in the world than ever. In truth, He now lives and finds his home in Everyman. Again, this was a miracle of His which I did not anticipate. Where I had my Loving Being in one man-God, He has found His Being in all men. That is how it should be. The task of co-redemption is in earnest, and I cannot do it alone. I must be united with my Son, and Man must be united with Him also. For Love has never been enough. There must be Light. And more Light. 'Let there be Light,' I said, and it is done. Now there must be Light and Love, and Man must help Me to find it. My Eye sees many such Knights as you, who long after it, as I do. Go now and tell my message."

When the Eye and Voice had ended, I was in peace. I knelt and prayed for our mutual salvation and did so with both little self-consciousness and full self-consciousness for what I was doing. Then I looked up. I was aware that mists were rolling in from the Sea, far away, and from under the earth. Then I knew that the King of the Sea and the Goddess of the Earth were coming back to the Center. In a moment, the Mountain turned to Gold and radiated a fantastic Light in all directions. It was a great Golden Triangle, with the Loving and Powerful Eye of God in the Center.

I was not deluded that my work was through. I felt privileged to witness this sight and knew that I would long reflect upon what I had seen and heard. I had no sense of exaltation, knowing that I now had to face an absent member beyond that Trinity, which would make it a Quaternity. And I knew that I had nowhere else to seek it but in myself. I had seen God's Wisdom, His Vision, His Humanity, His Love, and His Agony, but it was I who had to face, not His Power, but the one that dwelt inside me. In that task, I was neither alone, nor inept. For it required Everyman to do the same.

IV

When I came back from my third adventure, I was a more silent man. I knew that the task of knowing myself was more important than ever, and that my own struggle with the Snake-Son within me was the most significant work that I could do. I felt, too, the need to communicate what I experienced to other men, but I lacked the words to do so. In time, the momentousness of my experience waned, as I, like everyone, was caught up in the daily round of life. It was not that I lost track of the problem, but that my own feeling of power to do anything about it dissolved.

One day, as I was strolling in the forest where all of my

adventures had begun, I felt a creeping sensation on my back and the rush of air in my ear. It was as if a worm had crawled up my back and into my ear. I then heard a whisper:

"Look out, O Man, and not just within! I am there, and here, and everywhere! Come and find me!" I reached into my ear, half-expecting to find a worm, but I found nothing and had only an itch. I looked about in my perplexity, but saw nothing. Then, with another rush of air, I felt the wind in my other ear, and heard the words, "Come to the south!"

I knew, now, with whom I had to deal, and, in a trusting way, immediately set off towards the south. This mercurial Being, I knew, would not give me time to settle my affairs, but, if I wanted to pursue him, I had to follow at once.

I walked quickly, waiting for him to give me a sign. As I walked, the landscape changed fantastically. At one moment I would be walking in lush tropical jungles, the next would find me in cold arctic snows. Deserts and mountains came and went in the space of only a few steps. Cities with great monuments and forests with wild animals and men would appear and vanish with a change only in my breathing. I had the strong feeling of reality with each appearance and would be shaken the next moment by the changes. My belly and my heart were gripped alternately by them, but I resolutely kept up my pace. Without warning, the wind would whistle up my back and into one ear or the other, and I would hear the words, "You see?" or a crackling laugh. I had to confess to myself that I saw, but I did not understand.

After a time the visions I was presented with changed. Now the places I saw came slower and with a much heavier cast. I saw vast armies marching, and cities destroyed by war. I saw mounds of corpses in stinking piles, and great prisons where haggard men were in despair. I saw babies lying dead. Now the words came with the wind in my ear in a slower, heavier, and sadly ironic way:

"You see?" These two words seemed laden with meaning, but still I could not grasp it. Yes, I saw, but I did not see. I saw, indeed, but I did not understand. My steps were slower. My own quickness and eagerness were slowed by my failure to understand.

I dragged one foot after another now, not in fatigue, but in despair of grasping what, apparently, I was being asked to understand.

Finally, I stopped and fell to the ground. I was spreadeagled on the ground, lips to the dust. I tasted the dust on my tongue. I looked ahead of me and saw a long snake, thick and strong. His skin was a handsome black, with large red markings. He raised his head a few inches from me and spoke:

"Now, O Man, you know what it is to be ground into the dust! You want to know and to understand, and you do not! Well, lick the dust, as have I, for thousands of years. And you ask me why? I will tell you. It is because you want to know and understand!"

I accepted the words of the Snake, but still wanted to know: "Are you the Author of all this?"

"To know, to know!" he replied. "Of course, I am the author of it, and so are you, and so is Everyman who ever walked the face of the earth!"

Yes, of course, I thought, men have created all these things, and much of it was created by God—or by the Snake. There was nothing new in all that. What was the point of it all?

"Exactly!" responded the snake to my unexpressed thoughts. "Knowledge is Power, and what is the point of it all!"

"Are you telling me that it all leads to destruction and that Knowledge is the evil?" I asked.

"Questions, questions, questions! More knowledge, more power! More power, more destruction!"

Now, I became perplexed and irritated. This damned Son was just like his Father! Anything I did was wrong. If I asked a question, I was searching for knowledge which would lead to destruction. If I did not ask a question, I would still be stupidly wondering if I should abandon understanding altogether and simply live like an animal, which was out of the question. It was in my nature to know in the first place, and besides, this Devil tempted me to come follow him!

Laughter. Vast, rolling laughter. At first it was ironic and even sneering. Then it turned wide and joyous.

His laughter made me smile, though I felt rather like a fool for doing so. My irritation subsided, however, and again I had the peculiar feeling of no longer facing the Evil One. It was getting hard, indeed, to find the real Author of Evil in the universe!

The Snake was now arched on his back, making a large S, and chuckling quietly to Himself: "Devil am I? Yes, indeed. Disquieting and irritating am I? No doubt. . . . What can I tell you, O Man? How can I really help you on your way? Yes, I am known as Satan, the Hinderer, but only because I interfere with men's wilfullness, not because I am opposed to them. Indeed, were you to ask my Father, He would say that I care more about Man than I do about the Father, Himself! No matter, each to his own scapegoat!

"Yes, Knowledge leads to Power, and Power leads to Destruction. It is so. But, in my Father's hands, Creation was the Power, and, before I offered the fruit, with His unknowing assent, the Creation led to destruction. Every time God breathed, there was creation—and destruction. His weeping caused rain, as every child knows. His angers were volcanoes; his lusts became jungles in an instant and his depressions were vast deserts. His thoughts were stars, and his deepest reflections a galaxy. He could not help but Create, and in His new Creations, an older creation was destroyed. He did not know this—or rather, He could not accept it and pushed this knowledge off on me. He desperately needed to know

Himself. He needed a mirror for his existence. His first act therefore was to split himself. The first deed of God was that He divided Himself into pieces. In the beginning, there was One, then there were Two, then there were Four—and more. But He hated His division, and said, 'I'll make myself a Man, for company and pleasure.' But I knew, because He had given it unto Me to know, that He had made Man as a partner—to know Himself and to help Himself put Himself back together. But, since He made Man in His own image, Man, too, was destined to be divided. Because God loved Man, and hated His own division, He could not bring Himself to make Man aware of his division. That onerous task he gave to Me, His First Son, His dearly beloved and hated part of Himself. And so, I am cast out, after having done my duty. Like you, I know what it means to be rejected unjustly!

"For long, I was only pushed away, not cast out. I was the needed insinuator—the one who would, like you, ask painful questions. I would look into things, into men's hearts and even God's heart and I would see things. At last, my Father could no longer stand Himself, nor Me, and He came to earth again, to show His Love. And His Second Son, a God-man, set out to redeem you all. He did a fair job, if evaluation is permissible, except that he not only left Me out, but made Me the author of all the Evil in the universe! And why? Because I knew that God needed redemption Himself! That is the one bit of knowledge that the Father could not accept!

"My Brother did well. In His way, He tried to tell you, too, 'Ye are Gods!' he said. But few seemed to realize what He meant. So, He died, was sacrificed, and you know the rest."

At this point, the Snake stopped, and seemed to withdraw into Himself. I wanted Him to go on, but was fearful of getting into one of those paradoxical question-puttings again. All the same, I tried:

"But," I said, "Your Brother is said to have Ascended and that He would be born again."

The Snake smiled. "Do you believe it?" He asked.

"Well," I responded. "That is hard to say. I am a Jew, you know, though a Knight. But in my heart, I am also a Christian, and an ancient Greek, and some others as well."

The Snake laughed uproariously again, "Of course," He chortled. "I told you that I see into souls, and I see that you are divided! No matter, so are they all, especially those that think they are not!"

"Will He come again?" I persisted.

"Of course He will. It is so written."

Again, I paused. I needed to reflect upon what I had been told and, since the Snake seemed content to wait a little, I gave myself the time to think.

In actuality, many days went by before I could again speak to the Snake. Part of me was very much back in the world, in life, involved in the daily round and even intensely so. The other part of me remained there facing the S-shaped Snake in silent wonder. In this very act of living in both places, I had a deeper understanding of the Snake and of God's division: one knows and one does not know; one is there and one is not there. Now the division was less painful to me. It was, indeed, as the Angel once told me, that the need was "to know whether the other one is" both for God and man. The division was tolerable as long as one knew that there was a development, an end, a quest. What was more natural for a Knight than to be on a quest?

When I returned my full attention to the Snake, He smiled. I was aware of a golden crown on His head, and He softly repeated words that I had heard long ago and were now etched in my memory: "Summoned or not, God is always present."

After this time of silence, the Snake continued: "I have made you aware of only a part of My nature, which is 'to know.' As you are well aware, 'to know' is also a passion. It was written in the old books that 'to know' also means 'to unite with'—to passionately desire union. You experience Me in that way, too, as your passion to unite. Sex, you call Me, and a demon, and so I am, for I am satisfied with nothing less than total union. Restrain Me, you must! I know full well, for union without love is disastrous. Not only you know that, but many have known that. There are those that call Me Kundalini, for I crawl into the holes and crevices of the spine and to every center that I can find, to go up and up and down and down, until all that is to be known is known and all that is to be united with is united. Do not fear Me, though you are right to fear Me—but only if you do not know me and value Me. Without Me, there is no life, no press, no pull. There are those, both East and West, who would deny Me, and overcome Me, and reject Me. They are right to try, though doomed to failure. They can kill Me, and experience death themselves, but, as long as there is life, I am reborn. And after death, too, as my Father well knows.

"Passion I am, and passion I will be. Listen to Me and heed Me, and also do not heed Me. That is my message. If you understand you are blessed, if you do not you are damned."

I understood. One had to go with one's passions and restrain them. And one had to listen from moment to moment. The Angel's message was sound: "let each know where the other one is!" In the face of division, keep connected with the parts. And Evil? What was Evil? Evil was the division, not knowing oneself, where the Other was. Power without love; Love without wisdom; Wisdom without passion; fundamentally, God without man and man without God. I understood. And I trusted.

I looked up again at the snake. He had changed. I now saw a hermaphroditic creature, male and female, united, but back to back. Each wore a crown. I nodded and knew that there was union, but that it was incomplete. I knew that I had much more to do, more to know, more to love, and more to live, before the total union was possible. I nodded and bowed.

My honest submission to this being seemed to cause a change in Him. The Snake transformed back into his original form and leaped high into the air. He went straight for the marvelous golden triangle where the Eye of God glowed. He wrapped himself about this triangle and penetrated into its core. An explosion of light. Now the triangle was golden as before, but surrounded by the circle of the Snake, biting its own tail. In the center of the triangle was the Eye of God, with a human King on one side and a human Queen on the other, facing, and united. A funny arithmetic: three plus two equals four.

It was enough. And I went back to my life.

V

After my fourth adventure, I thought that I understood and could now live my life in a more meaningful and creative way—but I was mistaken. It was true that I understood much more and I experienced a greater sense of inner union, as well as a sense of greater union in the divine, but still. . . . Doubt and dissatisfaction again gnawed at me. Was this simply the greed of the old Adam in me, I wondered, or was the Snake sending me a message? After some time of letting the problem brew, I once again returned to my sacred place in the forest where all my adventures began.

I walked leisurely through the trees, enjoying their fine scent. I listened to the crackling of leaves underfoot and felt the chill of autumn. The reds, browns, and golden hues of the leaves played with the greens stunningly. As I looked at this great display of nature, I realized that what I had not seen in my encounters with

God, had been this: Beauty, Art, Joy, Play. Yes, play. Was this universe really so totally serious and desperate all of the time? Or was it my own serious nature that simply filtered out of all experiences just those that were hard and difficult and concerned with the dark and puzzling side of life?

Harkening back to my youth, before the Angel appeared, I recalled how I had responded to Music, to Art, to games with my friends. Yes, there had been Joy, but the Angel's stern "No" put an end to that. Was Play, then, only in Man's province? Were Art and Beauty Man's creation alone? As I looked at this forest, I realized that God must love beauty, too, or He would not have made it so dazzling since no eye but His had previously gazed on it.

Relieved, I sat down by the side of a stream to refresh myself. I lazily let my hand dip into the cold water and both welcomed and resisted the gentle flow as it coursed by me. I laughed at myself. Even when I wanted to be lazily playful, I had to test myself! I was God's fool, indeed!

It was then that I heard the singing. How can I describe it and not simply echo what poets have said? Yes, that is it! It was, of course, the singing that poets have heard and have attempted to translate into words and into music. I am neither poet nor musician, but I will try to tell you, in the simple language I have used until now, just what it was that came across my path.

I followed in the direction of the singing and came into a clearing. There, not more than twenty paces from me, but totally oblivious of me, was a girl of perhaps sixteen, sitting by the stream, and combing her long dark hair. She was pretty, yes, but not at all preoccupied with it. She was pretty in the way that the trees are pretty.

Again I laughed at myself. My own nature and even God's will, both for Himself and for me, was that I become as conscious of myself and of Him as possible. The chief sin was unconsciousness. Here, before my eyes, was a creature that seemed totally unaware and yet was the most beautiful being that I had ever seen! I laughed again and said to God: "Well, Sir, what do you make of that!"

Since no response from God was forthcoming, I settled back to listen to the singing. She sang songs that were gay and songs that were sad, and she sang them in language after language. I understood some of these languages, and I even remembered hearing some of the songs before. Others were utterly foreign to me, and in modes and styles that I tried to follow, but couldn't because they were unexpected in their changings. There were subtleties beyond my grasp. I wondered, how could this girl—clearly young, protected, naive, unknowing—sing in all these tongues with such authority? Her accent and understanding were perfect in those languages with which I had some acquaintance and I had to assume that this was also true for the many others. She could hardly have learned all these languages in her brief span of life. Was she, then, simply a great parrot, or—I caught my breath in disbelief—a Goddess? And why, I asked myself, was I so disbelieving? Why could she not be a Goddess? Was I, indeed, so prejudiced as to think that God could not manifest Himself as a Herself, and a sixteen year old, as well? I recalled my experience of the Goddess of Suffering, and chided myself on my limited patriarchal viewpoint. With that, I decided to keep myself open to what would happen.

I listened to the singing for a long time, keeping my eyes closed in order not to be distracted by anything else. Softly, she sang, and then loudly. Sometimes her voice was romantic or wistful, sometimes she sang passionately of love, of rage, of scorn. There even were martial songs which stir the blood against one's will, and my own blood responded. Then the songs stopped.

I looked up to see what had happened, why they had stopped, and was startled to see the girl bending over me, intently.

"Who are you?" she demanded, and "And what are you doing here?"

"I am just an ordinary Knight," I replied, "And I often walk in this forest. I heard your singing and was enchanted by it." I said this in as forthright a manner as I could, but I was feeling guilty at the invasion of her privacy, so I added, more meekly, "I am sorry to have intruded."

She seemed perplexed by this, but did not speak another word. Instead, she moved away a few steps, darted among the trees and brought back with her a woman who seemed to be in her late thirties, obviously her mother.

The mother was as stunning, in her way, as the daughter was in another. The elder woman was also dark, but full-bodied, more sensual, and experienced. As a pair, they were a marvel, and since I was still lying down, I was both awed and slightly frightened.

They looked at me sternly. I had the amusing thought that they must, indeed, be Goddesses, because every time I met another manifestation of God it was a stern one! With that, I laughed, got to my feet, and said, in my most charming, knightly way (gathering memories from my youth, when I was, indeed, as I have said, something of a ladies' man), "Ladies, I beg your pardon if I have disturbed you, but I can only plead that I have been utterly enchanted with your singing, Miss, and with your beauty, Madam!" I then flourished my hat and bowed deeply.

To my chagrin, the ladies were not, apparently, at all enchanted with me, and simply turned on their heels and walked off.

I was bemused. What did I do wrong? I was a gentleman, I thought, and this manner had its appeal with other such ladies. But was I really a gentleman? Inside? Obviously not, and I knew it. Perhaps these ladies knew it, too. I was impressed. I should have added, "At your service!" Ah, that was it! If they were, indeed,

Goddesses, they would expect that from me, of course. I had dedicated myself to the service of God, but I had failed to include my dedication to the Goddess!

With that realization, I ran after them, this time genuinely ready to ask their pardon–not for intruding, but for not being ready to serve them. I ran only a few steps and there they were in front of me, with broad smiles and open arms. Again, I was startled. Could they read my thoughts so quickly and change so radically in response to them? They were Goddesses, indeed!

"We are, O Knight," began the elder, in response to my unspoken question. "We have long wondered when you would finally realize it and seek Us out."

"I have not sought You out, good Ladies," I replied, "because I have been almost totally engrossed in the religion of the Fathers and of the Sons. I have been preoccupied with the problem of evil, and of consciousness, and, above all, the problem of meaning. But, I think, I have met you in another form, have I not? There, under the earth, in that great cavern?"

"No," the elder woman replied. "She whom you met was my Mother and indeed, only in one form. One day, please God, you will meet Her in another, which will not be so enlightening for you."

I chose, at that moment, to hold my tongue and not ask my questions. It was enough that I was now meeting with a human sort of Goddess. I was in no hurry to meet a fate that I was not at all sure I was ready for. I waited for the Goddess to go on.

"You have met Me, dear Knight" (I was startled and pleased at this hint of endearment) "at other times, and perhaps you did not know it. You have met me whenever you have felt attracted to a woman, felt yourself drawn to her as if to a beloved, or a long forgotten sister. For I am, indeed, that soul-sister whom you have encountered often. Do not conclude that I exist only in your imagination, or that you mistakenly experience me as coming from outside of you. No, that is not true. A man would like only too much to believe that, since it is so convenient. It would give him a chance to escape from life, but it is not true. Yes, indeed, I do make my home inside you, should you only desire it or acknowledge it, but I also live in them, in all those women to whom you are attracted, and—I must add—repelled.

"For, you see, my realm is life. My realm is love and hate and connections. My realm is a web, an invisible church of entanglements. The magnetism of attractions and repulsions, of involvements and estrangements, not only between men and women, but among young and old, and of these among themselves. People experience Me, and are shaken. They are shaken out of their masculine will and whisper of reincarnation, of soul-mates, of brothers, of sisters. In short, I am She who brings about union and its opposite. You ask for meaning. Do you not know that there is no meaning without Me!"

Here, the Goddess grew angry, and I had to acknowledge that She was right. I had given lip-service to Her, in my acceptance that there was no meaning without experience, but I was secretly, as She had hinted, gathering my experiences of life in order to be free of it. I was like a Hindu, I suppose, engaged in life and its illusion, only to be free of it. I took life as a sponge would take water, only to drain it into some private little vessel of aloneness. I bowed to her and sighed quietly.

The Goddess softened. She looked at me with compassion. "I know that is so," She continued. "In reality, I do not blame you for it. For you must, as a man, be a man, and free yourself of illusion and entanglements. But you only have to acknowledge Me, to expect Me, to understand Me, for I am not opposed to your blessed consciousness, I am only opposed to its one-sidedness. That is My nature, to bring together. The Angel once told you that the task is 'to let each know whether the other is.' That is true. But I am the one who brings the each to the other! It is not just you that has overlooked me, and forgotten me. God knows, you are better than most men in this regard! It is the Father. . . ."

Here the Goddess grew rueful and seemed to vanish inside Herself, just as She did when She grew angry with me. I felt that Her dialogue with me was also a dialogue with Another, which I dared not suggest to Her. She knew it anyway, I suppose.

She was silent a long time. I looked at Her, in Her silence, and felt echoes of deep thoughts and questionings that were going on in a language that I could not fathom at all. It was a mystery of a feminine thinking–a kind of consciousness which would, perhaps, always remain a mystery to me. I could only wait, in respectful communion with Her, knowing that I was not in real communion, but that I was just with my own images and not where She was. I smiled wryly to myself, feeling a barbed criticism toward Her. She was the one who opted for not only "letting each know where the other is" but also to bring about union, and now Her thoughts were elsewhere, quite apart from me!

"You are right, O Knight," the Goddess continued. "I am, indeed, guilty of what I complain about, and that is exactly where I was at that moment, speaking with the Father."

Her face changed again, from an intense and fathomless searching to a smiling warmth. Her Daughter, now, was playing with pebbles and leaves and humming to Herself. There was an atmosphere of peace, even of play, but there was also something uncanny going on.

The Goddess' face was warm, but strained. She had not, indeed, totally returned to me. I did not mind that, but I sensed a growing tension in the air. It was quiet, but the air was heavy, as if before a storm. I instinctively reached for my sword and glanced about me looking for the danger. The forest, too, was silent. No birds were singing, no wind was blowing. All the myriad forest sounds were stilled. I peered at the Goddess to see if She were aware of this strange silence. She only watched Her happy Daughter, playing innocently with the pebbles. There was an infinite sadness in the eyes of the Goddess, which reminded me of Her Mother.

I said nothing, but kept my hands on my sword. When the stillness was at its height, when I thought my nerves would crack with the tension, when I thought I could stand it no more, I heard an unearthly sound.

It was a laugh, but not a laugh, a cackle; and not a cackle, but a great, horrendous, female, blood-curdling sound which seemed to wreck the Universe or, at least, all the order in it. I shivered and trembled and drew my sword like a demon, ready to fight the Unknown.

There came, from out of the forest, a horde of faces and bodies, some whole and some in parts. There came men and women of every race—black, brown, white, red, yellow. There came creatures who were part man and part animal, all the kinds that I had ever seen in bestiaries and many more besides. There came plants with feet. And they came in a wild dancing, a mindless play and lust that threatened to tear us apart.

I looked to the Goddess, to see if She could stop this invasion. She observed the creatures, was sad but impassive. I glanced at the Daughter, now on Her feet in utter terror.

I knew that I had to fight. I realized that I would lose, and probably die, but I had to devote myself for the Goddesses. I leaped in front of them and fought like a tiger. I fought harder than I ever had in my life, and I was always known as something of a battler. I fought and I slew. Bodies were piled upon bodies as I slew; limbs and arms and blood and gore, until I was covered with it in a great pile all around me. I suffocated from the scene, the stench, and from the agony of my own wounds. I lost consciousness.

When I awakened, I was once again in the great cavern underneath the earth, where I had encountered the Great Mother Goddess. But the landscape was different. Instead of the starkness and the blue light, all was now in green and red and yellow. There was lush vegetation with forms and shapes which were fantastic to me. I was conscious of my environment before I was aware of myself. First, I felt pain and restraint. I was tied to a tree. To my left was the Goddess, also tied to a tree, and to Her left, the Daughter, in the same condition.

The creatures, human and otherwise, were all around us, demonically laughing and dancing. Now, they descended upon us again, incubi and succubi. They crawled into every orifice of my body and sucked all my juices—saliva, urine, semen, sweat, blood. At first, I was outraged, but I reflected: I have been raped in the spirit so many times, why should I be so outraged by a rape of the flesh?

When my head was free for a moment, I turned to look at the Goddess and the Daughter. The Goddess was unmoved. She stood in stoic and grand calm before this assault. Without having seen it, I knew that She, too, had fought like a tigress, but was holding Herself and Her humanity high before this assault. But then I saw the Daughter. Her face was tortured, and the agony in Her eyes was as great as that of the Great Mother Goddess whom I had seen long ago.

Then I heard someone crying.

I turned to see who it was that was crying. It was not the Goddess; it was not the Daughter; it was myself. I wept. I sobbed. The tears ran in a way that they had not since childhood. Nay, not even in childhood had I wept so. I wept for myself. I wept for what it was to be a man, to be human, and even to be a creature.

The tears, too, were consumed by the demons, and my pride

went. Not that I was humiliated—I was somehow beyond that. Rather, I felt that these demons and people were just like myself; they killed and raped and devoured and were, in turn, killed and raped and devoured. So be it.

Suddenly—with the same abruptness with which I had heard the great cackle—all was silent. The cavern was suffused with green light of every imaginable shade. There was a Presence. I knew that I was about to bear witness to the Great Mother, and in a very different way than I had seen Her before, just as Her Daughter had warned.

In the midst of the green light, there appeared a great Mouth with lips as red as the light was green. The lips parted and spoke, though the words came from outside Her and everywhere at once. Her words, unlike the crisp clarity of the Father, echoed and reverberated. With each word, there was born some creature, pouring out of her mouth. She spoke:

"For three thousand years, O Man, I have been rejected! For three thousand years! But you have known Me in a million guises: as lust, as hunger, as meat and bread, and earth, and wine. You have known Me, and lusted after Me, and rejected Me. The more you reject Me, the more I am as a demon to you. Nature is My realm, and it is as it is: in pleasure and in pain, in creation and destruction. You, O man, would despoil it and ravish it and devour it and consume it. For love, or for desire? Oh, no! For power, for consciousness, and for such other soarings of the Spirit as your malicious little minds can devise. But My day is coming, O Man! Now you see Me, in your wars, and your impotencies, and your hungers. Now you see Me. Until you accept Me, I shall crawl into every opening and devour every bit of you. Sovereignty!"

I was silent. What could I say? It was true that we men had exploited nature, harmed her, used her for our own ends. It was true that we men had so treated women—and the Goddess. It was true that we had rejected Her, or at least many of us had. But I had the feeling that she was speaking not only to me, but to Another. Her bitterness and resentment should be against the Father, really, since we poor mortal men were absymally ignorant, stupid and impotent. Dare I tell Her that? Dare I tell her that I saw Her traces, indeed, in both the Father and in Her Snake-Son? I said nothing. Words were not necessary. She knew, of course, "where the other one was." The lips vanished and there was silence.

I felt my bonds loosen and fall away. The Goddess, the Daughter, and I were now free and among men and the creatures. The men and the creatures had changed. Their forms were the same, but the demonism had disappeared. We wandered freely among them, and there was a sense of belonging all together.

I knew, though She had not said it, that the Great Mother was really against me because of my secret pride, my chosenness, my individuality. The Great Father could not tolerate His own unconsciousness (or mine), and the Great Mother could not tolerate my uniqueness. Had I really understood? Was She, indeed, opposed to uniqueness? No, she was opposed to that uniqueness, that chosenness, which set a man apart from other men, in pride and in isolation. We are all chosen, after all, with a divine spark.

With that realization, my heart lightened and I could get a glimpse of that day "when all mankind will be as brothers", and we mustn't forget the animals, and the plants, and the angels, and the demons. When the All will be as One.

The next moment found me in my sacred place in the forest. All was quiet and serene. Ahead of me, just above the trees, I again saw the Golden Triangle, shimmering. At its apex was the Eye of God, the Father. At the left corner stood the King of the Sea, God the Brother, all in blue. In the right corner coiled the Snake, God the Son, black and red.

Then, out of the depths of the earth, there appeared another triangle, dark and green with an intensity as great as the Golden Triangle. But this triangle was reversed. At its nadir was the Mouth of the Great Mother, as red as rubies or pomegranates; God the Mother. At the left corner stood the Goddess, radiant in red; God the sister. At the right corner knelt God the Daughter, in a lovely yellow.

Together, the triangles made a Star of David. I was astonished. The symbol that had been spat upon, rejected, was there in all glory and in a new light. I thought: It is right. From this union will come Another. The Messiah. The seed of King David. And this Son will be the awaited First Coming of the Jews, the Second Coming of the Christians, and the Reborn Son of the Greeks. So be it.

I bowed in reverence, and was suddenly transported into the Center of the Star. There was I, a king without a crown, just like all humanity. We all belonged there. I had hope. On that day, when He comes, the Star will come to Earth, and we will all be as One.

VI

My fifth adventure seemed to satisfy most of my doubts and questions, and gave me a new sense of purpose and well-being. I returned to my family and friends, eager to share with them what I had experienced. Most of them were moved by my story and understood very well what they were all about. New doubts assailed me, however. Was their reaction only because they knew me and loved me, or was what I had experienced of a more general nature? In short, would people who did not know me and care for me also find meaning and value in what I had discovered?

This question pressed at me and would not let me rest. Once again I was harassed from within to go on a quest, but this time the need was to connect with my fellow man.

Now I wandered in places I had never seen before. I met Jews and Christians, Muslim Arabs and Buddhists from Japan. I met Africans who had very different stories—all about animals—which moved me greatly. I met Hindus and Atheists. I would try to tell my story and got many kinds of response. Some would nod their heads and say, "Yes, that is the way it is." Others would say, "What a nice story!" These reactions pleased me. There were other responses, however, which puzzled me. They said such things as: "No, you have got it all wrong! That is not the way it is at all!"; "Yes, you have a partial truth, but the real truth is this (and then they would tell me their stories)"; "What mad fantasies! Don't you know that God is just a creation of men's imaginations?"; "Are you insane?"; "What presumption!"; "Don't bother me with such silliness!"; God is dead, why try to revive him?"; and, finally, "Heresy!"

I returned to my home bemused. What was I to make of all that? Naturally, I went to my sacred place in the forest in order to sort out what I had experienced. I sat down and rubbed my chin. My story spoke to some and not to others—that was clear. How could that be? I was sure that God had spoken to me. Could some of these people be right and others wrong? Or was it, indeed, "only a fantasy"? In any case, everyone seemed to be an authority.

In my puzzlement, I chanced to look up. There, before my eyes, was a gigantic tree. The trunk was huge and stretched higher into the heavens than my eye could reach. One could guess that its' roots reached down into the earth and spread through it in an equally vast way. I was stunned. I had never seen this tree before. Had it grown suddenly overnight?

I looked at the strange fruit of this tree. Instead of oranges and lemons and pears, there were signs and symbols. There were stars and crosses of every shape and description. There were circles, and squares, and crescents, and all manner of geometric shapes. There were phalli and breasts and other parts of the body. There were even trees and plants. Many of the symbols were rich and lush with many colors; others were old and dying. And buds, buds in great profusion.

As I looked on in wonder and bewilderment, I suddenly glimpsed my own Star of David, at the end of one branch. There it was, lovely and shining! The figures therein smiled out at me and waved. I waved back and felt foolish.

A moment later, there appeared, no longer in a mist but in a concrete way, the Angel of God, mounted on my horse. He carried a flaming sword, but He, too, smiled at me and waved. The Angel spoke:

"What you see before you is the Tree of Life. It was always there, but you did not know it. All the fruit thereon grows and thrives and dies. New ones take their place. The sap of the tree, the blood of God, courses through them, and they enrich each other. The fruits nourish mankind and help him live. When his particular fruit dies, he dies. Until he finds another one, his soul is dry. So it has always been, and so it will always be.

"The many fruits of the tree are immortal and man is immortal. So are you immortal, Sir Knight. Here have I stayed with my flaming sword since that first day, when the first man and woman did eat of that other tree. God, the Father, put me here, and said:

> 'Behold the man is become as one of us, to know good and evil; and now, lest he put forth his hand, and take also of the tree of life, and eat and live forever. . . .'

"But man was already immortal, though God did not want him to know it until he was ready. And man was not ready to know until he was ready to accept and understand what was meant when God said, 'man is become as one of us'. Now you understand, and the flaming sword no longer bars the way."

The Angel finished speaking and vanished into the tree. I fell on my face with joy and gratitude and, for the first time in my life, sang the praise of God.

After a time, I stood up again and looked at the tree. I knew that my sacred place in the forest was nothing else than the Garden of Eden, though I never knew it. I held out my hands, and the luminous Star of David came off the tree right into my palms. I did not eat, because I had no need to eat, but I put it next to my heart.

In duet, I heard the voice of the Angel and the Goddess saying, "Let each know where the other is."

So, here is my story, O Brother. Here is where I am. Where are you?

THE ARAB

THE ARAB

I

I am an Arab. Neither Christian nor Jew, nor any mixture, but simply an Arab. I am of the tribe of Ishmael and Esau, blessed be him who was deceived and betrayed. Unlike my friend, the Knight, my encounters have been with men, not Gods. That is not entirely true because, as Jews and Christians are aware, God is not realized apart from men, and if you wish to know God, you must know man, and know him in the flesh. I have nothing personally against Jews or Christians—the father of us all is Abraham, after all—though these people have committed many sins against my people. No matter, I am here to tell you a tale and not to engage in religious polemics. I respect you, Sir Knight, in any case, since you, after all, are on the same quest for Allah that we are all on. Enough! To my story.

Once there was a brutal blue calf. You must try to visualize this,

It should be easy for you to visualize a blue calf, but brutal may be somewhat difficult for you. I will explain in what way he, this calf, was brutal. He was brutal in that he ate grass without regard for anything. Not only did he eat his master's fine field of grass, and thus deprive all the other cattle of their fodder, but he also ate into the neighbor's fields. He did so incessantly, and with a greed and an appetite which was both wonderful and horrible to behold. He was not an especially large calf, and extraordinary in no other way except in his color and his appetite. What was the meaning of this strange event of nature? Why did this calf appear to us? We did not know.

One understood from the outset that this calf was unusual. Not only from his color, but from the fact that he weaned himself from his mother within minutes after he was born. He sucked a bit, licked his mouth, as if to say "That's all right, but I would rather be on my own" and promptly started eating grass. He could hardly stand on his wobbly little legs, but grass he could eat aplenty.

At first we were all amused by this funny little calf. We called all the people, from far and wide, to see our strange little animal. We petted him, and encouraged him, to which he responded not at all. After a time, however, the calf was no longer amusing. Rather, he became too much for his master. The master tried all sorts of ways to restrain him. He tied him up—but the calf broke loose. He confined him to a fenced-in place—but the calf leaped over it. He built the fence higher—but the calf somehow managed to dig a tunnel overnight. Now we knew that we were dealing not only with an unusual animal, but that, indeed, he was a monster.

A meeting was called of all the neighbors, for this is what Arabs sometimes do, in the face of a community problem. Each neighbor had a different idea of what to do with the calf. Some were for killing him at once, since he was such a menace to all. Others were horrified by this idea, since it seemed cruel. Still others thought that the calf was a special creation of the almighty and had, therefore, to be humored and respected, much as one behaved in the ancient days with epileptics. Still others tried to minimize the problem and played the game of hoping it would all go away. The meetings were inconclusive, so we all went out to smoke hashish.

The calf went right on eating. In their hashish dreams, some of the people wondered what would happen when this monstrous calf would grow up and become a bull—as if the extent of his destruction were not enough already—but they seemed strangely impotent to do anything about it. As for myself, I had the suspicion that the people really wanted the calf to continue his greediness, and that they had an inkling of what was to come. Since I did not live there myself, and since my view is, as far as possible, not to interfere in Allah's wondrous ways, I held my tongue and enjoyed my hashish with the rest.

A curious thing happened. When the members of the community seemed to abandon any effort to restrain this peculiar animal, when they simply left the matter to God, the calf, for the first time, pricked up his ears and seemed to notice them. Until that time, our precious calf had a marvelous indifference to all those around him. You will recall that he soon abandoned his mother's teat and showed every sign of total disinterest in anything except grass. Now, however, he came to where the group of neighbors were and looked at them. He was puzzled by their lack of interest in him—or so it seemed to me—and did not know what to do.

My neighborly friends quickly noticed this despite their hashish dreams, and slyly winked at one another. They puffed and waited. The calf peered at them for a long time. He then, of his own accord, leaped back into the fenced-in area that had been provided for him earlier.

We all thought: Allah has spoken. Do you need an interpretation of this event, Sir Knight? I trust that you do not. In any case, I am not going to provide it for I cannot. When you have heard me through, you will surely grasp what I am trying to say, beyond the words. I will go on, now, to another tale.

II

You will have grasped, Sir Knight, that one message of my tale is not to interfere in God's wondrous ways. Nature will restrain itself. That, no doubt, is a very bitter medicine for you to swallow, but listen further.

Once there was a marvelous fairy queen who lived alone in the heart of a forest. She was by no means a Sleeping Beauty, since she was wide awake. She was, indeed, beautiful beyond man's belief, but she had seen so much of the worlds, both natural and supernatural, that she retired to her fairy glen to be alone and have none of it. Many were the knights who came to woo her, but none could reach her. She was surrounded by nettles and by plants with gummy substances, the penetration of which caused a person to be hopelessly caught and entwined beyond the possibility of extrication. The great circle of these plants became the final resting place for many a warrior and knight. Their bare bones were ample warning for would-be conquerors.

One day, a Knight such as yourself came along, who was particularly pure in heart. Most of the other knights who dared to seek out the fairy queen came in the spirit of conquest, lust, fame, and other such worldly desires. This young Knight, however, was different. He was, indeed, like yourself, on a quest for the Almighty. He had, of course, a full measure of the generality of human vices, but was redeemed only by this one virtue.

Our young Knight journeyed to the glen of the fairy queen on the command of an Angel, and did not even know why he was so ordered. Now this, of course, was known to the fairy queen and, though her heart had been hardened by her experience of men's willfulness and greed, she took pity on the young Knight. She would certainly not yield to him, nor even answer his questions, but when she saw him struggling in the morass of nettles, gum, and bones of other knights, she mercifully made a path for him. The Knight lurched forward and fell panting and in pain at her feet.

After freeing him, the fairy queen promptly returned to her resting place and gave no other thought to the intruder.

The young Knight recovered from his breathlessness and the pain of his struggle and looked at the fairy queen. The queen ignored him. The young Knight spoke:

"Madam, I do not know why I have been sent here. As you probably know—for such has been my experience on each of my adventures—I have been sent here by an Angel, and I believe that I am supposed to learn something from you."

"Knight," responded the fairy queen, "you are very boring indeed. I took pity on you because you were pure in heart, and on a quest. Do you not see that I have had enough of the world, both natural and supernatural, and that whatever your desire may be it is of no interest to me? Go and tell your Angel that I am bored with him, too!"

Our poor young Knight was crestfallen. This was the worst affront possible. To be thought of as aggressive, deep, lofty, apart from other men—all of this was not painful to him. To be thought of, even, as a fool, provided it was the "fool of God", also was quite acceptable to him. To be called a bore, however, was the deepest wound of all, and he could do nothing except sit down and look sheepish.

Then he started to laugh. He began to laugh and laugh, until his sides ached and belly hurt. "Yes," he thought, "I am indeed a bore! What a boring fellow am I! I come to a fairy queen only because the Angel tells me to. I do not do it on my own accord, or out of my own desire. I do not really take any responsibility in all this, and so I am only a clean-cut, pure sort of thing, mother's little knight, perhaps." He laughed and laughed. "Yes," he continued, and now aloud, "those poor fellows with their bones bleaching in the sun, those bags of bones have more honor than I! They, at least, knew what they were after, knew what desire they had. Yes, madam, I beg your pardon, I am indeed a bore, and will now go back home and tend my garden."

With that, our Knight turned on his heels and started to walk back out of the sacred circle. The fairy queen got as red as a beet and screamed at the Knight.

"You are not only boring, you are also exasperating! Why, you, you. . . ." She spluttered in her rage, and the Knight was halted in his tracks. With a wave of her hand, the Knight was again embroiled in the nettles and gum, this time battling to get out.

In the midst of his struggle, he shook his head at the imponderability of women, both natural and supernatural, and decided that there was no purpose in continuing. He would do better to surrender and die as these others had died, leaving his bones as warning for his brother knights who might come in the future.

But the fairy queen, with her unpredictable nature, was not going to let him die so easily. Once again she parted the ways for him. Was she becoming aware of her own desire for the Knight? The Knight fell panting to the ground again. Now he looked up at the fairy queen with puzzlement in his face, and asked, imploringly, "Madam, what do you want of me? I have left you in peace, am willing to die like a dog and let my bones bleach in the sun, and you do not let me!"

The fairy queen fumed and spluttered. She was about to

encompass him once again in the nettles and gum, but she stopped and laughed instead. Now she laughed as the Knight had laughed—deeply, heartily, and with chagrin at herself.

"Knight," she said, "I beg your pardon. I see that whatever I do to you is wrong. I must confess that I did not know that I desired you myself. It is ever so much more noble to retreat from the world, both natural and supernatural, and be sought after, than to acknowledge that one is desirous oneself. Yes, I see that you have won because you did, indeed, know what you wanted, to serve God. I was furious because you did not want me, whereas I did not know that I wanted you."

The Knight rubbed his wounds and shook his head. "Madam, I no longer know what I want, nor do I know what God wants, and I really do not much care what you want. I am beginning to think that the Buddhists are perhaps right. Desire and wanting is the ground of ignorance, for God and man!" Thus speaking, the Knight fell to his knees and hit the ground with his fists.

Now the fairy queen grew puzzled. She looked at the Knight in hurt and anger, and then started to cry. The Knight was startled by her tears, and came over to her. "Madam," he said, "why are you weeping? I did not intend to hurt you."

"You did not hurt me, you fool!. . .Yes, you did. I told you I wanted you, and you ignored me. Do you not know that is the greatest sin against a woman, human or divine!" With that she arose and strode away.

The Knight mused to himself: "Yes, that is how a woman is—no, not a woman, a woman would be more human—that is how a goddess or fairy queen or sprite is. She sits there unmindful of the death and suffering of hundreds of men who know exactly what they want—her—and gets all aflutter if her needs are not subtly and delicately apprehended at once. Well, I am still alive, and very doubtful indeed whether I want her or not. She can just sit there until she gets more human!"

The Knight rubbed his wounds, and bolstered his pride. The fairy queen sat to one side, more peevish than anything else. They sat thus apart for a very long time. Then, at the same moment, they looked up at each other, smiled, and embraced.

III

Thus far, Sir Knight, my tale has been for you, to edify you in ways that might be helpful to you, since you are something of a moralist.

Before I tell of my experiences, however, I must first say something about myself. I am said to be a handsome man, and I believe it, though such things are, as everyone knows, in the eye of the beholder. I am also said to be an honorable man, though in a way quite different from the Knight. I am honorable in love. That is it. My morals are quite different from Sir Knight, and I have no wrathful Eye of God to placate at every turn. One might say that I serve a Goddess of Love—thought I think of it in no such grand or literal terms, since that would be to offend Allah, who will brook no polytheism. I know only that in serving love, I am also serving the Almighty, for that is my deepest nature and Allah put me here, I believe, to be myself and no other.

When I was a young man, I lived in a city far from here. I was a studious and serious fellow, much involved with my books and my plans were to become either a physician or mathematician. My family was illustrious in both realms and I wanted to follow my ancestral path. I was quiet and reflective, but not withdrawn from life. I enjoyed my friends and the luxurious life made possible by the wealth of my family, but my studies came first. Nor was I aggressive. My body was strong so that few cared to contend with me, but neither did I need to prove myself or seek out the competitive duels and combats of my friends. This was all as it should be—since it was understood that I would be a scholar or healer and no one expects such a person to be violent, even in Arab lands. The reason that I dwell on this fact will be apparent later on.

My life proceeded peacefully and amicably. I was betrothed to a worthy woman of a family of as high a standing as my own and we were pleased with each other. The wedding was to take place at the conclusion of my studies, which was only a few months away and I was in good spirits.

One day, however, as I was looking over the pages of an old volume at a bookstall in the street, I chanced to look up and caught a glimpse of the most beautiful dark eyes that I had ever seen. The girl was veiled and covered from head to foot, except for her eyes. When I saw them, my heart was stricken. To say that an arrow pierced my heart would be foolish. Say only, and more accurately, that I was possessed. I knew that I had to see that girl again, to gaze at her, to have her.

She vanished along the street, in the company of another woman. I hurried after them, but could find them nowhere. Shaken to my foundations, I knew that I could not survive unless I saw that girl again. Studies, marriage, career, all vanished as if they were only an illusion. I searched for her everywhere and made inquiries. It was impossible, of course, because how can one describe an identity from eyes alone? Yet the beauty in these eyes were enough to change the course of a life.

That evening I wandered, disconsolate, into the desert. A yellow crescent moon glowed in the sky as if it had an inner source of light, not reflecting the golden sun setting proudly at the horizon. I sat down on a rock and held my head in my hands. What was I to do? I knew that my life could not continue without that unknown girl, who was already in my thoughts as my beloved. The evening changed into night and I felt chilled. I gathered my cloak around me and started to walk. I walked aimlessly until I saw, in the distance, the red light of a campfire.

Coming close to the fire, I observed a wizened old woman, calmly cooking her supper. She glanced at me quickly and returned to her task. Unwilling or unable to utter a word, I sat down by her fire and warmed myself. We sat silently until the woman offered me a soup which I accepted gratefully to thaw my frozen bones and benumbed heart.

The woman spoke: "I see a young man lost in love. I see him finding his beloved and, in the finding, losing himself. I see heights of ecstasy and bottomless pits of pain." She expressed what I already knew, somewhere deep inside myself, and accepted. Such was the will of Allah, and such was to be my fate. A peace overcame me. I crossed her palm with silver and, without a word, walked back to the city.

When I returned to the city, I was still calm, though feeling a growing excitement at the expected re-encounter with my beloved. I knew that I would find her, and that my life would be changed. I also knew that it was the will of Allah. I let myself be guided by my steps and found my way back to the bookstall where I had first glimpsed her.

It was night, and the stall was closed, but life was continuing in the streets. The muezzin's chant of the evening prayer had ended and the people were swarming about. Among them all, just across the cobbled street, stood the girl, staring intently at me. I caught my breath, felt my knees quiver as our eyes united in irresistible attraction. I slowly crossed the street.

When I reached her, I looked deeply into those eyes which openly received me and drew me in. My soul plunged into their depths as into an unknown abyss where pain and ecstasy are as one. We said not a word to each other, for what was there to say?

I could not embrace her, since that was not proper in my city, nor could I spirit her away, since her companion was close by. After we gazed at each other for some few seconds of eternity, she slipped me a note and hurried off.

For a long time, I stood transfixed on the spot, savoring the memory and unwilling to leave the trancelike state I was in. At last, I lifted up my hand, holding the note, and held it tightly, though careful not to crush it. I dared not read it at that moment, for its' import was too great to be taken in at that unprotected place.

I hurried to my home and my room and only then did I feel free to expose myself to its' contents and allow whatever emotion they produced to take hold of me. The words were simple and brief: "I love you. Meet me tomorrow night." What more was there to be said? How many words I had read in books! And these were the most important of my life.

I slept hardly at all that night, but was filled with desire and restlessness. Only a glimpse of the moon, outside my window, calmed me and my agitated heart.

Next day I went through the motions of my life, but lived elsewhere. No one, I am sure, knew of my state, nor did I feel that I was dissembling. I found that one could live in two places at once, though the one seemed more like a dream. But which was the dream and which the reality? It did not matter. Reflections such as these came to me from habit and from the past, but they seemed to matter little in the face of the feelings that I was having. These feelings gave me delight I had never known.

That night I went to the marketplace and waited at the same place, across from the bookstall. A plan had been forming in my mind, but it was clouded by wild hopes and despair. Was it not possible that this light of my life would be my wife? Could I not fit into the fabric of my ancestral pattern this wild and irrational gift from the Almighty? It seemed quite reasonable. My parents were decent and loving people, far from reproving the experience of love. Even my betrothed could be made to understand and would surely be sought after by hosts of promising young men of the city. Yet something in me knew that this was all wish and illusion. The soothsayress had spoken the truth, though I knew not why. A sadness overcame me.

A moment later the sadness was lifted, for there, before me, was my beloved, veiled like a clouded moon, but radiant with the soft light that shines from her on a darkened night. We met, took hands, and walked out of the city into the desert. Without a word, we walked to a nearby oasis and sat down by its waters. The light of the same moon which was like my beloved caused everything to appear soft and textured, while the gentle wind made the palm fronds tremble just so slightly.

We reached out our arms and held shoulders, as if each was trying to embrace, grasp, comprehend, and adore the other at the same moment. I dared not lift the veil just yet, since I was conflictually filled with both longing to do so and dread. Instead, I let my hands gently fall from her shoulders and follow the outline of her body down the sides. The softness and hardness blended into a graceful line which went through my fingers, up into my arms and radiated through me until I trembled just as the palm fronds did.

My hands had their own life, and paused in their journey at her waist. For an instant, I hesitated, and was gripped with passion. I pulled her to me with force and reached behind her to press her to me. But the force was unnecessary, since she melted into me of her own will—or was it of a will higher than both of us? Our bodies met as if two broken pieces of a bowl were re-united into one vessel where only the seam could be seen.

We held each other so for a long time. The warmth of her body and her love calmed my agitated desire and made me human again. At last, I gently lifted her veil and kissed her deeply on the mouth, not even needing to gaze at that face for its true being was already known to me in an utterly imageless way. Our eyes closed and our souls met in the depths of that kiss—lips touching in that seamed and gentle way of the matching shards of a cup. Moments later our mouths opened and our tongues sought the hidden and moist crevices of the other. Now we were in total embrace, each searching and grasping the other in gentleness and violence, all at once.

It was enough. As if at a signal, we separated and sat down to gaze at each other. Need I say that she was lovely? Her face matched her eyes, with full and sensuous lips and rounded cheeks and curves and lines of endless interest and joy. I longed to follow all the lines therein, and yielded to my longing. She smiled as I did so, until, when I had marked out the glowing form to my contentment, I held her head in my hands and drew her toward me for our second kiss. This one was quick and playful and settling, as if to say, "and that is that, is that!"

We looked at each other and laughed. The merriness of her eyes and of her face delighted me, for with the depth and intensity that I had seen before, it was almost too much to add merriness and joy. Thus it was that the Almighty had sent her to me.

We had yet to speak a word, and my first ones were, "I love you." To these, she simply nodded and blew me a kiss. Words were. . . .what were they? Nuisances, meaningless addenda? Yes. Most of all, they were irrelevant. I did not know her name, her ancestry, her place, her station in life—all of which would be important in the world from which I came—and did not care. No, that is not true. I cared, but it seemed a violation to even ask them. For her part, she said nothing and asked nothing. She simply looked at me, sometimes held out her hand, to touch or be touched and she seemed content that we were together among the palms and by the water.

It grew late, and I said, "We must go."

"Tomorrow?" she asked.

"Tomorrow," I answered. We walked, hand in hand, back to the city, under the clouded light of the moon, and with a touch of the finger, parted where we had met.

Once home, I could reflect a little. Why were we both unable to speak? Did she, too, have this nameless knowledge of the soothsayress that our love was destined to be tragic? I tried to wipe this knowledge out of my mind. Tomorrow, I thought, we must talk and plan, for there is joy in life, and the doom-laden messages of soothsayers are often wrong. So comforted, I fell asleep.

When I awakened, I felt as if I had had a dream, but could not capture it. What was it? What came to my mind was the memory of the soothsayress' words: "I see him finding his beloved and, in the finding, losing himself. I see heights of ecstasy and bottomless pits of pain." Were these in a dream? I did not think so, but suddenly I realized that she said not a word about tragedy, or tragic endings. Losing oneself in the beloved could also mean to find oneself, could it not? Ecstasy and pain are not, necessarily, tragic. I felt comforted, but a small corner of dread persisted. I had fantasies of violence, but from an unnamed source. These, too, I wiped away and lightheartedly went about my day's duties.

That night, we met again and all dread was banished from my thoughts. We ran quickly into the desert, though it was darker now, with hardly any moon at all. We found our way to the oasis and embraced eagerly. I was wild with desire and she seemed to be the same. I clumsily removed her clothes and trembled in my eagerness, hardly aware of the new restraint that she was now showing. I felt it as a maidenish encouragement and it made me even wilder in my desire. I grabbed and I lunged and I took her, as some wild man might.

Then it was over. I was cold and hard, and did not know myself. Then I heard her crying, and looked into her eyes. The light had gone out of them, and now there was only agony. I could not look at her. I turned and ran. I ran, deep into the desert, deep into the darkness, as a hyena would run into a cave; as if knowing his instinctive demonism, hiding this from the world and, if he could, from himself.

I ran until I was exhausted and fell in a heap. First, all was confusion, despair, and agony. Exhaustion was blended with self-hatred and despair with confusion. When I recovered my breath, I ran again. I ran as if the only thing that would calm the violence directed at myself was running. Again exhaustion, again collapse. I must have run most of the night until, at last, I slept.

When I awakened, I was calm and not at all agitated. With clarity, I saw what I was: a man without love. In the recesses of my soul lurked a loveless creature, cold and hard and with a selfish brutality that was beyond my comprehension. I understood why I had refrained from the competitive games and duels. It was not because I was a gentle man, or of the scholarly type, but because I was loveless and not to be trusted. I understood my dread, and regretted my suppression of it. I understood, too, that I had to go into the world to find out who I was, or what I was, and find some way to scourge this demon of lovelessness.

I calmly returned to the city, wrote a letter to my beloved explaining what I must do, entrusting it to a friend. I took a few of my possessions, bade goodbye to my parents and my betrothed and left to wander the face of the world. I tried to explain why I must leave, but none understood. But leave, I must, and so I did.

IV

When I left my ancestral home, I knew clearly that I must make my way to the sea. Just as what had emerged in me was the opposite of all that I had thought resided in my soul, I knew that I must leave all I knew and go to its opposite in the world.

The days of my journey to the sea were long and uneventful. People were kind to me and there were no untoward incidents. The long days of walking also gave me time to reflect upon myself and what had happened. Slowly some perspective came to me and I saw myself more clearly. What had I discovered? That I had a deep capacity for love and its opposite—all at the same time. Before I had met my beloved, I was a quietly contented man, not subject to extremes of any kind. After meeting my beloved, however, I knew I was capable of depths of good and evil. I knew, now, why I had eschewed violence—there was a dangerous and greedy hyena who made his home inside my soul. I was no longer shocked nor guilty about this presence—since this was as much a part of the being that Allah had given me as my love—but knew that something had to be done about it. I concluded that the hyena needed to be fed. If he were fed enough and contented, perhaps he would not be so greedy to devour the good soul upon whom my heart wished to lavish its love. And where should he feed? Of course, where there were other hyenas and jackals and their prey. From stories I had heard as a child, I knew that a somewhat civilized jungle existed among soldiers and sailors. My hyena did not want to kill, only to devour, so it was the sailor's life that I chose. Hunter-sailor I became, and so harkened back to my ancestors of a dimmer past and the demands of an immediate present.

It was easy for me to find a ship that would have me, for there was a war at that time, and much need of men who would fight or work on those ships which carried goods and men from place to place.

The ship that accepted me was called the "Victory" and its crew readily incarnated the vision that my mind's eye had conjured. I saw their souls as animals, much like my own. First there was the Captain, an old and mangy lion who loftily kept himself apart from all the lesser animals. Then there was the Mate, an arrogant and cruel vulture who viewed us all as underlings to provide him what he needed. His first order to me, when he learned that I had been a student, was to give me the lowliest work on the ship. Perhaps he was right to do so, since I was still arrogant, not fully aware that I was, in truth, an animal like the rest. I did his bidding with the subtle obstructionism that the weak use against the strong.

Then there was the Bos'n, a weasel of a man—canny, clever, and self-serving. My fellow sailors included an able and clever tiger, hyenas like myself, and assorted dogs and cats. I resolved to stay close to the tiger, for does not the tiger provide prey which the hyena can devour? When I realized that the enemy of the hyena is the vulture, I was delighted with the rightness of my situation.

So the time went peacefully on our first days at sea. The animals were sharpening their claws with little fights, pacing the deck in their hungers and quietly going about their work, which momentarily distinguished them as men from the animals in their souls. I was easily accepted, once they knew that I did not think myself a lion as a result of my studies, and they heartily laughed when I told them of my animal visions of them all. This endeared them to me, for a man who knows he is an animal is far more to be trusted than one who thinks he is not.

Our first port was in Egypt, and we hungrily went ashore for our food. I attached myself to the tiger, an old and experienced hunter, as did several of the other hyenas and dogs and cats. He led us to a brothel, where a large variety of willing animals, of all colors and races greeted us cordially. There were fat ones and thin ones, tall and short—pigs, cats, and hyenas like myself. My comrades fell to, as soon as the tiger chose his own, a particularly hefty pig, and were joyous. My own hyena, however, perversely refused to eat. Even when cajoled, he declined, so I had to beg pardon and quietly walked down the stairs, to wander in the streets.

Before I had time to reflect upon the perversity of my hyena, and before I had even reached the ground floor, I heard a singing voice which startled me. I turned the corner and walked into a room with a dirt floor and bare, stained walls. The voice belonged to a gaunt Arab man, like myself, who was seated in a stiff chair, strumming an instrument I had never seen. Before him was a gaudily luxurious couch upon which sat a mountainously fat woman. She rested upon it like a sphinx, arms folded and eyes dreamily inward. Her dress was a bright red, with yellow flowers, and she wore numbers of bracelets. Her brown flesh billowed out all around her, but she was majestic in her ampleness. At her feet sat a mouse of a dog, as skinny and bony as she was fat and fleshy.

The Madame—for such she was in this house—motioned me to a chair with the merest blink of an eye. I sat down and listened to the music. The intense young tenor sang of love's pain and joy. I wept with loneliness for my beloved, but the songs soothed my soul, nonetheless.

Thus we sat, and for a long time. I drifted off into timelessness. . . . .I was brought back into time by the laughing sounds of the tiger and my friends coming down the stairs. Tiger tapped me on the shoulder—it was time to return to the ship. I bowed my thanks to the Great Madame and her Serenader, which they acknowledged with a nod, and my friends and I were soon walking in the night.

There was good natured teasing of the tastes of my hyena, but my comrades respected my stillness. We returned to the vessel as animals come back to their lairs.

Next day, the tiger and I set out across the desert to see the great Sphinx. We arrived, weary and hot, but were rewarded with a prospect of that eternal statue which spoke to our depths. The Sphinx put no riddles and we asked no questions. All was as it was, and should be. I knew that the perversity of my hyena was so because I did not understand him and what he wanted—no, that was not entirely true. My hyena knew what he wanted, but my soul knew, too, and now the one or the other could triumph. I must learn how both could be satisfied. I told the tiger these thoughts and he nodded his head in assent. He then looked at the Great Sphinx and said, "both must be fed to their full."

So ended my first voyage and my second adventure into the meaning of love.

V

"Both must be fed." With this thought of the tiger and myself at the foot of the Sphinx, I spent many a later voyage. I was lucky, indeed, that the "Victory" was destined to make a circumambulation of the globe. From Egypt our course was west and north and south and west again. We journeyed to the Arab lands and to lands of the Vikings. We saw the lands of the dark ones of the south, and the yellow ones, as well. And always I sought to attend to the needs of the soul and the needs of the flesh.

But rarely would they meet. The needs of my soul were met in the temples of religion and the temples of art. Strange and wondrous were the ways that the peoples served their gods, and I knew that they all saw Allah in their own manner. The needs of the flesh were met by the variety of the women I met and had—light, dark, ample, lean. The desires of the flesh were immediate and powerful, those of the soul lasting and more variegated. It seemed that my lusts were satisfied, but in truth they were not. The soul did not restrain the flesh, but would not participate in its satisfaction. So I tried to force the soul into it and then out of it. The former was impossible and the latter very difficult. I broke my Moslem law and drank of the fiery waters. This made me joyous and carefree, but did not drown the pain of my soul.

I tried to surfeit the hyena in every way that I could, sometimes with many women, sometimes in utter abandonment. This led only to vomitus and despair. By now I was indistinguishable from all the other sailor-animals and my tiger friend no longer accompanied me. It was as if he knew that I was become as a tiger myself and now must find my own way. Even the vulture and the lion kept their distance from me as I now became wilder in my attempt to kill the one side or the other in me.

The months went by and my conflict increased. The days and nights at sea, and the blessed needs of work gave me the time for reflection and pause. The days and nights on land found me hungrily seeking my goal.

Finally, exhausted, I came ashore in India. I was refreshed with all the new sights and strange manners. I was entranced by their music and by their dance. I was delighted with the temples and with their art. But so had I been pleased before, in all the other wondrous countries that I had seen. Neither delight nor new sights could satisfy me, however. What was I to do with the animal inside me who would neither be stilled, nor allowed full rein?

In despair of finding a union of body and soul, animal and feeling, I wandered about and found my way to the Temple of Kali, the great many-armed Mother Goddess of the Hindus. I did not know her story, and was not inclined to inquire too deeply into this polytheistic religion which would be an abomination to my still entrenched monotheism. I knew, in my depths, that my experience of all these other faiths was merely esthetic, and the true religion of my soul was the battle of the animal against love, of soul vs. body.

The Temple of Kali was small, as temples go, but beautiful. It was constructed of myriads of tiles of various colors. Within the holy of holies, I understood that the toe of the Great Goddess was enshrined. It seems that she was dismembered in the heavens, all her parts falling to places where temples were subsequently built. It was not the theology or the story which gripped me. No. There, in the midst of the altar lay a dead and sacrificial goat. His eyes were bulging, and many parts of him were cut away. The pilgrims had taken their holy toll of the animal and went away satisfied.

When I looked at the dead, staring eyes of that goat, I knew something that could not be put into words. I knew only that the goat was myself. I knew that what I had called hyena and tiger were indeed all that, but here was their grim representative. Ancestral memories were revived, and I remembered with pain the lamented goatskin of Esau and of his deception by Jacob. I remembered our father, Abraham, and of the miraculous animal which took the place of his son. I knew that the goat, this strange goat in a strange temple in a strange land, was that same goat which has plagued the people forever. Here it was, stilled and sacrificed.

I stood long at the altar, eyes magnetized by the eyes of the goat, vaguely aware of the buzzing of flies about his carcass. Soon I became conscious of voices. A little group of musicians and singers were chanting from their holy books, Mahabarhata or Ramayana. I did not know the words or the story, but was soothed by the hypnotic repetition of the voices. An old wise man, dressed in a simple white cloth, addressed me. He spoke wise words, I know, but I heard nothing. I understood one thing only, the goat was sacrificed, and I could love. A great peace overcame me.

As night fell and the crescent moon rose in the sky, a young man pulled at my sleeve, insistently. I was drawn out of my reverie and saw what he held in his hand. It was a magnificent star sapphire, a heavenly blue all around with a radiating white star within. I knew at once that this was to be the gift for my beloved. I purchased it with all the money left in my pockets and returned to my ship. The hyena and tiger were stilled and what remained of the bulging eye of the goat was the star sapphire in my pocket.

So ended my seafaring voyages and my third adventure into the meaning of love.

VI

When the "Victory" had completed its circumambulation of the globe, I found myself where I had begun. I was in excellent spirits and was glad to say a fond farewell to my companions, the good tiger, the dogs and cats and hyenas. The weasel was non-committal, as was the lion—for they had had little to do with me—but even the vulture gave me a grudging pat on the back.

With great joy I returned to my ancestral home, laden with gifts for my friends and family. I was greeted with warmth and pleasure by all, who were full of curiosity about my experiences. I told them as best I could, though my words came only with difficulty, for I was thinking always of my beloved. My queries about her were met with an uncomfortable silence all around. At last, I demanded to know where she was, and they told me. She was living, still, in the same city, and I excitedly set out to see her and present her with the treasured star sapphire from India.

When I arrived, I was trembling as I had when I first set eyes upon her, and this was in no way relieved when she opened the door to me. No longer was she veiled; now she was a glorious free woman of beautiful countenance and graceful figure. I let her speak no word, but quickly took her off to the oasis where our love was experienced. She was unquestionably overjoyed to see me, yet I felt her reluctance to join me. I thought that this, indeed, was the remnant of that fateful night that had sent me out into the world and I was sure that when she heard my story, all resistance would vanish.

It was so. As I told her of my adventures and conflicts, her eyes widened, and she listened compassionately. When I told her of the goat, and of my struggles therewith, she sighed deeply. When I told her of the sapphire, and showed it to her, and spoke of my love—she began to weep. She wept and wept for a long time, and I did not understand. Finally she stopped her weeping, embraced me, and told me, haltingly, her story. I will not repeat it in her words, as I was too stunned to take it all in, but, in brief, it was as follows:

That fateful night, when I had raped her, she was indeed darkened. The light had gone out of her eyes, not because of my lust and desire, which she welcomed, but because of my lack of love. Here I nodded sorrowfully. She did not blame me for this deficiency, however, but she blamed herself for her incapacity to evoke love. This statement astonished me so much that she had to repeat it several times. She blamed herself for her incapacity to evoke love in me! In despair, she received the message from my friend that I was going away, presumably forever, and was utterly disconsolate. My friend was kind to her, befriended her, and in truth, fell in love with her. My beloved was healed thereby and gradually grew to love my friend. Shortly before my return, they were married and were very happy together.

This news shocked me. Many feelings passed through me: hurt, anger, despair. We sat silently for a long time, and then I knew what I had to do. "Let this ring be a token of our love, a love that was meant to teach us to love. I love you, and will love you always."

She looked up and accepted the ring, as I carefully placed it on her finger. I embraced her and chanced to look up into the heavens. There, in the crisp night air, hovered a marvelous crescent moon, its curved edges glistening, almost enclosing a shining star of Venus. That emblem of my people was also my own, and I knew that it was a living symbol of my capacity to love.

Then my beloved and I made love—and we were happy.

We returned to the city in peaceful joy.

In the days that followed, I had time to reflect upon what I had experienced, and what Allah had set in my path. I became aware that what had really interrupted me in my studies was a realization in the depths of my being, but unavailable to my consciousness, that I was insufficiently capable of love, and that I could never become a healer without this capacity. The experience of my beloved, and all the adventures as a consequence of it, were absolutely necessary for me to enhance this capacity. I now felt right about becoming a healer, and soon resumed my studies. My education for love was further advanced when I saw my betrothed. She, indeed, had loved me deeply, and I did not know it. She had waited patiently for me, and now my love, in truth, began to flow freely to her. We grew closer and closer, loved more deeply. In time, I married, in love; in time, I became a healer, in love; in time, with my beloved, I became a friend, in love.

So ended my fourth adventure into the meaning of love, and so ends my tale.

Thus it is, O Knight, that I meet you here in your garden, which is also my garden. Each of us had his Eden, and here we meet. Come and embrace me, O Knight, as I embrace you, in brotherly love and friendship! Look, there above us, our ancestors, Jacob and Esau, are also embracing, in the Tree of Immortality! Look there, in the heavens, and on the Tree, do you not see it? There I see my crescent moon with its star, and I see that my star and your star are one! Let it be so, O My Brother; let it be so in heaven and on earth, that men are brothers and as one!

THE "RONIN"

THE "RONIN"

I

I am a Ronin—or rather, I have been a Ronin, and am no more. A Ronin, my friends, in our language, is a warrior, a samurai who has no lord. He wanders in search—because a man without a master, a warrior without a lord, a disciple without a guru, what is he? Do not answer, for you two men, Sir Knight and Sir Arab, already know what I mean. I can tell this by your stories, though I am puzzled by much of what you say.

I only know that I am here with you now, in that place that is called Eden for you, Sir Knight, and Paradaizo for you, Sir Arab, and that, in truth, is the same for me—though we call it "The Pure Land." It is, indeed a miracle for us all to be here, as you would call it, Sir Knight. I am loathe to call it that myself because the miraculous has no special place in my view. There is no need for such a word since all life is miraculous.

My view on the matter is expressed by one of our Masters, who said, "I do not rely on God; I respect Him." You can see at once, Sir Knight and Sir Arab, how we differ.

We have come together for a purpose, it seems. We have come here to understand one another and to embrace one another. This we can do only after we have told our stories. I am desirous of telling you my story, but first I must tell you, Sir Knight, and you, Sir Arab, some of my reactions to your stories. You, Sir Arab, have already done this for the Knight, with your first two parables, which I find most interesting. Thus I must tell you my own reactions, and then get on with my own tale.

Compared with my experiences, Sir Knight, yours seem more complex, with emotions and divisions which seem different from my own. For me, there is only one triangle, not two. My experience of myself consists of my "self" with all its faults and sufferings, the saving force of the Buddha, and finally, the experience or the reality of the Wordless realm: Emptiness, Sunyata,. Suchness, Naturalness; whatever the word. Just one little triangle.

I have a difficult time feeling such symbols as God, Goddesses, Angels, Snakes. I understand bits and parts which parallel Buddhistic thoughts. Such as the idea of the incompleteness of God without man. Amida's Vow, for example. He chose never to seek absolute perfection while even one sentient being suffered. Or Amida, too, as a parent, (because of its emotional meaning, not metaphysical), and man, his children. But Amida can't be a parent without children.

Most of all, the union of opposites is a central idea in Buddhism. Actually, it is the only important idea. There are numerous opposites which are stated as: This world is, as is, the Pure Land. The world of Birth, Suffering, and Death is, as is, Nirvana. Defilement and Ignorance is, as is, the Supreme

Understanding. Man and the Absolute Truth are, as is, One.

In your story, Sir Knight, from the Buddhist standpoint, the snake, the witch, the goddess, the horse, the forest, the God, the ocean, the maiden, the flashes of light, and even you, O Knight are all One.

For you, Sir Arab, I have only compassion. Your way seems simpler and more direct to me. Maybe you are more Oriental, like myself. I too have had to do with the animals, as you will see, though our solutions are different.

Gentlemen, it is strange. I feel close to you both because our goal is the same and the intensity of our drive is the same. But I feel different because you want to know and experience all the parts and thus bring them into union, while I go from the standpoint of denying everything, even the denial itself.

You know, I really have nothing to say. Life is like a sword, glinting in the sun. As simple as that; there is nothing to say. And we live on the edge of that sword; one slip and one meets death. To be able to die without fear is all that matters. Until then, just drink your *sake* and do what you must. Wander the earth, like a lion. Like a lion, die when your time comes. Leaving no trace. For a man who had nothing to say, I've said quite a bit! Perhaps I have something in common with my Western friends, after all. Ha!

Now, to my own story.

As I have said at the outset, I have been a Ronin, a warrior without a Lord. It was not always so. When I was a youth, I apprenticed myself in a school of swordsmanship. We were many, we students, and we served our Lord and Teacher devotedly. I was a reserved type, and accustomed to staying by myself. I was inclined to be cold and distant, even though my burning heart was filled with desire and emotion. It is often so with us, a fact which Westerners are not able to grasp very well.

I trained long and diligently. I struggled so hard, in fact, that I was often exhausted and in despair at my inability to reach my goal and master my task. In time, however, I grew very proficient—so proficient, indeed, that I was able to defeat all my fellow pupils. At length, my master acknowledged that he had nothing more to teach me. He blessed me and told me to go forth for further enlightenment. I bowed and went forth in joy and anticipation. I traveled throughout the land and sought encounters with swordsmen of every shape and talent. Sometimes I was defeated and sometimes I was victorious and with every encounter my skill grew. I was able, in time, to find other Masters who took me further in my craft. After many years of effort, I was able to perfect myself to a degree which seemed satisfactory.

It came to pass, however, that when I returned to my ancestral home, I was honored, but deceived. My skill and talent were beyond question, but my former Masters grew old and narrow. They were jealous, it seemed, of what I had accomplished and were in fear of losing their power. As it is, sometimes, with the old who cannot bend gracefully, they turned ever more rigid. I sorrowed, for it is in the nature of my land to respect the old and do all possible to avoid the shame of losing face. I tried to keep my peace and do what I could to advance our common school of swordsmanship. In time, pupils came to me to seek me out as a Master. They sought not the Elders, and it was for this, I think, that the Elders increased in their jealousy and irritation. Gossip grew, and I know not what was said of me.

When the time came for me to be fully acknowledged as a Master in my own right, the Elders banded together and looked piously down their noses at me. They nodded their hoary heads and said that I was not ready, that I was more a butcher than a swordsman, and so on. At first, I could not believe my ears, and I laughed. When I saw that they meant what they said, I grew both furious and disconsolate. What could I do? They refused to reason or discuss. They looked for my submission, without even being honest enough to openly demand it. They hid in their pomposity, for they were, no doubt, afraid of my swordsmanship.

There was nothing to do except leave the Masters and the School and wander alone in the world. A Ronin. A warrior without a Lord. A disciple without a Master. A Master without recognition.

I wandered for a long time. After a year or so, I was no longer furious at the deception and betrayal by my former teachers, and was able to realize that what they said had a grain of truth in it. I was Master of my craft, but not master of myself. I was, indeed, still attached to fame, recognition, power—in short, to desire. I knew full well that the swordsman's craft was nothing without Enlightenment, and that I was, in truth, immersed in the illusion of this world—bound up with ignorance and desire.

I resolved to retreat into the forest, where I could meet myself alone, without a Master, without assistance and without a light.

II

I retreated into the forest where I remained alone for many days and nights. At first I could think of nothing but my own despair. I was alone and lonely. This was a shock to a man like myself who had been very used to thinking of himself as a lone one, who can wander the world without need of anyone. Ha! I thought, this is salutary in itself—I must have been attached to the idea that I am alone and a lone one. My secret desire for fame and recognition is no better and no worse than this secret illusion that I can be utterly non-attached to people.

So, I accepted my loneliness and despair and came running back to my friends. I acknowledged all this without losing face and thus could return to my isolation and aloneness in a new way. I understood that one needed one's aloneness and isolation, along with one's need for family and friends. My mountain retreat was no place but a state, and a condition to which I could go at any time.

With this, I decided to look at the state of my soul. It was clearly an animal, a kind of ox or bull. I was well aware that my main preoccupation over many years had been to somehow cope with that animal inside me which was black as black can be, and wild and unruly and given to fits and starts and wanderings of all sorts. That animal of my wildly ignorant and lustful soul. Every desire that I had ever known was contained therein. Even the desire not to desire was contained in the hairy breast of that wild and snorting creature. Yes, I had seen him in every state: asleep, lusting, chaotic, well ordered and disciplined, wild and adventuresome, frightened, joyous and aggressive. I did everything possible to tame him. I restrained him with ropes. I whipped him with as many lashes as I could manage. Yes, I had done all these things. I had even given him his full way. To which he responded with whims and chaos and hungers which immediately set the rest of my soul into guilt and despair all over again.

I was no stranger to the animal of my soul and all his movements. So this time it was no small surprise to see that he had whitened considerably! That was extraordinary! After all these years of taming and fighting and struggling with this passionate bull of my soul, with all his rages, lusts, disregardings—now I saw him, indeed, whitening, whitening, whitening. How was this possible?

Now I had to reflect. All these years of my effort and now when I simply accepted my needs to be with people, and accepted my needs to be alone as well, now my poor bull was whitening. I could only conclude that he had whitened because I had accepted him! But I had also to conclude that I could accept him because he had whitened. Yes, a koan, indeed. The sound of one hand clapping. It is the same. The bull whitens because you accept him, and you accept him because he has whitened. So that is what those old foolish Masters were always talking about? Well, so be it. I will not challenge it; here in front of my nose is a whitening Bull! Indeed, I shall have to see how it is that he whitens. Will he wander off again? Shall I follow him? Shall I let him go? Should I discipline him?

Oh, there is despair! All the rights and wrongs, all the shoulds and shouldn'ts. Then my bull is black again, and one must start from the beginning. How will I ever learn that what is, is what matters? How will I learn to accept that I cannot accept? Oh, oh! There he goes, down and around and biting his own tail, and I whip him and defeat him, and he laughs and is morose, and I am a fool once more! Ha!

Now I simply stay with him. There he is, white and black, with the rope tied into his nostrils; but the rope hangs loosely. He looks at me; I look at he. He smiles, I smile. I go sit upon his back. Will he accept me? I sit, comfortably. Then he senses my anxiety, and he throws me. I am back on the ground, and he laughs. I laugh as well, but I beat him again. He groans, and I laugh. He laughs and I groan. He is not yet ready. I am not yet ready. I cannot sit upon his back, but I can walk with him, and by his side. This I can do.

So, we walked together for many days. I held the reins very loosely—so loosely at times that it was as if I did not hold them at all. Often I would look at him to see how he was. Now, when I smiled, he smiled back. That in itself told me that he was a most remarkable bull-ox. A smiling bull-ox? Yes, that, too is like the sound of one hand clapping, or where your lap goes when you stand up.

I rejoiced: the Smile of the Bull-Ox! Now I laughed. I laughed and laughed and laughed. Everything was becoming very amusing to me. Was I going mad? No, surely not. The cosmos was a very great joke: It was the sound of a Bull-Ox smiling.

Now I could sit and play my flute. I played at first carefully and delicately. I did not want to stir up this smiling bull-ox. But no, had I forgotten? Music can charm the beast, and so it could, and so it did. I played sad songs and mournful ones, and I wept. I played happy songs and I laughed. Then I sang. I sang every song I knew, and many that I did not know, but simply made up. My voice was first parched and squeaky, and too loud and too soft. It needed an oiling, or a tempering just the way that my sword did. I tempered it. With sweet water, and wine as I could find it. Heated rice-wine, how softly it goes down the gullet! How delicate it is! How little it affects you! Until you stand up and are required to sit right down again.

But such a fuss about my needs! That is too demeaning of the swordsman! With that, the bull turned black again, and snorted and ran about, and kicked me and made me very nervous indeed.

You know of such bull-oxes in the West, do you not? Yes, of course you do, I had forgotten. You, Sir Knight, surely know of that tradition of the vaulting of the beast, and you, Arab-San, you know full well of the tradition of the slaying of the beast. Yes, that is how you are, are you not? You master and you slay. Yes, I know that you understand it as a way to master yourself with grace and charm and courage. But do you love the animal? No, love only to slay it, and eat it, or sacrifice it.

I cannot say you nay, for I, too, have fought this creature and have longed to slay him. I cannot slay him, for I am slayed thereby. I cannot tame him, unless I am tamed. He and I are one. But being one is nothing if I cannot mount his back and walk with him peacefully home, playing the tune upon my flute. That I long to do. That desire is illusion, too, and down and black he goes, and down and black I go too.

> Will you listen black-white ox?
> Will the music calm you?
> Does your ear harken to its sound?
> Or do you fear I'll harm you!
>
> You are right to fear, you know,
> For I am blacker still than you.
> You are only a beast,
> An animal, fancier than me.
> But I have a mind that will not be stilled
> Deadlier by far than thee.
>
> But we can not be parted:
> Neither you from me, nor me from It.
> And if I can not be parted from me,
> Then neither You from It.
> So fear not, oh ox.
> For two are one, and three are one
> And the saving force of the Buddha is
> Upon us.

III

Many days we wandered, the bull and I. Of course we wandered together, for we could no longer be parted, Now I saw him whitening, whitening, and I was joyous. Then I saw his whitening was too white, as if all the life and joy were going out of him, and I grew worried, lest my bull become a cow and just be content to chew the cud all day. At this, my bull laughed. Yes, he laughed indeed. To you it might sound like a snort, since it comes from my bull and not from your own, but to me it was surely a laugh. A great deep laugh, that began in the belly and worked its way up and out. As if he were to say, "Oh, my master, you have tried to tame me and make me good, and now when I am, you grow irritable and think me too tame. Who is it that must be tamed? Hunger of a soul? Or power-tyranny of a master?

Thus it was that I imagined that my animal spoke to me. I, indeed, could imagine it, could I not? For he was and is the animal of my own soul and who, if not I, can know his language? I listened to the animal of my soul and I ruefully agreed with him. The tamer must be tamed, and if there is no love, there is no point. Thus the flute. Ah, to play a flute without love is impossible, is it not? I played once again, but aside and near him, my ox-bull friend, not astride him.

I did not know why I did not try and ride him once more, but I waited. Then I saw. What did I see? I saw a cat leap upon his back. I saw a man dig a goad into his side. I saw him teased by a cape. All this I saw. Ashes! said I. I have always thought that the whitening of my bull, his taming has always to do with me. Now I see. There are those others, those cats and goads and people and capes.

My ox-bull does not know what hits him. In a moment, he is snorting and raging and stuck and does not know who has done this to him. Then they say, "What a wild bull! What a vicious fellow! My!" I do not know it either, and lament that it is all my fault. Oh, precious bull, friend of mine! I have forsaken thee. "They" have been able to fool me and thee. Whether they have wanted to or not. Oh, good bull, we must become canny, you and I. The willow on the bank is green, and can just stay that way, but it, too, can be crushed by a boot. Bull, you must see and smell and hear. Ah, now, that is the reason for all those sense organs! Was I blind? Indeed, I was! I thought that all his sense organs had to do with inner vision alone! Ah, what a fool, what a foolish fool of a fool of a fool! Yes, these are to tell him when there are cats and goads and brutes and capes about. It is enough to know that he screams because he has been pierced!

Ah, brave bull! Now we dance, you and I! Let us dance, you on all fours, I on all twos. We dance, for I have discovered it. I have discovered what every fool in the world has already known! Ah, congratulations to me, and now, I will listen to thee, friend Bull. When you snort, I will guess it is because you have been hit!

Ah, brave bull, you do not speak.
And because you do not, I am slow to understand.
And so slow am I, that I am more foolish yet.
And you go down, and I go down, and we neither of us know
What has happened to us both.

When the ox-bull and I completed our dance, I took him down into the world again with me. I was ready to test my new insight and to see if, indeed, I could ride on his back, get off again, and be aware when he was being stabbed.

We walked peacefully into the city, and no one remarked about my bull and myself, for we all have ox-bulls, have we not? We all agree not to pay attention to each other in this regard, do we not? It is all so that no one will really criticize us for our animal souls, is that not true? I believe it to be. It must be added that the ones who criticize most are, in reality, quite unaware of their own animal souls. These, poor things, are either old and dead, like the elders, or have mashed their animal souls beyond any hope and thus are resentful that any other animals are alive. Very sad, but painfully true, I think, don't you?

No matter if you agree or not, my ox-bull and I came into the marketplace to see if we could be accepted. Sometimes I did it angrily and badly, sometimes elegantly. Then there were those who shook their capes at him—they were hungry for games and competitive events. I was tempted to bring out my sword, but realized that that was no longer an issue at all: I had to protect my bull without provoking another and being cat-like, cape-like or goad-like in return—if I could. Sometimes I could and sometimes, I could not. Ah, was that it? Was I now really so free and detached that I was free of the desire to be non-attached? With that, my bull fell down in the mud, I atop him, and muddy, too. Now I laughed and laughed, and my bull laughed too.

Now see me there, can you? I am walking peacefully in the marketplace atop my ox-bull. I am playing the flute peacefully, and I laugh. Sometimes I laugh, sometimes I cry. Sometimes I am angry, sometimes I am peaceful. The bull falls down and the bull gets up.

I drink when I am thirsty, I eat when I am hungry. Now and then I sleep, and am as lazy as can be. Now and then I have desire, and now and then I hear fear. Fear is what I hear—or desire is what I hear. But I hear and not fear—or rather, I hear fear and hear desire, but I no longer fear desire. Do you know what I mean? Look at the rose! How it grows! Listen to my tune as I walk and sit on the back of my bull.

Oh! Ox-bull, I love thee.
Oh! I know thee.
To sit sweetly upon thy back-
No reins.
To quietly walk home—
No reins.
Or to fear with thee and follow that—
No reins.
Your snout turns upward to my tune.
My flute turns downward to your rhythm.
Is it noon, with sun aloft?
Or night, with moon serene?
Ah, ox-bull, what does it matter?
Man and Bull are one.

IV

Now, the animal has gone out of sight, and I sit alone, atop the mountain, looking at the darkening sun and misty moon. Rainy it is, and cloudy. Nature is sad and beautiful. Yes, you surely know how our nature is, for you have seen the paintings of our Masters. Nature copies the paintings of our Masters, does it not?

It is nice, to sit serenely, with whips put away. Now despair has taken me over once again. It is not the animal, poor soul of a bull-ox, who has nagged me and tormented me and driven me and kept me from my peace. No, it is not he. Well, let me say, in fairness, that it is no longer He, this bull-soul of mine. No, not He. Nay, it is Me. . .Yes, yes, yes. It is the I, the Me, the one who Speaks, in His God-Almightiness. That is the one who puts me in despair.

What a pipsqueak is the little ego, pompously and vainly sitting atop it all. Thinking that it can, or should lead the animal at all. Yes, the animal has gone out of sight, all right. But the Man is still here, the Man that I am! The vain and stinking man that I am. Ah, this I saw in the Elders. Their vain, pompous, little pretensions, lording over their fellow creatures, as if they knew, at all, what is best for another, or how he should be! Ah, and that awful little creature is, of course, me, too. It is I that is vain, and ambitious, and cruel, and it is, save us all, the "I" that wishes to retreat from the "I."

Let me fall away from myself. Let me bury my head 'neath the mat, 'neath the wood of the pillow. But I cannot escape myself. Wherever I look, I find myself. It is the I who seeks to escape. It is the I that I find when I do escape. It is the I that I see in thee, no matter how I disguise it and change it and move it and account for it.

Oh, give me my sword, for now I know what to do with it! Oh, I must plunge it within—take it into my belly and rip and put an end to this Me—this bloated little me. Death, you are not to be feared, you are to be welcomed as the ender of this meaningless and pompous little kabuki drama of mine. Silence! Even my tongue, as it speaks, continues the proclamation of the I. Silence, tongue. Silence! The one who proclaims silence, who demands it, is also the pompous little tyrant. Oh, oh, oh! The groans come out of my belly, as if the sword were already within. The groans are not from pain of the wound, self-inflicted, but are pains that self inflicts them. Where can I flee from self? Where can I go? I follow me everywhere!

Has it always been so? Was it this that Gautama endured? Is it this that leads them to hold up one finger? Or a flower? Or to keep one's finger to one's lips? Or to slap the other in the face? A thousand ways of saying, "Do not ask me, for I do not know! Not only do I not know, but if I were to speak, I would already show that I do not know, and that this pompous little ego of mine is already thinking and proclaiming that it knows." Yes, surely these great and wonderful Masters knew that. The demon of it all is the "I", the little me. No, not your I, but my I. As I say it, I proclaim the specialness of My "I". Oh, pain, oh, agony, oh wounds of the soul much greater than that of the flesh.

Where can I go to escape me? Where can I hide? No use asking the question. For the questioner is always I.

Let me turn to you. If I look at the you, then, perhaps, I escape the I. So, I look at you, and what do I see? Ah, it is already finished, because it is the I that questions what it sees. Even if I were to question it another way, it could only report that it is the it, is the it, is the it, is the it, into an eternity of its that are I's.

So then, if it cannot be escaped, then let us love it. Ha! Now I escape by calling me "us." Like a fancy court. Or a school of swordsmen, all contained within the One that is Me! Oh, your Lordship of Myself, must I now address you as a plural, as a school of Lords? Fine, another way of illusion and self-deception. Oh, most great and glorious and pompous little ego! I bow down before you, for who could possibly be great enough to bow before you and be received by you, than you yourself! It is not enough that I touch my head to the floor to you, I must be totally flattened. There, does that please you?. . . .No? It does not? Because it is still only the I that does it? Totally flattened or totally flattered—it is the same!

Let me run screaming into oblivion!

Will death, then, do it? Will that beloved state dissolve once and for all this sated samurai self which seeks self and self alone? No, surely not. For the wheel of samsara will continue. Life after life, kalpa after kalpa, aeon after aeon, until all karma is dissolved. So, then, pompous little man, if not this ego, then another, and another, and another. Until the sands of time are all piled up on the beach of eternity.

Nothing, then, little Ronin; nothing, then little Samurai; nothing, then, little nothing, except to accept this pompous little ego of yourself. Nothing to do but accept it. What was it that the great Master once said: "One day you will find that the one who needs all your care and love is yourself." Ah, now I see what it is that he meant. That is what he meant, he meant—that is what he meant. Now, I can sing my song. Shall I sing it? Yes.

The great little "I" shall love
The great little "I" shall love
The great little "I" shall love
The wicked little "I".
The great little "eye" sees the wicked little "I"
The great little "eye" sees the wicked little "I"
The great little "eye" sees the wicked little "I"

It sees and is blind to itself.
The great little "Eye" needs the wicked little "I"
The great little "Eye" needs the wicked little "I"
To see.
The wicked great "Eye" sees the good little "I"
The wicked great "Eye" sees the good little "I"
The wicked great "Eye" sees the good little "I"
And stabs itself with the sword.
Weep not, great Eye. Cry not, little I.
And who is this who says, "Weep not, cry not"?
Is it not another "I"?
No, it is not. It is not.
Who is it then?
And who is it then, who asks?
It is Nature who asks.
It is Nature who asks.
It is Nature who asks of itself.

I repeat: It is Nature who asks,
It is Nature who asks,
It is Nature who asks
Of itself.
And who is this who says, "I repeat"?
It is "I", of course, it is "I".
Do you understand?
Do you understand?

I do; I do.
Eye do; Eye do.
Aye, do; Aye, do.

And there, way up in the air,
There it is: A circle fair.
Sunyata: Suchness
Mandala: Muchness.
And Man has Gone out of Sight.

A tree stands in the forest.
Its trunk arches and bends.
No miracle. All do it.
But see: How one side of trunk
Grew round,
And other side of trunk,
Grew round,
And both meet again,
Making a hole.
A hole, is it?
Or a whole?
An empty nothing of everything,
In the middle of the tree trunk.
And that is what is meant
When we say: The tree is treeing.

A flower sways in the wind.
Its petals hold onto its power.
Does it love itself?
Like a woman stroking her breasts?
Yes.
As the roots love the ground.
Little roots: fine flower.
Great roots; gross flower.
Roots of the flower.
Roots of the tree.

They sway and bend and arch
And seek their Source.
Up into heaven, down into earth.

And that is what is meant,
When we say: The flower is flowering.

The painter sees the tree-hole,
Though he is blind.
The painter hears the flower,
Though he is deaf.
The painter smells his art,
Though he has no nose.

He tells us all,
Though he cannot speak.
And man is a painter,
Is he not?
And knows the sound of flowers,
The smell of visions,
The words of pictures.

And that is what is meant,
When we say: the painter is painting.

For man is manning
And trees are treeing
And life seeks its goal;
Which is: to be.
The bee is beeing,
Why can't we?

The Source.
It speaks:
Where, in the thunder of the Name,
Is the ghost?
The one who speaks without body?
Does he exist?

Apart from Nature?
No.
Nothing, then is supernatural?
No, all is natural.
And the best must be Super-Natural.
What is most natural,is.

Even anti-natural?
Yes. Even anti-natural.
For nature has its opposites,
Nature *is* its op-o-sits.
Strange word, listen:
Op-look! O-oh! Sits-be!

And that is what is meant,
When we say: nature is naturing.

VI

So I came down from my mountain, and no one knew that I had been away. No one knew at all, at all—no one knew at all. That, Sir Knight, is a miracle, I grant you. That is the saving force of the Buddha that is upon us.

For when He is with me and I am He, I have bliss-bestowing hands. I walk with my laughing face, and paunchy belly, and I am at home with wine-bibbers, vagabonds, and tramps. As well as warriors and teachers and geishas. And wives and children and ants. We and they are all Buddhas, are we not? Yes, we are. Buddha and his Bo tree, and you and your Tree of Immortality and I? Yes, I. Now, I walk without a sword. Now I carry a staff, and a lamp, and people come to me for bliss and enlightenment.

What do I tell them? I say, "Go away, there is nothing to know!" For now I know that what the Old Masters have said is true: There is nothing to know. I also know—and this is the sad and wonderful part—that we all have to find this out for ourselves and in our own way and in our own time, and many times over, and with many gurus, and with no gurus.

So, come my friends, Sir Knight and Sir Arab, drink with me and embrace me, as I embrace me, as I embrace thee. For my tree is as yours, Sir Knight, and my animal is as yours, Sir Arab. My triangle, too: My self with all its faults and sufferings, the saving force of the Buddha, and Sunyata: the suchness of things. My triangle, too.

Look, look, see!: The Great Circle of the Rising Sun, Setting Moon, and Empty Hole! You see it there in the trunk of the Tree? It can contain your Star, but need not. It can contain your Crescent, but need not. It is all one, as I have said, and we have said. So, my brothers, I salute you as Buddhas!

JULIA, THE ATHEIST-COMMUNIST

JULIA, THE ATHEIST-COMMUNIST

My name is Julia. I have no idea how I came to this strange place; it is not my idea of Paradise at all. As a matter of fact, I am—or have been—an atheist for a good portion of my life. To me, Paradise has been a myth. I accept that this is where we are, though I cannot tell if I am in a dream or not. Perhaps you are all part of my dream—or I am part of yours—I cannot tell.

I can say, however, that it is strange. You, Comrade Knight, look like something out of the Middle Ages. You, Arab, seem like a man of the eighteenth century. Or, if you are of my century, you are not like any Arab that I know, with your cattle and fences, but more like a cowboy! Ronin, since I know nothing of the Orient, I cannot tell from whence, in time, you come, but I would guess that you belong to the early nineteenth century.

I say all this, not because time matters to you—you would have said so if it were—but because it is important to me. You all seem somewhat timeless, eyes on the spirit and eternity. You do not even mention your names, as I do. You seem to be nameless, though I know better than that. Perhaps men are more impersonal than women are. All your differences are resolved in "The Quest" and, specifically, the quest for God, or Union, or Enlightenment. You are ready to take all eternity to find it. I don't know if that is particularly masculine, or because you all seem to belong to another age, but at any rate, it does not suit me.

I am clearly a child of the twentieth century. I feel myself to be very mortal, indeed, and am convinced that there is only one life—that into which we are born and suffer and die. I believe that it is our task to make the most of this life and to improve conditions on this dreary planet, for us and for our posterity. It is mankind that is to evolve and produce Paradise on Earth, not individual men, and not God.

Well, enough. Let me tell you my story, since this seems to be what we are all here for. You will understand my views from it, rather than from my troubling to give you a lecture about it. I became disenchanted with lectures and polemics long ago.

I was born in 1926, in the common era, in a forested region in eastern Poland. There were only two houses in our little area, both belonging to members of our family—or, more accurately, to my Grandfather's families. Each house was made up of children and grandchildren from his two marriages. Not that my grandfather was a bigamist—oh, no! He was a pious Jew who had managed to outlive his first wife. She died in childbirth with her tenth child. At the age of 72, the time of my birth, my grandfather was enjoying his full patriarchy, having sired 20 children and 40 grandchildren, of which I was the last.

I saw hardly anyone except the members of my family for the first seven years of my life. There was an occasional Polish peasant from whom we bought foodstuffs, or an itinerant peddler who brought us news from the world outside, but mostly the people I saw were brothers and sisters, aunts and uncles and cousins; some full, some half, but all happily mixed up together in a squabbling, loving, impoverished way.

At the head of it all stood the proud figure of my grandfather. He was a giant of a man, for an eastern European, and he walked erect and firm with his seventy-odd years. When he sat in his large chair, he was awesome. How the family ever managed to get such an imposing chair, I don't know. It had a red damask seat and back, carved oak arms and legs—really a Spanish throne, in my memory. When grandfather sat in his chair, it was as if God were presiding over the fate of the world. Too much noise or chattering would distract him from the reading of his beloved Torah, but he would show his displeasure with a roar and all would be silent. He would return then to his reading, puffing his pipe and stroking his long white beard. If my grandfather was not God, Himself, he was surely a direct descendant of Abraham, Isaac, and Jacob. We grandchildren called him "Zaideh".

My grandfather was not a figure out of the Middle Ages, as you are, Comrade Knight. He came directly out of the Old Testament. I believe his psychology must have been like that of the pre-Christian era as well. Yet I always enjoyed being with him, talking about the family history or about the woods which he seemed to know so well. Our family, he said, had been in the Polish forests for about three hundred years. We never owned the land, of course—how could Jews own land?—but there had been a tradition of leasing land, cutting the trees and selling the wood. Fortune had waxed and waned over the centuries: sometimes the family was wealthy, but usually there was barely enough to eke out a meager living. Because we always grew a few vegetables, and had a goat and chickens as did every Jewish family in forest or village in Poland, we managed to live reasonably well. We always had chicken on the Sabbath, for example.

Before coming to Poland, he said, his grandfather's grandfather's grandfather, back three hundred years, lived in Germany. There the family also worked in the forest and it was there, he thought, that they learned their trade. The sojourn in Germany had been brief, since they were expelled—in the typically sad history of the Jews—and came to Poland. Before Germany, the family had been in Holland, where they were mirror-makers and lens-grinders. That much he knew for certain. There was a tradition that the family had previously been in Spain and had been expelled during the Inquisition. That seems likely in terms of my present knowledge of history and the movements of the Jews. Before Spain, North Africa, and before North Africa, Israel, which was left long, long before. Every year, at Passover, Grandfather would sit at the head of the table and, at the end of the Ritual, shout, "Next year in Jerusalem!" How loud and joyous was his shout and our answering echo! Our life in the forest was good, nonetheless.

My grandfather loved me especially. I resembled him a little. My skin was fair, and my eyes blue like his, and my temperament was not unlike his. My hair, though was different. I had dark, very curly, almost kinky hair, whereas he had straight red hair in his youth. His hair and my hair proved that we were hardly a "pure" family, racially. Clearly, Russian cossacks and, very likely, African Negro, figured in the past history and wanderings of our family since the destruction of the temple.

If my grandfather were the archetype of the patriarch, my grandmother was the archetype of the matriarch and great Earth-Mother. She was big and buxom, clumsy and good-hearted, full of good humour, earthy wit and laughter. Sometimes she chattered too much and Zaideh would roar for silence. She was silent, but by no means afraid of him. "Bubeh", as we called her, had her own domain, and the Queen was just as royal as the great King. My grandmother loved me, as she loved all the children and grandchildren, by kissing us, patting us, blowing our noses, feeding us cookies, and protecting us from the wrath of offended patriarchal males. Her daughters were constantly berating her for her inefficiency, especially the daughters of the first marriage, but she took the criticism with good humor and ruled us all with love and warmth. Everybody loved her, despite their irritation with her.

My mother, her middle daughter, was her great champion. Mother was far more efficient and intelligent, though less able to be warm than Bubeh. My relationship to my mother was straightforward and matter-of-fact. We were probably very much alike in many ways. We seemed to have an unspoken understanding. She and I understood that we had to take care and be efficient, lest everything collapse; yet our love was such that we did not mind the other, inefficient females.

My father, however, was another matter altogether. He was a thin, silent man, with deepset and passionate eyes, always looking off into something else. He was rarely quite "there". It was not that he was a bit mad; no, not that. He was really something of a mystic, I think, though he was an ardent Communist consciously. My father had been a "catch". He had come from an educated family, and not only—as the other males—in Hebrew and Talmud. He had been to the Polish schools and even had graduated from the Gymnasium, the High School. He could speak several languages and had a surprisingly romantic and violent past. Surprising, because when one looked at him, one saw a small and quiet man—not at all one for violence. He had seen a lot in his life, however. He had run prohibited Communist literature from Russia into Poland, tried to organize workers, led students, been in jail. His passionate nature had captured my mother, and his education was impressive to my grandfather, who deplored his politics and atheism.

Despite my father's hopes and aims to change the whole world, he was rather impractical, and could rarely manage to earn very much money. He would earn an occasional ruble as a translator, but he needed very little and was pleased to live in the kind of socialistic community of our little houses in the forest.

He was a decent father and took it upon himself to educate my brothers and myself whenever he was at home. When I was very little, he would tell me stories of all kinds that he would make up. I had only to give him a topic and off he would go into the wildest kind of fantasy. I loved it very much. I would especially ask for funny stories. These he found more difficult to create, but, seeing that I would grow hilarious and give a gross belly laugh like my grandmother to all of his attempts, he was encouraged to bring up whatever humor he could find. I was such an appreciative audience, I think, that he was amused by me in return. He was much harder on my brothers when it came to learning how to read, to write, to spell and to "do numbers." In fairness, he was also harder on me when I reached the age of five or so, when I began to perform the regular sets of lessons. I rarely gave him difficulty, unlike my brothers, so that his wild temper would seldom awaken itself in relation to me. When it did, I would cry and run from the room, which made him feel badly. I tried to restrain these little tantrums of mine for his sake, for I, just like my mother, absolutely adored this Great Man.

Now that I reflect on it, it is amazing that we had two Great Men in our household. Grandfather was, indeed, God; and God of the Fathers, of History, of the Torah, of the continuity of life both spiritual and material. For Grandfather was also God of the Forest. He understood the plants and the trees and whatever little animals would manifest themselves in that place. He was also indomitable and conservative, orthodox and a benevolent despot.

My father, on the other hand, was the God of This World. He was for Change, for Humanity, for Life, for Liberty, for Progress, for Making a New World. He was against the Capitalists, the Tyrants, the Exploiters, the Prejudiced, and so on.

Father and Grandfather respected each other and treated each other in a warm, though reserved manner. Each knew that the other had different views about life, politics, and especially about religion; but they shared goals, strangely enough. They wanted: for mankind, peace on earth and the brotherhood of man; for themselves: independence, good family life, friends, and the chance to pursue their intellectual interests.

My grandfather would say about Karl Marx: "A Jew who is not a Jew! Who ever heard of it! Paradise on Earth, yes, but without God? He has it all upside down! Too much goyische thinking in his head!" To which my father would answer, defensively: "All your religion, and all your Jewishness has brought the Jews nothing but pogroms, pain, and poverty! Where is your God at pogrom-time? No, we must make Paradise on earth, but *we*, men must make it, and not wait for some Messiah to come on his white horse!"

That was the extent of their discussion when they got on the topic of communism or religion. They, neither of them, could really talk with the other on those topics, probably because both were so thoroughly committed to what they believed. Secretly, I think, each knew that the other had similar goals. Many times, when I was older, my father would say to me: "Don't tell him this, but I do believe that he is a greater Communist than I! He is generous, wants the best for everyone, is ready to sacrifice for what he believes in, is a good and loving man." And my grandfather would say to me, on our occasional walks in the forest, "You know, your father is really a religious man. He wants all those things for men that God wants, and he is really religious in the right way: against hypocrisy, exploitation, and to bring Eden on Earth. God, anyway, loves atheists because they spend so much time thinking about him!" With that, he laughed, gave me a hug, and picked a flower for me.

Now that I think of it, these two men have been instrumental in my views, for I am fully and dedicatedly a Communist, though not nearly so naive and impractical a one as my father, and am an atheist like him. On the other hand, I believe in God, all right, but one created in men's imaginations, out of their conditions of life. I know, like my grandfather, however, that a Jew must be a Jew. My views will become clearer later on. Right now I want to continue my story.

I could go on to describe my family: the lazy aunt who was a Communist, too, but only because she felt that whatever anyone else had was meant to be hers; the show-off cousin who always ruined our Passover Feasts with her need for attention; a conceited cousin, smart and insufferable; the thieving uncle who stayed with us just for what he could get; yes, these unpleasant ones, and the many, many uncles, cousins, aunts, who were loving, generous, intelligent. And my brothers: those passionate, bright, difficult fellows who combined so much of father and grandfather. I weep as I think of them. I weep for them, dead, and I weep for myself, who has lost them, and I weep for the world, which has lost all the wonders that they would have brought to it. I cannot bring myself to say more about them right now. Maybe later, when I have brought you up to date about what happened to us all—maybe then, I will be able to tell you how good and generous and wise and wonderful they were.

Now, I can tell you that my childhood was happy and gay. I walked freely in the forest, alone or with my grandfather. I was safe with the birds and the little animals that would appear, and was always welcomed by the workmen, both family and others, who were busy cutting the trees. I loved to watch them at their work, pruning, paring, sometimes watering—for the forest was, in part, like a garden that they cultivated in order to produce a good crop. Part of the forest was wild and unattended. You know, it was something like this place. I would not have thought of it as Paradise—at least in my communist view of things—but I agree that my early childhood, my first seven years of life, was Paradise, indeed. Love, warmth, play, cheer, study, family, variety. Yes, a whole communist society and the forest, too.

When I was seven, however, a part of the family was compelled to move to the city. I was not clear about it at the time, but it seems that by 1933, an economic depression, originating in America, that golden land where everyone was rich, affected Poland deeply. It was now difficult to earn one's living. We could go on living on our own vegetables, but it grew harder and harder to sell the wood. The place would support only part of the family and the rest had to find sustenance elsewhere.

My father knew most about city life, so it was clearly our part of the family who would be the ones to leave the forest and try to make our way there. The great unity which had been in our family was giving way. Some of the people were Zionistic, and they wanted to stay in the forest until the time when they could emigrate to Israel. Others longed for the opportunities of the promised land of America. Still others accepted things as they were and preferred to stay where they had always stayed.

It was easy, then, to decide. The Zionists and the Conservatives stayed in the forest with the grandparents. The Communists and the ones who wanted to improve their lot in America went to the city. We were about evenly divided, so nearly twenty of us went to the city to live. As I think of it now, our four groups: Religious, Zionist, Communist, "Americans"—demonstrated the forces affecting all Jewry at the time very well, indeed. I, myself, have been each of these, at one time or another.

So, many of us moved to the City. It was sad to leave the others, my grandparents, especially, but there was a certain adventure connected to going to the great City. Parting was made easier with the knowledge that we would visit Bubeh and Zaideh and the others when we could. So, just after my seventh birthday, a new phase of my life began.

II

If the first seven years of my life were those of the seven fat kine, the second seven were leaner. Paradise gave way to another reality, but it was not Hell. The infernal reality came only during the last part of the second seven years.

It was exciting to come and live in the City, after our forest and country life. There were so many new things to see and hear. First of all, there were all the people, none of whom were relatives. On second thought, they weren't all that different—they were Jews after all! We lived in the Ghetto, in two rooms, just as crowded as we had been in the forest, but now the crowded conditions extended to our environment, as well. In the forest I could always take a walk and be utterly alone, if I wished. Now this was not possible. People were everywhere. The shops and dwellings were hard by each other, but the crowding gave warmth, and I soon found a way to retreat into myself to be alone, rather than wander in the woods.

Besides the numbers of people and buildings instead of trees, what struck me most about the city was that the Jews seemed to walk bent, or in fear. Where was that pride that I saw in my grandfather when he walked in the forest? These other Jews did not have it—or rather, they only had it on Sabbath, when they walked to synagogue. What a sadness, that these men had dignity only in their worship and only on this one day, but not in their everyday lives!

When one left the Ghetto, it was like going into a foreign, hostile country. I did not understand this. In the woods, we all did pretty much what we wanted to do. There were rules and limits, of course, presided over by grandfather, father, and mother, but we felt free and safe. Now I felt neither free nor safe.

By the time I was ten or eleven, I better understood this sense of unease. First of all, my father was a Communist, making him suspect among not only the Poles, but the Jews as well. In addition to that, my father had taken on the age-old shrinking fear of the Jew in the alien and hostile land. It was an alien and hostile land, even though my family had lived there for three hundred years.

I became aware that the Poles were hostile to both Jews and foreigners when we went to school. It was made clear to us that going to school was a privilege which the Poles were only grudgingly granting us. Every day my two older brothers and I would walk to school safely enough, but coming home was often an agony. There would be cat calls, throwing of rocks, and shouts of "Jews" and "Christ-killers", especially at the times of our holidays or at Easter. My brothers were in continual fear of being beaten up.

They held their heads high, though they were quaking inside, and we hid all this from our parents. It was good that we did so, because they would have felt horrible about our situation, but powerless to remedy it. I was not the butt of jokes or pranks, but I suffered deeply for my brothers. It was not much better in the school. The teachers were brutal and often sadistic, especially when it came to the Jews. I had a first-hand experience of what I later learned was typical in our history: being forced to defend one's view when to do so is considered heretical and punishable with strict measures. It is like being called a witch when there are trials and witch-burnings—that is how it was to be a Jew in school in Poland in those days, as well as to be a Communist, later on, for me. In short, it is having to testify against oneself.

There had always been pogroms and anti-Semitism in Poland, we knew, but the increasing intensity, apparently, was a consequence of the rise of the Nazi movement in Germany. We suffered, but somehow managed to keep our wits about us.

Life in the city grew worse and worse for me. The experience of anti-Semitism on the part of the Polish youth proved to be more painful than I first realized. It felt strange to be a foreigner in one's native land. But I cannot blame it all on the Poles. I also began feeling alienated from my fellow Jews in the Ghetto. I could not explain this, of course, in my early years, and even now I am at a loss to understand it altogether, but I do know that I steadily became more isolated and alone—more unhappy with the world as I found it and with myself.

As I grew older, I became conscious of myself more and more and did not like what I was beginning to see. I found that I was not pretty, though not ugly either. My hair, I despised, because of its kinkiness and my inability to do anything with it. I grew heavy, and awkward, had thick legs and an ungainly walk—like a duck. I became increasingly closed, irritable, sensitive to the point of being touchy and withdrawn. My main solace was reading.

Thus I would be in the winter—withdrawn, neurotic, fat, unhappy, sensitive. In the summer, I would return to the forest, my Utopia. There were not only my grandparents, who made me feel beautiful and whole again, but also my cousins. We would play, dance, walk, talk. We would hike, swim, run, or sit quietly together. I was alone when I wished to be and had all the company I desired when I craved that. It was lovely. By mid-summer, I was always human again—thinner, healthier, tan and gay. Autumn and the return to the Ghetto would renew the pattern of withdrawal. It is hard to explain, though easy to describe. It was not that I was deprived of love, for my parents loved as best they could and this was more than substantial. Nor was it the lack of people about—for I could have had as many friends in the city as I had in the forest. I can only say, irrationally, that I was cut off from my own Utopia, the Forest, and that this was enough to make me ill, detached, and half-alive.

Life continued in this manner until my twelfth year. My father had been active in radical organizations, and I read more and more about such things. I was strongly attracted to the Utopian future of the Marxists, where each would receive what he needed and would give what he could, but it all sounded like living in the forest with my grandparents and cousins. Besides that, I was seriously religious, in an inner way, and could not accept the atheism. My father would talk to me about Communism, kindly and lovingly, with a glowing glimpse of the future. His vision was of the brotherhood of man, peace on earth—a Jewish vision, a Christian vision, and a Communist vision. But for him, the atheist, God was excluded. I did not understand this. My religion was not very developed and differentiated, but I believed in God, all the same. I vaguely believed that God was located in the trees of my beloved forest. So I disagreed with Father.

In my twelfth year, as I have said, deep changes were beginning to take place. The ominous rumblings from Germany were growing louder, and we lived in fear of what would happen to us if and when the Nazis invaded Poland. The Poles were bad enough, we knew, but the Nazis were even worse. In the midst of our worry and fear, my father grew ill.

We all have crucial life experiences which more or less mold us. These experiences, it is true, are not simply that one is molded and affected from outside, with no inner aptitude. That would be the naive environmentalism of those stupid Communists I subsequently knew and, I am ashamed to admit, like whom I also was for a time. I know that this outer experience also meets an inner core or aptitude, and that there is a basic, even historical, necessity in individuals and in the nation, for these events to occur. It is a strange magnetism, I think, of forces in interaction, and I do not in the least think of it as mystical. It is a kind of psychological-material synchronicity, a meaningful concatenation of inner and outer events from which none of us is free and most of us would wish to escape. We escape by fleeing either outward to the world, people, life, or inward to fantasy, dreams, thoughts. None of us really can escape, altogether. When these events occur, we know, even at the moment, that they are crucial for life. It was just such an experience when my father grew ill. His illness was no mystery. We knew what it was: cancer. It began in his throat, and moved into his chest, and it grew with a rapidity which was astonishing.

The man had always smoked a lot. It was only in the Forest, that he did not—consume himself, I almost said—when he did not smoke at such a great rate. Yet I do not know if it was the cigarettes that caused his cancer. My grandfather, after all, was an almost equally prolific smoker, though, it is true, he smoked and puffed on his pipe, rather than cigarettes. He did not, in short, inhale all the nicotine that my father did. Father's lungs, no doubt, were as black as they could be. Yet I do not believe that it was the cigarettes that caused my father's cancer. I think that it was the meaningful moment, the conjunction of events, inner and outer, which produced it. Father was consuming himself and was ready to die. That is what I think. His spirit and desire were more than his frame—thin and scholarly as it was—and the time—hellish and impossible as it was—could bear. So he consumed himself and died. I did not understand it this way at the time, of course. I saw only that Father was ill, suffering, pale. I saw the nearness of death for the first time in my life. We had already heard that Jews were not only displaced, beaten, put into camps in Germany, but were already dying for the crime of being Jews, and this was hard to believe. Now, however, death was much closer. Father was dying and we all knew it.

What could I do? I did what was deepest and best in me at the time: I prayed. I prayed to God to save this dear, compassionate, gentle man. I prayed to that great God of the Jews, who is open to human misery, who can change not only the course of history, but the course of individual life, the God who is passionately involved with His people. I prayed to this God. I prayed with the intensity and depth of my love, of my anguish, and even of my neurosis. Thus did I pray.

My father died. Yes, he died. I had asked God, I had promised God—I dare not tell you all the things that I had promised God I would do if only he would spare my father. It would only show you, as it does me, that I conceived even then that God could be bribed, cajoled, wanted sacrifices from men and would only then use his power beneficiently, but only perhaps. This was the God to whom I prayed. I prayed in vain. My father died.

At first, I had no feeling. I was numb. The funeral was as a dream to me in which I was merely a robot, not a dream with feeling or action or suspense or drama. I went through it and did not even weep. The daze lasted weeks. Mother cried, relatives cried, and Bubeh, dear Bubeh—she wept and held me and stroked me and looked for my tears, and she knew and wept some more. My sorrow was too deep for tears.

At last I went to Zaideh. He would know. I told him—dear Zaideh—of my prayer, of how I had asked God to spare my father and that He had not done this. My grandfather sat quietly. He was silent a long time. He then spoke with a cool and timeless depth. His words were brutal. He spoke in Yiddish, and in a way that I cannot translate. He reminded me first of years before, of the stories that I had been told about the first World War, of how my father had to go to war and was in danger of losing his life, and of how my grandfather's sons were also called up, and had to serve in the hated army of the hated Poles. My grandmother had wept and moaned, but grandfather had said, "If they have to go, they have to go; if they are wounded, so they are wounded; and, if they die, so they die." He reminded me of this story, which I heard a hundred times. Each time I heard it before, it was as if the different characters of the two people, Grandmother and Grandfather, were being extolled and cherished: Grandmother weeping and in agony, Grandfather cool and detached for all eternity. The archetypes lived and one heard of them. Besides, no one died, so it could be merely an entertaining story. Now the genuine event occurred, and I saw the eternity of my Grandfather. I saw his coolness and I was astonished.

I looked into Grandfather's eyes. I looked deeper into those eyes of the same blue color as mine but vast and bottomless. I saw into them and that which I saw changed everything. The words and the demeanor said one thing, the eyes another. In the midst of those eyes were suffering and anguish, the enduring of pain that I have rarely seen before or since. Those eyes revealed the suffering of the Jews, and of men, from time eternal. They showed the suffering of the man who knew he was in the hands of God, and that God's ways were different from man. My grandfather was Abraham, and Isaac, and Jacob, all in one; more than that, he was Job. I loved him, and I loved his suffering.

But something cracked inside me. An illusion, a faith, a belief was broken. All I knew was that God was dead. I denied Him. It was then that I became an atheist. That, as you will see, is the central fact of my story, though I will tell you many other things. You will see in my story what this all means. But there, before my thirteenth birthday, I lost faith in God.

III

The next months are somewhat vague in my mind. My father's death catalyzed the family into action. It was expected that war would soon come and the specter of the Nazis was very great for all of us. We knew that we had to leave the country, but this was impossible, since there was no money for that. Failing that, the old, the feeble and the young had to leave. We had been receiving frantic letters from some distant relatives in America, who were, like us, terrified of the Nazis and wanted desperately for all of us to come to the Golden Land of America. There was enough money, at this time, for only a few. After full family discussion, it was decided that my grandparents, my mother, and myself should take the tickets and come to America. My brothers and the others would somehow take care of themselves for a time, until more money would be forthcoming. There was much protest about this arrangement—from my grandfather who wanted to stay in the land of ancestors, and from my grandmother, who hated to leave any part of the brood unattended. My grandfather was convinced to leave when he was reminded that he always hated the Poles anyway, that the land was never his nor his ancestors, but was always leased, that the true promised land was Israel, to which we might all go one day, but that we were poor and had to earn some money first. Grandfather listened to all of this, needed the guarantee that there were plenty of orthodox Jews in America, and then agreed to go. Grandmother was reassured that soon the rest of the brood would be brought over and was given a solemn promise of this by my mother—something that she was to bring up again and again when the awful truths were later known. I am getting ahead of my story. At this point, it was agreed that Bubeh, Zaideh, my mother and I should go.

Once this was decided, and the money for tickets received, we quickly set out for Danzig. We were full of excitement about going to America. I can still remember the ferment of the port, and of the people. Just the other night, I dreamed about it once again and saw it as clearly as I see you all right now. The Summer of 1939, the people in their caps, shawls, starched clothes. The atmosphere of fear, even panic. The feeling that the world might be coming to an end. The anguish on the faces of the Jews, especially. The Poles seemed less aware, and only an occasional face had real fear in it. My family, with our own blend of fear, excitement, hope, and sadness at leaving our loved ones and our beloved Forest.

It was then that I was able to put aside my grief at the death of my father. The vision of the pain in my grandfather's eyes, earlier, had enabled me to weep, and weep I did, copiously, for days. My grandfather comforted me, my mother comforted me, but my grandmother comforted me the best—she wept with me! Oh, did we weep! We wept together for days until, at last, we were wept out. My mother's grief was greater than our own, no doubt, but she did not have the gift of letting her emotions go, and thus she contained it all. I suppose she felt the need to be strong, take care of us. She must have known, even then, that not only was her husband dead, but that her family would be separated and that she might never see her sons again. Now that I think of it, she was the bravest woman that I ever saw. I do not believe that I could endure this myself.

But now, at the ship in Danzig, I could let my grief rest and I could think of a new life, a new beginning in America, the Golden Land. As it is with the young, hope and new life are powerful and take precedence over death and separation. I had now passed my thirteenth birthday, and, although I was not a boy and subject to Bar Mitzvah, everybody knew that girls matured more quickly than boys, and if boys become men at thirteen, I was surely about to become a woman.

We had hardly arrived in America, in noisy, frightening New York, when war broke out. I remember the day very well, because it was the day that I had my first menstrual period, September 1, 1939. I was 13, becoming a woman, the war broke out, and I bled. My mother was lovely. She had warned me beforehand, so I was prepared, but I was awkward and embarrassed, nonetheless. When she gently slapped my face on both sides and said words like "put-put, Mazeltov" I laughed. It was a ritual, and it meant I was a woman. She laughed, too. She did not know what it meant, but knew that her mother had done that to her, and so, she did that to me. Mother then called my grandmother into the bathroom, to tell her the great news, and my grandmother promptly performed the same ritual. Then we all sat down and laughed uproariously, almost forgetting that I needed care. It was a lovely experience, I think, one which helped spare my neurosis from attaching itself to being a woman. With all my "mishigas", as they say, my fundamental being as woman has never been questioned or hurt, thank goodness.

All the same, it is interesting that the day that Poland was invaded by Germany, the day World War II officially broke out, the day that began the Holocaust for the Jews, that was the day that I bled and became a woman. There had been a meaningful correspondence between the death of my father and the death of God. Now there was a meaningful correspondence between the death of the Jews, and my bleeding and becoming a woman. The profundity of this is beyond me, but, despite my rationality, I accept the meaningfulness of the symbol, with all its ambiguity, without question.

We listened carefully to the news each day after that, wondering about the fate of my brothers and the rest of my family. Our relative in New York was far from rich, so again we were crowded into his two-room flat, along with his wife and young children. They were kind to us, and we were all glad to share our common fate as Jews, but it was also clear that we soon would have to fend for ourselves. At this point, we were glad to have any shelter at all and could laugh because things were just like in the Old Country, in this, the land where streets were paved with gold, except that now the animal that lived with us was not a goat, but a cat!

We could tell nothing about our family from the news of the war, but we felt better that France and England were going to fight. Surely they, civilized people that they were, would defeat the Germans, and we would soon be re-united with our family.

Our mood was tense, but hopeful, and Mother made arrangements for us to go to California, where she had already been promised work as a translator, and as an advisor in the film industry. This sounded very glamorous, and I thought that America might be a Golden Land after all!

Living in Los Angeles proved to be immediately pleasant and easy for us. Mother got the job that was promised and her pay was very good. Indeed, she often said that she was earning more than the combined income of all the families of our two houses in the Forest, plus half the Jews of the Ghetto in the city. She remarked about how many Jews there were in Hollywood, how vulgar they were, but how nice and considerate all the same. Many were rough in speech and ill-tutored, for a Jew anyway, but underneath, she said, they were generous and loving. I did not know anything about that. All that I knew was that soon we had a warm and friendly home in the Hollywood Hills, that I had my own room to myself, that all sorts of interesting people were coming to our house, that my grandparents were content in the new place, and that Mother was making a new life for herself. We now had security, warmth, and a good life. There were many trees again, and lots of good places to walk in the hills, even if it was not the Forest.

Despite our good fortune, I was still quite unhappy with myself. My kinky hair grew worse. My piano legs and duck walk made me more self-conscious than ever, and I seemed to be unable to do anything about either. I was quite aware of boys, but terrified lest any of them approach me. If only my brothers had been there, I thought, they would pave the way. That was where we all were most unhappy: we missed my brothers.

The news from Europe grew more and more ominous: Poland defeated, France and the Low Countries invaded and defeated, as well. Only England survived and with little chance of eventual triumph. America was supportive but afraid, or inept, or isolationist.

Worst of all, Russia had deceived us. My father had been Communist, it is true, but of the Trotskyite persuasion. Though he continually hoped for the World Revolution, for the triumph of the World Communist State, he did not have much regard for Stalin. All the same, we still had great hopes for the first Communist state—even those of the family, the majority, who were not Communist. There was expectation that something new would emerge out of such an experiment. When the Russians invaded Finland, we were greatly disappointed, but rationalized that they had to defend themselves against the Fascist base near their chief city, Leningrad. When they invaded Poland, we were shocked, especially since they had made a pact with Hitler. This we could not rationalize so readily, but still, we could not believe that a Communist would be so bad as a Nazi. I still read avidly in the Communist literature and was deeply impressed with all the Russians had accomplished. I loved the Russian films. Despite all evidence to the contrary, I was sure that the negative things could be explained, were just capitalist progaganda, or were temporary expedients in the face of threat.

More horrible for us were the reports of the concentration camps in Germany and elsewhere. The Jews were being destroyed, it was said. We could not believe it. When Russia was invaded, we were glad, for now the "good people"—Communists and Western democracies—were united against the common foe. In time, our people would be free.

Thus the years went, until America was in the war. It is a history known to all—at least all who lived at the time. That history is not what I wanted to tell you of my story. What I wanted to relate is what happened to my soul, the inner story of my life, as well as the outer events.

These crucial events began to occur after the war was over. When victory was achieved, we finally learned the fate of our fellow Jews: six million dead. When my grandmother realized the full extent of what happened—the death of sons, daughters, grandchildren—she went mad. At first she moaned and groaned and complained, asked questions, and blamed everyone for not bringing the others with us. All attempts to reason with her were impossible. She let herself go altogether, fell back into a shell, and simply died. It all happened so fast that it was hard for us to realize it. She was quite old at the time, over 75, but like all the peasant types of my family, there was every reason to believe that she would go on living in good health until 100. She simply died, however, and her death had a certain rightness about it. She was relieved of her suffering, at least.

In caring for Bubeh, mother hardly had a chance to grieve for herself, and, when she did, she did so privately. It was as if she, too, had cut herself off, as if the loss of the sons was too much to bear.

I moved toward my grandfather, who sat silently in his chair, puffing on his pipe. He had been silent all through the later years—reading his Yiddish newspaper, taking his daily walk, saying his prayers, going to the synagogue. Now he was more silent than ever. The deaths of all the Jews went into him to the marrow, but he said nothing. The deaths of our personal family members seemed only a part of this larger whole. When my grandmother died, he took this in, he absorbed it in the same timeless way.

I went to Zaideh to speak to him. I wanted to ask him how it was that his God, whom I had given up at the death of my father years before, had allowed this to happen. When I came to him, however, I dared not speak to him thus. Why should I be so cruel as to push my atheism upon him? I loved my Zaideh. After my father, there was no other man who was so fine and upright and decent. So I went to him to comfort him. I went to Zaideh, not for answers, not for help and solace, but as a loving granddaughter. I went with love and warmth, with tears in my eyes for his suffering. When I went thusly to this great old wise man, this silent rock, this Job, this Moses, this Abraham, Isaac and Jacob, this patriarch who was the same as all the Jewish partiarchs who ever lived—this man took me in his arms and wept. He wept and sobbed and held me to him; he said not a word, but cried and I cried, too. It was not the end of the world that this man, who was for us, as little children, the representative of God on earth, could not answer us, for he, too, was human.

We wept, and then my mother came, and she wept, too. We cried, together, the three of us. For days was it? For weeks? Or was it just minutes or hours? I do not know. We held each other closely and wept for what it was to be a Jew, and a Human Being. The strange thing is that my grandfather's faith was not shaken. When I later asked him about this, why he did not give up his faith in God with such horrible events, he answered simply that it was not a question of his choice, for God had already chosen. He, Grandfather, was chosen, all Jews are chosen, and one could neither get out of it, nor change it. One could only pray to God to release us from His wrath and to bring us under His wing of love.

I was touched by my grandfather's faith and his endurance, but I was still an atheist and a Communist, though in a way different than before. I could not formulate it then, for that had to wait until later, but that night I had a dream.

In my dream, I was down low, under the earth, being oppressed by the burden and pressure of earth all around me. I pushed my way up to the surface, where I was free again, and could breathe. Here I caught a glimpse of my family, but just a glimpse of them, waving happily at me. Now I wanted to go toward them, but I felt a pressure, another pull, driving me up, up off the ground. I tried to work against this pull upwards, just as I had tried to overcome the pressure downwards before. I tried to hold onto the ground and the trees, but the pull dragged me up into the air. I was frightened and angry at being pulled away from my family, but the force would not be denied. As I ascended, I was told or I knew—I am not clear which—that I was being brought to the presence of God. Now I was more frightened and angrier. I was unbelieving, and thinking this a trick. Then I changed; in the dream, I changed: I decided to bring my complaint to God. I decided that I would rise up to God and complain to Him about how He treated Man, how terrible He had been to His Chosen People, and how He was not entitled to be worshipped and prayed to by the people, and how I no longer believed in Him, anyway.

With this infusion of anger, of questions, firmness and rage, I heard a Voice. It said: "She speaks truly of the Lord, listen to her." I found myself sinking back to the earth, gently, easily, until I found myself safely resting in my bed.

This dream made a great impression upon me. I came to a peace which I had never known before. I also came to a firmness that I had not felt. It was as if my anger and my questions and my atheism—especially my atheism—were being sanctioned and encouraged by God! What was that? That God affirmed my atheism? I did not understand this fully at the time, but this has been the chief paradox of my life: my atheism is God-given, and I worship the Highest in that. So I do believe at this moment. Much else happened in my development later on—of which you will shortly hear—but this paradox has stayed with me. I rose up to God and complained to God, and rejected God for his unwonted cruelty to Man, and to his Chosen People. I aver that I am an atheist and that God has agreed with me, and has told me that I speak truly of God.

So, now, my friends, so it was that the third seven-year cycle of my life came to an end. With the first, I came out of the Paradise of the Forest into the City; with the second, I rejected God upon the death of my father; with the third, God affirmed my rejection of Him, and embraced my vision as true. I discovered paradox, and came into my own search, which is why, probably, that I am fortunate enough to find myself among you able and illustrious men in this place of the origin of us all, Paradise.

IV

In 1946, before my 21st birthday, I decided to leave America for Israel. The dream had been decisive in my development. It had said nothing about how I was to live my outer life, but, all the same, I knew that I had to do this. I was an atheist in a special sense, and I was deeply aware of this, but I was also a Communist, though not as yet in a special sense. I knew that I could not stand my fellow Communists, most of whom were simply greedy, power-hungry, domineering little people. I was glad that I had never joined any organization so as to get myself into trouble with Communist-hunters.

I was now more Zionistic than ever, and felt that whatever my fate as a Jew and as a Communist was, that I would spend it in Israel. As soon, therefore, as my studies were completed at the University, I made ready for my trip to the Holy Land. By this time, my mother was well ensconsed in her work in Hollywood and had met a man of whom she was deeply fond. He, too, had lost his spouse, was lonely, and wanted to marry her. It seemed right for Mother to embark on a new life, just as I was ready to go abroad and be fully on my own. It felt natural that Grandfather should come with me to Israel, while Mother would continue her life in America. Thus it came to pass.

In the Fall of 1946, I completed the third seven-year cycle of my life and went to Israel with my grandfather. Zaideh had now spent as many years in the twentieth century as he had in the nineteenth, but he was almost as strong as ever. We both knew, however, that at ninety-two, he was going to Israel to die. He was doing this for the whole line of our family, for those who had come out of his loins and had been burned in the ovens.

It was a great and meaningful voyage. We went slowly—on a ship, and it was a Jewish ship. My grandfather marveled that here was a ship both owned and run by Jews.

When we arrived, the land spoke. It said, "Welcome, oh Jews! Shalom! Welcome to you, for you come Home, at last." And it was a homecoming! We kissed the land, and felt its dry warmth. The trees and the stones spoke to us, and everywhere we went, we rejoiced at the names of the places—places which had names in the Bible and in history, but had—almost—been forgotten as realities. My grandfather was so joyous in Jerusalem, he danced. Oh, how he danced at the synagogue of the Chasidim! He danced and he prayed. In truth, he had never been a formal member of the

Chasidim—he had been a traditional Jew—but he had read, he had studied, he had watched, and he had talked. Now, now that he was in Jerusalem, of whom it was written, "If I forget thee. . . .", he was in the place of his soul. He danced and he wept, and he was home.

He was, indeed, at home in the Meah Shearim of Jerusalem, the old city of Jews living, really, in the middle ages. He was at home, but I was not. After a time, when I found that he would be happy and taken care of, I left him there and went to live at a Kibbutz in the Gallil, which was as communistic as one could desire.

During the years in Los Angeles, I had spent summers in a Zionist camp, where I had been quite happy. It was, indeed, a repetition of the pattern I already knew in Europe: winters of neurosis, introversion, unhappiness, study; summers of outdoor life, walking, being with family or alone in the forest, happy. Now, in Gallilee, I was in a perpetual summer camp in the forest, along with a new "family"—all my fellow Kibbutz members. It was as if the remnants of my neurosis fell away, for I was at one with everyone in work and play and study. Work, comradeship, dancing, community. It was lovely. It was my nature to be extraverted, and now, at last, I was on my own soil and living my own life.

Shortly after my arrival, there also arrived a handsome young American who looked upon me with a fire in his eyes—what more could I ask? Now, in my fourth cycle of seven, Paradise had returned. The young American and I were married, and it was a source of great joy in the Kibbutz. We danced all night. Even my grandfather, whom we brought from Jerusalem, now became reconciled to all the pain and evil in his life. He knew that our family line would continue. I would surely give birth to a son.

Life was good. In 1948, the War of Independence came, and we fought for our lives. That war is well known. Needless to say, we gave everything we had, and the celebration of our own land, of proclaiming the Jewish State after two thousand years—this was almost too great a moment in history. The war was hard, all the Arab states united against us, but we won and the land was ours.

We went back to our labor and our life, to build our Jewish State and to welcome back from the Diaspora, all the Jews who were now clamoring to come. It was miraculous, and the flood of emotion made me almost forget that my special "Chosenness" was atheism. I had to reflect upon what my Communism would be. I had seen too much and known too much to be the naive Communist that my father had been—the Trotskyite believing that all men would soon be brothers, that the workers of all the world would soon overthrow their rulers. I had seen too much for that, and knew that the era of nationhood, of states, still had a long way to go. I knew that the Jews, above all, had to have their own State for a very long time. I also knew that what the Russians had done, their abridgement of freedom, would not be tolerated as Communism, and that Marx, too, had turned everything upside down. What kind of a Communist was I? Hardly one at all. Yet, I was.

After a few years of routine, of work and the regularity of life in our Kibbutz, I began to have periods of depression, without knowing what it was all about. I no longer felt joyous in my work, which was to care for chickens and sort the eggs, nor did I feel happy when I awakened in the morning. I loved my husband, there was no doubt of that. He seemed intent upon his activities, and very busy. He not only did his daily task—which was to care for the trees in the orchards—but in his spare time he continued to work on his dissertation for his doctor's degree.

What was it that I was experiencing? Was it a further disillusionment with the Communist way of life? Was it a breakdown of the meaningfulness of life? I did not know. When I tried to communicate these feelings to my husband, he was sympathetic, but he did not really seem to understand, nor to connect with what I felt. I suppose that I did not convey to him the depths of my despair. How could I? It seemed too absurd to speak about depression and despair when I answered every question with a statement of satisfaction. Did I love my husband? Yes. Was I happy to be married? Yes. Did I feel that I was doing a meaningful work in the Kibbutz? Yes. Did I like it? No, not any more, but I did not despise it either. Was I glad to be living in Israel? Yes, indeed. Did I feel patriotic and believe that I was living in an important time in history? Yes, a man's question, indeed, not a woman's, but I felt that it was important. So, all questions that would be asked of me, I could answer either affirmatively or in a way that could not account for my recurring times of lassuetude, depression, crying spells.

There was only one part in my life that seemed to have a connection with my state: I was not getting pregnant. For the first few years of our married life, my husband and I were pleased not to be having children—we wanted to know and experience each other first, before the distraction of a family. It was not that children would be a burden, financial or emotional, in our lives. Not that; for the Kibbutz was organized on Communistic lines. Though the babies stayed with their parents at night, they lived largely in a nursery with other babies and children, and were cared for by nurses and teachers. Parents would be with their children in their free time, and when both wished, but there were no family house units, as such. We were not fearful of the responsibility, since the whole community took care of that. We just wanted to have no other people to distract us from our emotional connection with each other.

After a few years, however, we no longer felt this way, and were ready to have children. We wanted a boy and a girl, at least, and were looking forward to that pleasure. I also felt that it was important to my grandfather that I have a son, for his sake, and that the strong, healthy line that came out of him, so destroyed by the Holocaust in Europe, would continue with me, his granddaughter. My husband and I even agreed that if there were a son, we would give him, as a middle name, the surname of my grandfather's family. When we told Zaideh our plan, this gave him great pleasure and, as they say in Yiddish, "naches." It was as if this would be the final crown to my grandfather's long life and make it possible for him to die happily, despite the enormous tragedies.

Yet we were not having children. At first, we thought that it was just a question of time, and that the children would soon come. I, after all, came from a highly prolific family, and my husband did also. We went to be examined. It appeared that there was nothing physically preventing conception, from either side, and our respective contribution to having children–sperm and egg–were both quite normally viable. Why we were not having children was not known, and, therefore, "psychological."

At first, I rejected psychological explanations as being no explanations at all. It was just another way of saying that the reasons for our not having children were not biological. My husband would make little jokes in the English language, saying such things as "my wife is impregnable, no. . .unbearable. . .no, inconceivable."

I was rather annoyed with these jokes, but realized that he, too, was pained and that his jokes were merely regressions to his American sense of humor, which was not very deep. I realized, too, that my own reaction was to fall back to my Polish-Jewish touchiness and paranoidal feeling of being demeaned. Finally, we both wept together in each other's arms, and admitted that we were desolate about it. Our sorrow did have the effect of bringing us closer together for a time. Now, at last, I had an outer situation and event to which to attach all my despair and unhappiness, but I knew in my heart of hearts that my inability to have children at this time was not the only reason for my despair.

It was 1953. My husband had received his doctoral degree the year before. I was twenty-seven years old and my grandfather was now—praise God, I would say if I were not an atheist—ninety-nine years old. For some time, my husband had been speaking about going to Switzerland to study postdoctorally to become a qualified psychotherapist. It had been his desire for a long time, but it seemed to be difficult to find the funds to do so. I, too, looked forward to a change—in truth, I missed Europe, and its green. Even though our Kibbutz was in the north of Israel, and there was forest, I knew from my childhood how the rain-swept forests of Europe can be, and I missed them. I thought that perhaps I, too, could be analyzed, and find the cause of my barrenness. For now, in my heart of hearts, I was beginning to believe that my inability to have children was of a psychological origin beyond my conscious awareness. I had read in psychology and felt new vistas open up to me, but was still, as a Communist, something of a doubter and scoffer.

When my husband received a grant from an international association to study in Switzerland, however, and the Kibbutz placed no objection to our going, we were both overjoyed. In 1953, the fourth seven-year cycle of my life was coming to an end, and the fifth one was to begin. I began to feel meaning and pattern in my life again—not that I understood it. Rather I felt that with the move, the meaning might emerge.

All that remained was to see my aged grandfather, who was very weak and living in a home of Elders in his beloved Meah Shearim in Jerusalem. I visited him a month before our scheduled departure, knowing that this would be the last time that I would see him alive. I talked to my Zaideh, no longer spry, nearly blind, quite weak, though apparently aware enough to be sensitive to my need to see him and make it right with him before I left.

"Oh, little Julia," he said, patting my head. "I know why you come now, before you move again from our land, to pursue your husband's career and your own need. I know, little one. I know that you will miss me, and that we will not see each other again. I know that you come in sadness, for not giving me a grandson and a granddaughter who will continue my line and my tree. Please, do not grieve for this, for it is a sign from God. I do not believe it to be a punishment. . . .no. . . .I believe that you, like me, and like all of us Jews, are chosen. You, dear Julia, are chosen in a way that neither I, nor even you, as yet, can fathom. I am ninety-nine years old, and I have been chosen by God to live long, and watch the destruction of great numbers of my people, and to see the death of my parents, and my brothers and sisters, and my wives, and all my seed but one, and why the Lord has given this unto me is a great mystery. But the Lord has also, in this same era and in this same time, given my people back its land—that for which we longed for two thousand years, and He has brought me here to live in it, and to worship Him, my God, in His Holiest of Cities. This, too, He has done. The Lord giveth and the Lord taketh away, and He giveth again, and mysterious are the ways of the Lord. . . .You, little Julia, are like Sarah, to me, of old, and of our father Abraham. For she, too, was barren, and she was the ancestress of our line. Do not tell me, Julia that I am wrong, that I put too much on you, that you are far from Sarah, but just an ordinary Jewish girl. That may be so, but I feel you to be otherwise, and that you are the end and the beginning of a new era for the Jews. Perhaps not you alone—I do not burden you with that, but leave it to God. You, like Sarah, are burdened, and barren. God will come to you, and make you fecund and creative and of a new line, and you will feel—as did Sarah—the breath of God in your name, the Ruach Elohim. That breath will make you fertile, and a new line of the Jews will come forth from you, and the line from which I come will be continued. Such is it that comes to me, and blessed be thee, my sweet Julia, the last of my seed."

Zaideh put his hand on my head and then turned his face to the wall. I knew that a patriarch of old had spoken to me and I trembled in awe. It was my beloved Zaideh, the ordinary man that I had known all my life, but, at the same time, he was Abraham, and Isaac and Jacob, and the last of the Patriarchs. God had spoken to him, and given me a message. I was shaking and crying and at peace—all at the same time. It was as if, at last, the deep darkness in my soul which I had lived with for several years and which had come up as a wordless despair, was now being reached by this old man's words. He was connecting with the dark, abysmal place and making it meaningful. He was not giving an answer, but he was, as the Quakers say, "Speaking to my condition", and my being was responding to him.

After a long time when I could recover myself and speak to Zaideh, I spoke again. But he was asleep. He seemed to be smiling in his sleep, as if joyously beholding the vision of a happy place, or an answer to his soul's desire, and I did not wish to awaken him. I went to my room to sleep the night and rest from that encounter. That night I had the first dreamless, peaceful sleep that I had had in a long time. I awakened refreshed and ready for the new phase of my life. When I went to bid goodbye to Zaideh, I was not surprised to be told by his nurse that he had died peacefully in his sleep during the night. Zaideh had forgiven my my barenness—nay, he had promised great things from it, and now he could die, with the assurance in his own soul that his life was not in vain, and that I would continue his seed. Praised be the Lord of my grandfather, for making him happy. But let it be acknowledged that I was following my own path of being the atheist, for thus was I chosen.

We buried my grandfather in the land that he had finally attained and with him we buried a long and wonderful and painful history. The day was beautiful—the sky clear, but unusually cool. The people came from all over for the funeral of my grandfather—it was a great event. Mother came from America, and it was as if all the Jews of the Meah Shearim were there to celebrate him. There were tears, it is true, but there was joy and a feeling of peace—for my grandfather had come home to Israel and to his God, and all was well.

V

In the Fall of 1953, well after my twenty-seventh birthday, my husband and I took up residence in Switzerland, in the city of the "Great Psychologist", to study at the Institute which bore his name.

How can I convey the feelings and impressions that I had upon my arrival? Before we arrived, in the slow Dutch freighter that we had taken from Haifa to Genoa, and on the train from Genoa to Zurich, I had many thoughts and impressions. I had summarized the first seven years of my life as in the primordial paradise. The second seven years took me from this Eden into a gradually worsening purgatory to a horrible hell at the end. The third seven-year cycle found me in a gradually improving purgatory in America, and again finding paradise in Israel during the fourth seven-year period. This time, however, during the last half of the fourth cycle, I had a kind of paradise outside with an unknown and increasingly hellish purgatory within. Now I was arriving in a "psychological holy place"—as distinct from a religious one—which, hopefully, would help me mend or bring together these heavens and hells into a livable unity. Or, at least, give me some explanation for it all. What was psychology for, after all? My husband had no such deep problem at the time. He was there simply to be trained better, to be educated better, and to do his proper work in the world. If he had any deep inner problems, they were not apparent to either him or me, and he was just glad to be in Switzerland, finally studying in the place he had long desired to be.

Our arrival set the atmosphere. We emerged out of the train station in the late afternoon on a rainy, dreary day into a wonderful old European city. I immediately felt something stir in me. I could not formulate it then, but now I can see it as a coming into life again of a whole period of my soul. If Israel represented the ancient and deepest layer of the human part of my psyche, as well as the most modern and recent part, then America represented the generally modern part, but Europe was everything in between. Europe was from 70 C.E. to the nineteenth century. America was the nineteenth century and into the twentieth, but surely Europe was everything in between. In a way, this represented my own life as well. My grandfather represented Israel and the whole dim past, where I was raised in a forest, similar to the beautiful forests that I had seen on the train coming into Switzerland, and these buildings, these old buildings looked rather like those in Poland, too. I was going to live again in the continent of my birth.

We were quickly settled in our little apartment and taken by friends up an old cobble-stone street to acquaintances of theirs. There we sat, in a fine old, quiet living room, with an old tile stove, in the midst of Swiss cleanliness, positively burgher-like comfort and security, looking out of the window to the great lake of the city. We sat there quietly, nibbling cheese and drinking wine. How can I tell you what I felt? It is in the heart to say: I wept inwardly with great joy and felt that I had come home.

That is a strange thing to say, isn't it? For a Jew, for one who was born in a Polish forest, for one who lived long in America, for one who also felt that she had come home when she went to live in Israel—all of that is an unexpected background for one who feels she has come home in the rainy, quiet atmosphere of Switzerland! It was so. I could not explain it then, but now I understand it somewhat: Israel represented my spiritual home, the home of ancestors and the spiritual meaning of my life. Switzerland, however, was a home for my soul, the womb-like place where one could be safe, go into one's self, be well fed and clothed and warmed, attended to and educated from within. Israel was the home of the Fathers, Switzerland the home of the Mothers. I wonder if others see it that way, too. Or is it only me? Virgo, the Jungfrau, after all, is an astrological symbol for Switzerland, so it makes sense to see it as feminine. That others may not see it that way might be because the Swiss women are not notably attractive compared to Italian or Greek or Spanish women, or even French women. There are many pretty Swiss girls, but I think too of those dried-up, thin-lipped ones who are terribly tight and constantly cleaning their floors! I stand firm, however, in thinking that the beautiful Swiss landscape, its care for beauty, comfort, positive order, is, indeed, a good mother.

I was very happy that first evening, enjoying the wine and cheese, looking over the beauty of that remarkable lake and city.

My husband and I settled into the life of the city, as students and foreigners. It was perfect, for the Swiss know how to treat both—leave them alone as far as possible, as long as they do not disturb life. The Institute was ideal, for it was filled with people from all over the world, old and young, many coming to study to become psychotherapists, or simply to continue their own development.

There were quaint old ladies from England and America, whom my husband at first deplored—they were so unprofessional and unbecoming to his desired image of the proper psychotherapist—but I rather liked them. Later on, even he admitted that they often knew a great deal more about psychology than he did, and finally he liked them as much as I did, and came over to the view that it would be terrible were this to be just another professional institute with so many dull, deadly serious young men and women out to improve their role and income. Praised be the old ladies, the young strange men, and all who made that place into the unique and alive place it was.

There were many teachers and speakers. There were the regular faculty, who had spent long years with the Master, and the visitors from all over Europe and, indeed, from other parts of the world. Even from Israel, I was glad to see. They lectured on mythology, religion, psychopathology, and all manner of related things.

The main thing was one's own analysis. That was it. One was "in a process" and that was a secret, private thing, that people did not discuss with each other very much. They could talk about deep matters, about theory, people, and all the usual things, but they didn't talk much about their analytic work. I liked that a lot, and from being a scoffer about psychology, I became pleased and positive, and a booster. It was not long before I was "in analysis" as they said, myself. I had planned to do so, of course, for I had to find out about this deep, dark place in my soul which was inexplicable.

Very soon my husband and I were safely on our "inner journeys"—he working with a woman, and I with a man. The man that I saw reminded me very much of my grandfather, a big man, seated in his big chair, puffing on his pipe, saying little, but seeming very deep and wise—a kind of Swiss-Gentile grandfather. He would grunt and comment sparingly, but he kept my nose to my own inner work, and gave me the atmosphere for the deep and clear questioning of myself that I needed so much at the time. We had a number of friends, of course, and good ones, whom we saw often, but the main thing was "the work."

Mornings one would get up, write down one's dreams, "work on them", go to analysis, and then to classes. After lunch and chats with friends in the restaurants, one would have another class, come back home to read and study. The evenings would be free for talk—good students' talk—or study, or cafes, or movies. It was a good life, and we loved it.

What of the search into my soul? After the initial searching into the darkness, it became clear that part of my darkness was that I knew just too little—that I had been insufficiently educated. I needed to read and to study, and so I did. I studied at the Institute and I studied at the University as well. I studied psychology, of course. I very much resented the idea that I might be a psychologist or become an analyst, like my husband, because that seemed too much like following his path, and I wanted babies anyway. My soul insisted otherwise. It seemed to say that part of my barrenness was lack of education and that I had to study. I had a "big dream" in which a Voice with great authority told me that I was to become a psychotherapist. The authority of this voice was such that it could not be denied. I tried to reject it and promptly got quite ill with diarrhea and nausea. When I accepted the "voice", the illness cleared up at once. Both my analyst and my husband agreed with the "voice"—another example of male solidarity—and I had to submit.

I must confess that once I embarked on this path, I did not find it disagreeable. The work was hard, but interesting, and there were, of course, those lovely long vacations in spring and summer when we would travel all over Europe and see the great historical and cultural wonders—plus, of course, the cafes, the people, the food. It was fine!

I studied, I learned, I analyzed, and I seemed to be following "my path". Still I was "barren", and the great inner darkness would make itself felt as an unknown cloud in my dreams, or a door unopened, and I could not get at it. Even using the techniques of "active fantasy", of carrying on a dialogue with the figures of dreams and fantasy, even this great technique of the Master failed to bring this gloomy darkness into the full light of consciousness. I uncovered much, and understood my childhood, my relation with my parents, especially that with my father. I relived and healed the neurosis of my adolescence, and I "developed", but I could not reach the darkness or the barrenness.

In time, I completed my studies at the University, was myself a Doctor, just like my husband. It felt very strange to be one. I felt that I was not at all intelligent, nor able, but I did understand a few things, and believed that I might be able to help people with my care and concern, if not my capacity to understand intellectually. My husband had enough of that for both of us!

After 1957, I was fully occupied with the Institute and my post-doctoral studies to become an analyst and psychotherapist. Our other life became less and less important—and the only big event was the war which Israel quickly won against the Arabs. It was over so quickly that we had no chance to go home and fight. We were delighted with the outcome, of course, and sorry that we had not helped. We were also glad to be out of the wars and concerns of the world, safely covered up in our little nest. It is amazing, now that I think of it, how much we both needed that period of nesting! I am not clear, even yet, why we needed it so much, but it was deeply life-giving at the time.

Still no answer to the deep darkness. Yes, now there was a good deal of inner light—I was much more aware of myself, of the world, of the history of the spirit and of the development of consciousness. I was aware of my roots and what had formed me, and of my commitments, but still. . . .

It seemed to have to do with the problem of evil, the problem of six million dead Jews. More personally, it had to do with the death of my brothers, who would have been so much more creative and valuable than I. Why was I alive, and they dead? Was what my grandfather said true? That I was meant to be like the ancient Sarah, to have children when old? If so, why? There seemed to be no answer to these questions, no matter how hard I, or my analyst, worked.

It sounds as if only superificial things were dealt with in my analysis, or, if deep, that the deepest part of me was untouched—the part where the essential darkness was. If that is the impression which I am giving, I wish to correct it. No, that is not the case. Indeed, let me say that I finally understood the paradox under which I had been living for so long: That I was an atheist, and chosen to be one by God. I understood it thus: Man has always had a God, and this image of God is really a projection of the Self, of his own totality, of the ruling principle within his own psyche, of himself and the world, of which he is unconscious. The image of God, in short, is a psychological projection like any other, though its potency and mystery and importance are greater than any other. I understood that man's image of God changes in accordance with his general development. I also understood that his general development is contingent on his environment, on his society, and on the way he makes his living. In short, the Marxist part of me was also satisfied, but at another level. Man is conditioned by his society and his history, and it is real, but not only material in the way Marx saw it. He, like an alchemist, was projecting his visions into matter: it is real, but psychic. I also saw that man needed Community, or *communitas*, in the Christian sense, and that modern man, having lost it, needed it desperately.

I understood the paradox that "God had chosen me to be an atheist and a Communist" to be translated into a statement that the Self, the highest totality of me, had selected the function of my ego to be a challenger of all current and past images of this totality (God), and that I was meant, by this same unknown and unknowable totality, to reject all of those current images of God. In short, when people said, "God is dead", they were saying the psychological truth that the old image of God was no longer viable or believable. My task was to deny all images, even the image which transcended images. *That I am the atheist of God means nothing less than that I serve that image of God which is beyond all images, beyond all past, present and future understandings, in short that I am indeed Jewish, and have no images of God at all!*

That, to my delight, makes me, indeed, a Jewish atheist for God!

My Communism became clear to me, too, in the sense which I have already given it. We are all brothers and sisters. We live under the same archetypal and general psychological reality. We are meant to live together in that foreseeable future when men will be brothers on earth. Again the paradox of a Jew who can be a Communist is resolved: The Jewish image of Heaven realized on Earth at the coming of the Messiah! Such a Communist, in hope, am I!

So now, when I quote what I said the the beginning—"There is only one life, we have to improve conditions on this dreary planet, and mankind has to evolve and produce Paradise on Earth, not individual men and not God"—these words, indeed, sound atheist and Communist, and indeed they are, but now you will understand that they come from a religious and psychological atheist and Communist, which is quite an individual matter, indeed!

These solutions are far from superficial, in my opinion, but they still did not reach that ultimate blackness of which I have spoken.

I could not solve the problem of evil entirely! All the same, I had come to some inner acceptance, understanding, and reconciliation.

With this relative peace and understanding, I thought that perhaps my understanding of evil was much too dark, and that now, in truth, I might become fertile, as my grandfather had said that I would. We were, in point of fact, nearing the end of our stay in Switzerland, and had less than a year to complete our studies. In the midst of this relative peace and understanding, my husband painfully told me that he had been deeply attracted to another, and had been unfaithful to me.

I was seared to the depths of my being. Evil was no longer an academic issue, intellectual; nor was it a personal issue of my own darkness. No, evil was worse. Evil was the pain of guilt and fear, and of being torn apart into little pieces! I suddenly realized the guilt of my having insufficiently cared for my husband. I realized the guilt of deep and dark possessiveness, and of not wanting him to live, nor myself. I felt the fear of his leaving me; I felt the fear of being alone; I felt the fear of being thought of as a fool; I felt the humiliation of all of it. And throughout, I felt love. I wanted him to do what he had to do; I felt strangely open to him as I had never felt before; I felt torn apart and open at the same time. I felt as if I had been raped by life. That was the evil: I was confronted with the ultimate darkness of betrayal and of love and openness at the same time. Worst of all, I knew that my husband was, in his way, in the same place. I did not understand it altogether, nor did I want to know, really, but I knew that he loved me, and did what he must.

In the midst of the suffering and agony, I walked again in the forest. The forests here were much like those of my childhood, and I had often gone to them on the outskirts of the city, for solace, meditation, or joy. Now I went in agony and desperation. Whatever I did was wrong: that was the greatest evil of all. In the midst of my agony, I had the fantasy of my grandfather coming to me. He was full of infinite compassion and care. Tears welled in his eyes as he patted my head and comforted me. After a time, I stopped crying, and he said, "Julia, as I told you, you will be as Sarah. I can only tell you, that until today, you have been as Sarai, loyal and true and devoted, and a handmaiden. Now you have felt God's darkness, and you have been impregnated in the spirit. Just as Sarai became Sarah, you, in truth, will, inside of yourself, change from Julia to Juliah. You have felt the spirit of the Lord. Now you will, yourself, be the mother of new creations. You will suffer much, but you will create."

My grandfather vanished, in the fantasy. I really felt that he was as a ghost, coming from the dead. After that, I had a measure of peace.

That night, I was impregnated by my husband, and I knew that I had been touched by both man and God. Atheist, yes; Communist, yes; but now, I had *known* God, as Sarah had known Abraham, and I was a girl no more.

The depth of this experience made me more silent than ever. The few remaining months of our stay in Switzerland were largely those of getting ready to leave—saying goodbye to friends, and so on. Only one event had the significance of this depth. That was my final visit with the Great Psychologist. I had completed my studies, as had my husband, and we each, in our time, had arranged to have a final interview with him. My husband's came first, and when he returned, he seemed serene. He apparently had gotten what he wanted or needed, and was at peace with himself.

When I went, it was strange. I was very quiet, could hardly bring myself to face him, feeling a great numinousness in being with him, yet shy and embarrassed. We chatted a bit. I told him that I had found his books difficult to read. He answered, "They were difficult to write." I told him of one which had moved me the most, and he nodded and sighed, and said that that was the most difficult, painful, yet important experience—the deepest confrontation with evil. At that point, I burst into tears. I could not help myself and wept uncontrollably. The Great Psychologist, Swiss and Gentile as he was, proved to be much like my grandfather. He waited quietly, did not even ask me why I was crying, but then began to speak in a soft voice about himself, his own life and sufferings: his voyages, experiences, even to his betrayals and being betrayed. I looked up in wonder. Now I knew that he was a Great Man, and not just a Great Psychologist, for he spoke to my condition, from a depth within his own, from an instinct which was just right. He risked all. He risked being a fool, a madman, and presumptuous, but he had infinite regard, I felt, for my suffering, and for his own, and did not intrude. In short, where I had been raped by God, he lovingly repaired this rape. He did so out of his own experience of being raped by the same God. I came away healed.

VI

In 1960 my husband and I left Switzerland. I had finished the fifth seven-year cycle of my life, and was now aware of how this cyclic character had affected me. For reasons of my husband's career, and his own inner calling (for he had his own deeply religious experiences during this period), we had to go back to America to live, rather than return to Israel. I had no such calling, but like Ruth, felt it deep in myself, deep in my own being, to go whither my husband would go.

We returned to America, and started our life there. True to my experience, I had been impregnated that night, and in regular time, I gave birth to a lovely daughter. I was much fulfilled, though I felt a twinge at not having provided both my husband and my grandfather with a son. I laughed, though, and realized that, luckily, I was not Sarah, but Julia, after all, and I was not about to have an Isaac like her. I knew that I had gone through an archetypal experience like her, but, thank goodness, did not have to live her faith. Obvious evidence: I was thirty-four when I had my first child, and not in my nineties!

In the years that immediately followed, my husband and I adjusted rather well to the new life. He had been an American, so it was both easier for him, and more painful to come back to the land where he had never felt at home with his soul and spirit. I knew that my spirit and soul did not belong there, but also knew that the "flesh" was there, and I was having children in the flesh. I discovered that for a woman, children of the flesh are one's real homecoming, and that is the first and initial task. All the rest could come later.

It was enough for me for several years. I had two daughters and then two sons, twins! With the sons, I had a dream that I was with "the Mothers." I was with my mother, who was still living in actuality, and with my grandmother, and with a great and unknown creature, who was, I suppose, the Great Mother. We were all laughing with joy. These two sons seemed recompense for my two brothers. It was a secret among us that the souls of my two sons were, in actuality, the souls of my brothers. So I was mother to my brothers reborn! I was sister to my mother, and wife of my father! Incestual things in the spirit; shocking, I suppose, but deeply satisfying within.

I had not solved the collective problem of six million dead Jews, but I felt, in my soul, that two of them were reborn through me!

For several years, I was fully involved in caring for my children and making a comfortable home for my husband. The spirit of our home was good and warm. It felt like the good days of my childhood in the Forest, though now we had several rooms, and not one goat! We had dogs and cats, instead, with an occasional bird, turtle, or lizard, cared for by our children.

After four years, our financial situation had much improved, as such things do in America—that is one of the great things about it—and we were even having luxuries. The children's needs much occupied me, but I began to have spiritual longings which were unsatisfied. At that time, my husband and I took a trip to Europe and Israel for a holiday and to visit our friends. I saw my old analyst and had a dream—how convenient for me, don't you think?—that showed clearly that I should begin to practice the work for which I had been prepared: psychotherapy. I laughed about this "convenience", and upon our return, I did begin to see patients. At first I worked only a few hours per week, but with time and as my children were more and more in school, on a larger scale.

This work proved absorbing to me. All that I had learned was put to the test, and there was a new place of connection between my husband and myself. We did not wish to discuss the patients, themselves, but to discuss our feelings and reactions, dreams and situations. Our relationship was much better, yet I was aware that my maternal feelings were mobilized much more readily by my children and my patients than by him. The problem of the "fathers" and of the "mothers" had been greatly healed for me, in analysis, in being a mother myself, in bringing me closer to my own mother, but there were still areas in which I was deficient.

During some of this later period, I was able to stand by my husband better, as he went through betrayals of various kinds, even at the hands of those friends whom he loved and thought loved him. I now knew that he was experiencing what I had experienced some years before. I could not put this into words for him, but I knew it, and I felt that he knew that I knew it.

My feeling, deep as it was, was now beginning to be felt all around me. I was less afraid to express it, and it was having its effect. My husband's experiences, however, were also having an effect upon me. How could it be that these people, people that he had known and loved, and presumably, had also loved him—how could they betray him so, and not even be aware of it? I fully understood the inner grief and agony of betrayal. I understood, too, that one might not know what to do about it, but I could not comprehend their lack of consciousness, their righteousness.

My thoughts went deep. Were these people, like the Communists, about to destroy my faith in psychology? My faith in Communism had been challenged and destroyed by my experience of Communists, who had proved to be greedy, power-driven, and, in some ways, more frightening than non-Communists. Were psychologists—those who through insight and self-knowledge were going to be the inheritors of the future kingdom on earth—were these people going to disappoint me? Were they not living up to my expectations, the way the Communists had not? Yes, of course. Now I had to think more deeply, about both my Communism and my psychology. I had resolved the paradox of my atheism in a deeply satisfying way. Being an atheist for God, as I have said, was enduringly satisfying. Shall I say it again? Yes, I shall: "I am an atheist of God, which means nothing less than that I serve that image of God which is beyond all images, beyond all past, present or future understandings, in short that I am indeed Jewish, and have no images of God at all!"

This, as I say, was deeply satisfying for my atheism, but I had no such deeply satisfying understanding of my communism, except in the future "Brotherhood of man" when the Messiah comes. Somehow, this statement seemed inadequate to me. It was all right some six years earlier, but now it seemed thin, in comparison to the enduring symbol and understanding of my atheism.

What is more, the Communism and the psychology were drawn together, or identical, in a way which surpassed my understanding. More and more, this intellectual dilemma occupied me. Was I forever doomed to have my ideals shattered by the realities of life? It was true that my experience of the "rape" by God was tremendous, but one of those per lifetime seemed enough. Yes, my grandfather had assured me that I would suffer, but I did not feel that such a particular kind of suffering had to be relived.

So, what did it mean that psychologists failed to be psychologists and Communists failed to be Communists, and yet these two viewpoints had within them the highest ideals of my life: individual development and totality for the psychologist, and collective joy and redemption for the Communist? Perhaps my idealism was at fault—I expected too much, of others, of myself, and even of the realization of ideas. Yet, where had my own "creativity" come, when had I become impregnated? When I was torn apart by the divine paradox, by the good and evil in God? I could take the good and evil in God, but I could not take it in man? Yes, that was it! What presumption! I could accept that God was both good and evil, but man, somehow, had to be better; had, even, to be better than God!

So, I thought, is that the flaw in my reasoning? Is that why I cannot come to a deeper place in my Communism and psychology? Because of the inflation and expectation? Yes, they are neither one very individual, are they? In which case my psychological views fail in the very thing that they admire, they are not individual! And my Communism fails in the opposite direction; it is not very communal!

What shall I do about it? Develop my own psychological theory and thus satisfy the ultimate demands of my psychological ideals? Go out and save the world, or, at least, a part of it, and thus satisfy my Communist ideals? Both of these sounded wrong to me—the first because I had no new theory, really, and the second because it is very much against my temperament. What to do, therefore?

I found myself in this state of mind when the Arab states were once again threatening my beloved Israel. Israel was all alone, but, in lightning-like fashion, like the Maccabees of old, they whirled through the opposition and captured all, with a minimum of loss of life. All my old Kibbutzniks were in it, and I loved them. How my husband and I wanted to join them and fight! But we could not. Now the Communists everywhere were against Israel, and I knew that all the outer Communism was the enemy of my deepest identification—spiritual, soul or flesh. Yet I could not abandon my ideal: all men are as brothers—to each what he needs, from each what he has to offer.

In this state of mind, I went to sleep. I dreamed—or, at least, I think I dreamed. For I found myself in this forest, or one very like it. Because to tell you the truth I do not know if I am dreaming. I do not know if all of you are parts of my dream or if, in fact, I am part of yours. No, I am caught in a solipsism which does not hold water. I know only that I am here, and that I have had such and such experiences. I will leave it to someone else to determine whether it is inner or outer. Let me, then, simply go on with my story.

I went to sleep then, and dreamed that I was in a forest. In the dream, I felt relieved to be in a nice green forest again, which was like those of Poland and Switzerland—ordered and tended, and not so wild as those in America—and I could sit down and rest. In my dream, I rested long by the water, and drank deeply thereof. At that point in my dream, I dreamed that I fell asleep and had a dream. It was a dream within a dream, hence my confusion. In my dream, I saw my grandfather smiling at me, and embracing me. After him, came the Great Psychologist, who did the same. Then came the turn of my father, and I wept to see him again. There was a pause as I thought of how I had missed him. Then I embraced the three men and they embraced me. We made a circle and bowed our heads together. The circle then broke and my husband appeared. He smiled and I ran to him and embraced him, and he held my hand. Suddenly my two dead brothers appeared, as if in the flesh, and I gasped as I saw them. As I went forward to touch their hands, they changed into my twin sons, back and forth, proving that the dead two were the living two. I was overcome with all of this, when all the men, led by my grandfather, united in a circle. Grandfather, father, psychologist, husband, brothers-sons—all six of them turned into two triangles which joined together as a Star of David—a living Star of David, and I knew what it meant when one said, God has become Man. They danced a Hora in a circle and my joy was great. Their circle changed from the dance to the Star—back and forth. As it did so, I became aware of my grandmother, smiling at me, too. "Bubeh," I cried out and ran to her. Just behind her was my mother, holding in each hand the little hands of my daughters. I joined the women and we all held hands and danced a hora of our own, laughing and calling out to the men in the other circle. We were five, they were six, and they all were ten—my own *minyan*—plus me. We made a very large circle—all eleven of us—and danced until we were hot and tired and exhausted. When I thought my heart would burst with happiness, a strange thing happened. Suddenly, there was a silence. The men withdrew and formed a line; we women withdrew and formed a half-circle. To my astonishment, our feminine half-circle, which was moon-like, became a sickle; and the line of men became a kind of hammer. The men invaded us, and together we made a hammer and sickle: the Communist symbol. At that moment, my father spoke and said, "This is our Commune, that of family and those who love each other. We welcome into it all who belong there. It is not family alone, or Jewish alone, for is not the Great Psychologist with us, too? Ours is the beginning of the family of man, and the brotherhood of man, both potential and actual. We will live the actual and hope for the potential."

The Great Psychologist then spoke and said, "What you see as the height of your ideal, and your attitude and your way, the Communist hammer and sickle is to me, dear friends, a Psi—that Greek sign of my ideal devotion, Psychology, the study and devotion of the Soul. That is in the Service of the Self and of Men. So, I embrace you."

I awakened from the dream within the dream, and found myself here in your forest. It is not Paradise to me, or is it? And it is not a dream to me, or is it?

I do see your tree, Sir Knight, and it is amazing! I see there. . . .do you see it? I see the Hammer and Sickle—that symbol of work and the brotherhood of men, and I see that it is also a psi. I see that it is psychology that unites them and what more can I say? For the Great Psychologist has said it, and my father has said it, and Knight, good Knight, you do, indeed, seem like my Brother and I embrace you. And you, good Arab, and good Ronin, you are my Brothers, and I am your Sister, for you, too, as my father said, belong in my circle, do you not? Yes, you do! My symbol fits yours, does it not? Yes, it does!

SYBILLA, THE NYMPHOMANIAC

SYBILLA, THE NYMPHOMANIAC

I

My name is Sybilla. Julia, like you, I want to tell my name; I also like to know names. In my feeling, this desire is not just a feminine or individual trait, as you seem to think, Julia. My need arises from pain. I have had more than enough of experiencing men and Gods with no names. The nameless, the impersonal, has occupied a large part of my life. It has brought me hurt, pain—no, how can I even use these pale words? The impersonal and the nameless have brought me agony. That will be apparent from my story.

I am glad to be here, and I belong among you. I know that, though at one time I did not believe that I belonged anywhere! That, too, will be understood from my tale. Where shall I begin? I suppose I should explain why I should be called "The Nymphomaniac." I would prefer that my story unfold as it is, and, in due time, you will understand how it was I have had that title. Ah, titles, that brings me to the beginning of my story.

I was born in Alexandria of an Egyptian Crown Prince. That is what I was told by my mother. I tell you that is what my mother told me, and I tell you in such a way as to make you doubt whether I believe it. Well, in point of fact, I do not believe it. I believe my mother's story all right, but I am not convinced that I am her daughter, let alone the daughter of an Egyptian Crown Prince. Before I explain that, let me tell the story as my mother told me. It is a little sad, a little sordid, and a little beautiful. All three. At least I think it is all three.

My mother, may her soul not suffer again, was a pretty little Greek girl, on holiday from the country. She happened to meet a handsome young sailor one day, who was also on holiday from his ship. The young sailor, in point of fact, was the Crown Prince of Egypt, learning to sail ships, as young royalty do. He was on shore leave and wandering about in the Greek capitol city when he espied my mother, with her golden blond hair, brown eyes, and marvelous figure. The Prince was dark and handsome and Arab. They looked at each other and fell in love. At first, the Prince would not tell my mother who he was—he wanted to be loved for himself, of course. My mother was so loving and loyal, obviously devoted and genuine, however, that he had to be honest with her, and told her the good news. You may detect a note of irony as I tell the story. I have seen so much of life that such pleasant little fairy tales make me sound a little wry. I am sorry to be bitter about it—I had thought that all bitterness and regret and irony had vanished from my soul, but apparently not. Perhaps, the mere telling of my tale will dispel the last remnants of bitterness that reside therein. So, let me go on with my mother's story. In truth, I am more sorry for her pain than for my own.

The couple fell in love, as I have said, and swore undying

devotion to each other. He got away from his ship, and she from her family, both with lies and excuses which were readily believed since they had been so truthful and ingenuous before. They traveled to the great holy places of Greece on a kind of pre-marital honeymoon. The sights were an all new adventure for my father, of course, but so was it also for my mother, who had lived the life of a happy peasant girl.

The couple was much in love, my mother tells me. They spent their first night in Delphi, where, she says, I was conceived. My mother told me that night was one of ecstasy for them both—they felt that they were totally united with each other, that their love was destined by God, both his Moslem and her Greek Orthodox Christian God. That may well be, but I think differently. My view may have sounded strange to you before, when I said that I do not believe I am my mother's daughter. Now I can explain. I do not think that it was the Moslem God nor the Orthodox Christian God that sanctioned and brought together their love the night I was conceived. No. I believe that the Ancient Greek Gods and the Ancient Egyptian Gods were let loose that marvelous-terrible night, and I was born as a consequence. A blessing, you might say? Wait until you hear my story and see if you still think so.

My mother and father fulfilled their love near the Omphallos, the Navel of the World, the Center of the Universe, on the hard ground, late at night, under the stars, believing that they were having a great lark. Well, may the Gods forgive them, they were young and carefree and unknowing. They—at least my mother, I am not sure about my father—suffered enough for that night, I think, and I have suffered for it, too, but, they, at least, had their pleasure and joy.

After a few days, my father returned to his ship and my mother to her farm, he promising to write to her soon, as soon as he could get his father's consent for marriage. My mother was radiant and joyous. When she returned to her family on the farm, she told her parents and family the story in the naive belief that they would be happy, too. Naturally, they were shocked and skeptical. They simply beat her. Such were some peasants in those days, and, I suppose, such are some peasants at every period of history—and not only peasants, as I can tell you from my experience, but city folk, too.

My mother wept from this pain and disappointment in her family, but she took heart in the hope that her prince, who was, of course, *the Prince,* would take her to a new life.

Time went by and there was no word from the prince. My mother missed one menstrual period, and then another, and it was clear that she was pregnant from that fateful night. At last, a letter came from my father. In it he announced, tearfully, that his father would not give his consent to the marriage of a future king to a common peasant girl, even if the girl were the finest in the world. It was not a matter of cruelty or love, the young prince could have all the love affairs that he wished. No, the prince was betrothed, without his knowledge, to a proper young princess of a different country, and this arrangement was good for both countries; their personal feelings and desires had no bearing in any of it.

There it is. You have heard such tales before, no doubt. All very impersonal, isn't it? That is one of the "objective", detached arrangements made in the name of family, country, morality, or God. This "impersonal arrangement" was my mother's chief blow in life. It nearly destroyed her. Her parents, when they ascertained the facts, were much nicer to her. They felt guilty for being so cruel to her, apparently. Now that their bleak view of life and human nature was vindicated, they could afford to show a little of their Christian charity.

My mother, bless her, was not taken in by this hypocrisy. She refused to submit to their view or to that shown by the prince's letter. She was determined that she was going to give birth to me and care for me, no matter what. She also refused to let the prince know about her pregnancy—out of pride, naturally. In that, thank goodness, she was fully Greek. If he could not go against his father's conventionality out of love and conviction, then she was not going to force him to do so out of duty. She was not going to substitute one duty (his to his father and country) for another (to her unborn child). She left her farm in Greece and went to Alexandria, in order to be near him in some way. Since she was a talented seamstress, she was able to support herself very quickly.

And so, I was born. Is it not, as I have said, a sad, and sordid and beautiful story, all at the same time? Like a fairy tale, is it not? But my life is no fairy tale, as you will see.

I was born at home and easily, despite the apparent curse upon my mother's fate. I gave her no great cause for pain as a child. I was a pretty little thing, with dark eyes and skin like my father, blond hair like my mother. My hair, however, was rather darker and streakier, and not so pure and golden as my mother's. Still, the light hair and dark skin were an unusual combination and I was a point of interest among people.

My childhood was happy. I in no way felt rejected, unloved or cast out, on the one hand, nor "chosen" on the other—as you seem to have felt, Julia. We lived simply, among lots of poor people, but there was enough to eat. The "ghetto" life was warm and cozy for me, and not a horror as it was for you, Julia. You, sir Arab, will probably understand this better. "Quarters" are different from "ghettos", after all.

My mother was not bitter about her fate. She seemed content to be a seamstress, take care of me, and have her small pleasure in life. I played and danced and sang and was petted by everyone—rather spoiled, I think, but not too obnoxiously so. My mother told me the story of my father, which made me feel—how shall I put it? Not "chosen" or special, but. . . .something unusual. I guess I have no word for it, even though I am Greek. All I can say is that it made me feel good and that there was only one Sybilla. That's it! What I felt was not that I was "chosen" nor "special" but that I was one of a kind. There were no others like me and there never were any others like me, nor would there ever be! This had nothing to do with being good nor bad, virtuous nor talented, just "one of a kind." I still think so, though the many "impersonal" experiences that I have been subjected to have knocked out any special joy in this fact. It just *is* so.

That, my friends, is my background: just a Mediterranean girl born of a Greek mother and an Egyptian father, but brought up on the streets of Alexandria and with father absent. Happy, all the same? Yes. My mother loved me, and all the males around us adored me and bought me sweets and good things. Until I was thirteen. That is another chapter in my short but impassioned life.

II

At the age of thirteen, my life changed. How can I describe how this change came about? If I use the word "desire", you will, perhaps, understand me, especially if I add the word "sex" to this. But you will understand me, I fear, only in terms of customary categories or values which may be prim, lascivious, natural, ordered, religiously lawful, or some other. These do not encompass what I have experienced as "sexual desire." I can hear some cynic say: "Oh, she just awakened to sexual desire and felt, like all young adolescents, that this was the first time that such a thing ever happened."

I can only tell you it was different, and I think I am qualified to be an authority in this matter, as you will soon see. It happened like this: At first it was nameless—a kind of warmth and good feeling in the body, which combined itself with an itch, a desire to rub and be rubbed. It was a diffuse, but good, feeling. I was reminded of my experiences in my earlier childhood. I had often had sexual play with the little boys of the quarter. We would hide behind the buildings and examine each others' sexual organs—fondling them, licking them, sniffing them, like the little animals that we were. We laughed and enjoyed ourselves a lot, suffering no pang of guilt nor needing more than that. We were healthy little animals, playing.

Which makes me wonder why I was so hard hit when I was thirteen. That is not quite accurate—I know very well why I was so devastated at thirteen, but I did not find that out until a number of years later. At thirteen, suffice it to say, I felt a strengthening of these desires and pleasures, but was, at first, by no means disturbed by it. I understood that sex was somehow more serious—not just play—but I was heartened by it, felt more grown-up, and was not threatened very much. My breasts began to grow and I became more and more flirtatious.

I experimented in love making with several of the boys I grew up with, but our desire had natural limits and I felt no great shame nor difficulty. There was only one experience which I found disgusting. There was an old man who had been watching me for some time. I knew that he was lascivious and I was somewhat repelled by his greedy and beady eyes. One day he came close to me and whispered in my ear that he would give me good things if I did what he wanted. I trembled with disgust and irritation and tried to pull away. He grabbed me hard and squeezed my breast. I fought hard and slapped him across the face, even drawing blood with my nails. He let go, and I immediately felt sorry to have hurt him, and even felt some compassion for his need. I said some few words of apology for hurting him and told him that I would have to go home.

That incident reminded me of the time when I was quite small, perhaps five or six, when another old man gave me some candy and asked me to walk him home. I did so, and he asked me to hold his penis while he urinated. I laughed and felt peculiar—not because of the act, which seemed rather exciting to me, but because he was like one of the fathers, and one did not do that with the fathers, I thought.

I tell you of these incidents not because they are interesting, but because they are, in fact, not very exceptional, but could happen to any normal girl. I think that my reaction was normal, as well. Indeed, with my experience of life since that time, I believe that I was healthier than most along the sexual line. If I had been allowed to develop normally, I would probably have had a rich and meaningful love life. My loves, then, might have been pleasurable rather than, as it later turned out, a story of agony.

No matter. I must try and tell my story as it happened. If I am tempted to justify myself or elicit your sympathy, I will deny the intrinsic reality of my individual experience. I would be horrified to do that. I do not welcome judgments, evaluations, sympathy, or any kind of comment, which is so much "impersonal" nonsense, unless you are ready to share with me what you, yourselves, have experienced along this line! Do I sound defensive and hurt? Yes, I suppose I do. Despite all my efforts, there are still traces of my wounds—they heal only slowly, I suppose.

Enough of my defensiveness. Let me be open about what happened! After this first period of flowering, I felt an increasing intensity of desire. I began to be obsessed with the image of penises, breasts—wanting to suck on them, lick them. At the same time, I was preoccupied with the desire to have my vagina penetrated by increasingly larger penises, which would overwhelm me and fill me up. Nor did I just fantasy about these things! No. I began to find boys my own age and somewhat older to fulfill some of these desires. They were inexperienced like myself and sometimes rough, and sometimes too weak; but even with the older ones, I was never quite satisfied.

I had not yet had orgasm, and, from what I heard, that experience would relieve a person of desire. I began to masturbate and did have orgasm, but found it was only partially relieving. It was, somehow, not enough; I wanted a partner. One day, after a few months in which I was obsessed with sexuality and every day seeking someone out, I had an experience with a mature man. He played with me, licked my sexual parts, had me do the same to him and, finally, had intercourse with me many times. I finally did have orgasm and found relief.

My passion was mitigated only temporarily, however, and I was soon ravenous again. I was beginning to feel guilty about all these acts, without knowing exactly why I felt so guilty. Perhaps it was only a nameless shame. It was not a sexual law that I was violating, I felt, but something in me as a woman. A woman who could not be satisfied with one man, even many men, what kind of a woman was that? And love? I did not know what it was, but I knew that whatever it was, my sexuality was not that!

At last, in desperation, I told my mother about what was happening. At first she was shocked, but, good mother that she was, she quickly commiserated with me, and took me to a doctor to see if I could be relieved of this excessive desire and to see if I were ill. The doctor examined me carefully, and I grew quite excited. He did, too, poor man, and we were soon having sex. I both hated him and felt compassion for him, just as I did for the old man before. I realize, and knew even then, that I was as much to blame as he was. I did entice him, after all. I think that I was not to blame with the old man, however.

The doctor warned me not to speak to anyone about what happened, and I agreed. I went back to him again and again, for "treatments". These consisted of sexual activity. This was, I suppose, treatment of a sort, because I had temporary relief, but, of course, I was not "cured." I also could not tell my mother about it, since I did not want to hurt the poor doctor. At last I had the courage to tell the doctor that he was not helping me and that if he did not stop, I would have to tell my mother. This frightened him greatly, and he promptly told my mother that he was unable to continue seeing me.

My mother then took me to another doctor, and the same thing happened. This time, however, I realized that no one was going to be able to help me, and that I had to do whatever I had to do alone. The second doctor was easily disposed of–he was more a fool than anything else–and I told my mother about my real situation. We sat down together and wept. My mother finally told me that since my birth, she had worried that she had violated the Gods. She had an unspoken fear that she was going to be punished for a nameless transgression. She did not believe that she had, in fact, really transgressed the Christian or Muslim God–even though she had broken their law. She had done so out of love, and "dear Jesus" (as she said) would be forgiving. Rather, she feared a nameless God that hovered over her. She wondered if she now, through me, was being punished. She wept, and tried to take it all upon herself, even praying that the nameless God, if offended, should take her and not her poor, innocent daughter. I felt deeply for my mother, but knew that her martyrdom would be of no avail. I did not know, myself, why this was so–it just was. I had to live my fate as it came to me. When I told my mother this, she crossed herself, and was satisfied. It is Greek to accept one's fate, and it is Muslim also. She loved me for it, and for not blaming her. How could I blame her? Can one blame the storm for thundering and lightning? So, at 13, I became a woman, came to my own fate, and was ready to kill myself. Only my desire kept me alive.

III

I was a woman, at 13. I had achieved my full height and full physical development. I was quite attractive and had a rounded, pleasing figure. Despite my inner turmoil and doubt, I appeared to others as if supremely happy and full of life. Only my mother and the few boys and men with whom I had relations had any inkling of what was beginning to happen. Mother and I alone knew of its seriousness. We tried to hide it, at first, but it became impossible. My mother gave me cold baths, she rubbed my parts herself, she even gave me her breast to suck on, thinking that perhaps this would relieve me (one of my lusts was to suck on penises and breasts). I was deeply touched by her attempt to relieve me, but it was fruitless. The lusts would not be denied, cooled nor hidden. At last, we both gave up, and I went into the street.

I tried to keep some semblance of decency and humanity, but soon I was known everywhere as the girl who would have sex with anyone. I hated this and was deeply humiliated, but it was true. My mother was laughed at, and soon the decent people (why is it that everyone is "decent" when you have trouble, which is to say that they do not wish to help?) did not bring her sewing any longer. She was laughed at, as the mother of "that nymphomaniac." "Sybilla, the Nymphomaniac," I was called.

Soon, my mother had no money, and we had to earn a few pennies in some way. I strove with all my might to restrain myself for the sake of my mother and I became a prostitute. It was not that I minded being a whore—I was already much lower than that in my own eyes—it was only that I did not think that I could restrain myself sufficiently to charge money for that which I needed so desperately. I would myself pay all that I could, if I had the money.

Being a whore proved to be an effective, though temporary, solution. At last I had a place in life. I earned a few pennies, enough to take care of the minimal needs for survival of my mother and myself. I seemed to be part of the human race again.

As a whore, my experience widened. I no longer had to be furtive in my need to get men; now I could solicit them openly. Since the amount of money did not matter to me, I went with all kinds: young, old, fat, thin, handsome, ugly. I experienced them all. There is little, in the way of sexual depravity, that I do not know. Nor do I put this on the men alone, since I not only accepted, but desired every such depravity. But my desires were never really fulfilled. The horror of it all was that whatever I wished, and would then try to fulfill, would immediately be followed by terrible self-revulsion and guilt (towards what I did not know) and then another desire of equally intense nature. I was doomed to live a life of desire, fulfillment, guilt, reawakening of desire, and to repeat this cycle in such a way as to wrack me with pain and agony. Yes, I know, there are many people who have desire and must go through such torments and conflicts—but I wonder how many of them have had to live them as I have?

Sometimes I would talk to my sister prostitutes. Most of them were frigid—hating men and using this way only to earn a living. They were difficult to awaken sexually, required a great deal, and as whores, both stimulated themselves extensively and earned their bread. Usually, they had a pimp who was also their lover and who, of course, took away all the money that the girls earned. My sister whores had love where they were despised, and gave love where they, in turn, despised. This was the more typical kind of life, though there were also girls who were just poor and found this a good way to earn money. These remained prostitutes only briefly. They soon married or found someone to take care of them. All in all, the girls and women I met as prostitutes were not so different from women in any other class of society—they were only more open about things and more independent. The same can be said of the men—I saw a cross-section. Being a prostitute, I suppose, is like being a doctor—one finds out about the secret places of men and women: their agonies and loves and desires. One even has the pleasure, sometimes, of fulfilling these, or starting some young lad out right.

You may have noticed that I said "women." Yes, it is true. I had a desire for women as well. Not as strong, but there all the same. And even women would pay me—for many such have this desire also. I laughed at this side of it—luckily I could hardly take that part so seriously. I did meet those who were as maniac as I for such sexuality. I merely nodded to them, and felt that I had to deal with my own madness.

For a few years, I managed to make my way, and had some kind of life as a prostitute. All the same, my desire was not fulfilled, and the epithet, "nymphomaniac", stayed with me. Indeed, I became quite mad with my insatiable desires. After a time, it became known that I would have all kinds of sex without any payment whatsoever, so that no one, now, would help me fulfill my role as prostitute. I was reduced to taking all who came and I had no place in society at all. I walked the streets, clothes torn, almost nude. I began to grow dazed. I think that I finally lost my humanness, and was taken by everyone who wished. I remember vaguely that I was picked up by a pimp who promised me a few pennies.

This pimp had me on a stage, having intercourse with animals. I remember it only vaguely, for I was now almost out of contact with reality altogether. The humiliation was total, though I recall feeling that the animals had more warmth and humanity than the people. I remember. . . .I remember. . . .no, I do not really remember. That whole period is more a dream than a memory.

I finally wandered away from the city, out into the desert. I was determined, now, to die. Many times, over the years, I had tried to kill myself, but I had been unable to complete the act. Now, I decided that I would starve myself to death. I knew that I could not control my sexual desire, but had the happy thought that I would soon be too weak to seek out its fulfillment. Hunger, after all, when deprived, is stronger than sex! Even when the latter is monstrous!

I wandered into the desert, many, many miles. I walked day and night. I drank (for I found that thirst cannot be denied! It is stronger than hunger or sex), but I did not eat. I tried to wander far from men, for every time I would see a wandering group, or a caravan, I would still feel compelled to rush up to them and take all of them sexually. At last, even these turned me away, as I must have looked quite terrible.

Then I laughed. Finally, I was relieved–not of the desire, that never left me. I was relieved of any possibility of fulfillment, since I was now so horrible to look at that no one would have me. What had happened to that beautiful, healthy girl who was full of life? At 18, I was near death, and happy to die.

In this state, I wandered; I do not know how long. I came to the Sphinx, and, in a cave nearby, I stumbled in, ready to die. In my delirium, I thought I saw a figure of a man sitting there. With my last remaining conscious thought and breath, I called out to him to take me sexually, and then I fainted.

I do not know when I awakened. Indeed, I cannot, in truth, claim to have "awakened" in any real sense for many months, even years. In retrospect, I see myself as having been totally possessed and largely out of contact with outer reality for those three years that I spent in that cave. It may be hard to believe, but I spent three years, until I was twenty-one years old, in the cave. One might say that I gradually emerged out of madness, or was healed, or was simply bizarre, but none of these is the way that I see it. I will try to explain what happened, as best as I can.

When I "awakened", as I say, from the initial faint, I was still quite delirious and probably near death. The man who had been sitting near me was now standing and I saw him as clearly as anything could be clear in such a state. What I saw was Christ, crucified upon His Cross. There was sweet Jesus, suffering mightily upon his rack of pain. I cried out, "Oh, sweet Jesus, forgive me!" The figure came down off the cross and gave me water to drink. At that moment, for the first time in many years, I was relieved of the terrible pain of desire and tormented lust that had gripped me every moment. I rested, and knew that I was not going to kill myself.

I wept softly for a long time and then slept. When I awakened again, I was not nearly so dizzy nor vague as I had been with my previous vision of the figure in the cave with me. Now I sensed not him, but a larger-than-life-size figure emerging from inside me. I was shaken and awed to see a huge figure of a male human body, with the head of a hawk. I was astounded by it and looked to see if my companion saw it, too. He seemed not to notice it: He hung limply from the nails punched into His hands and feet, His head falling on His chest. I was full of compassion for His suffering, but was powerless to do anything about it.

The Hawk-Headed God, for such is what He was, I am convinced, spoke. "You are dead and in the land of the dead. What you have heard from your mother is true. On the night that you were conceived, the Gods of the Greeks and the Gods of the Egyptians came together. We came together not in animosity nor in wrath nor in rivalry. Indeed, we had not planned to come together at all. It was the act of your parents which brought us together. This is a sin of pride according to the Gods of your mother in Greece, but is no sin according to us, the Gods of Egypt. At first, we merely felt uncommoded by the action of your parents, and allowed a relatively mild fate to take its course. But we, like your parents, had not reckoned upon those other Gods, of more recent origin: your Christian and Muslim Gods. We Egyptians have no rivalries nor jealousies—our sway, after all, is the oldest of all. We allow new Gods to thrive. The same can be said for the Greek, but your Christian and Muslim upstarts are far too youthful and rebellious. So we had a war within your soul. (Ha! I find that even I change, for I use the word 'soul' and not Ba and Ka as I did of old. No matter, even the Gods change, I suppose.) In this war, you have followed now one of us and now another. Perhaps now you can understand your desire followed by guilt—different Gods are being served! This conflict has finally brought you to us. You have surrendered, which has erased the sin of pride which your parents had toward the Greek Gods. At that same moment, we came to an agreement. We agreed to have our sovereignty serially and not at one time, for that would kill not only your body, but your soul, too. We do not wish your destruction, but wish you to find peace and even help us to reconcile ourselves with ourselves. We did not ask it, but now we need you. Thus, now, you die to the world and in these three years, you will reconcile us, your Egyptian Gods."

With that long speech, which I remember very well, indeed—delirious as I was—the Hawk-Headed God faded. I was astonished at this and knew not what to make of it. This big impersonal God, with no name that I knew, was now kindly and warmly informing me of the most huge, incongruous thing of which I could imagine. Yet, it made sense to me, and I was strangely stilled once again from the torments that I had suffered. If I was mad, I was glad to be so! I thought of the name I had been given, "Nymphomaniac", and was able to accept at least the last half of the appelation: "Maniac." I laughed: Better to be a Maniac than a Nymphomaniac! The laugh died on my lips, however, for in a moment I felt a huge pressure from within me.

It was as if all the sexual desire that had hounded me and beaten me and tormented me all these years since I was thirteen was suddenly gathering itself into one large unit and forming itself. Then, manifesting first as a vapor, and later becoming solid, there came out of my eyes, nose, ears, mouth, vagina, anus, a figure which gradually grew and formed itself into a creature which was as fantastic and gigantic as the Hawk-Headed God had been. This one, however, had the body of a woman and the head of a cat. This Cat-Headed Goddess said not a word. She merely looked at me and penetrated, with her look, into the marrow of my soul. I was aflame with desire and sexual passion. She then looked from me to the figure on the Cross and I knew what I had to do.

I hope that I do not offend any Christians among you, or the Christian sentiment among any of you who happen to profess another religion, when I tell you what happened. I can only say that my mother, whom I have always dearly loved and treasured, is Christian, and that I am Christian in part, as well. If what I say offends you, perhaps you had best look to your view of Christianity, for I do not believe that it should offend. Christ is God's Son made flesh, is He not? And flesh includes that animal part of ourselves, does it not? And He is a God of Love, is He not? Enough of my questions and apologies. I do not wish to be defensive, for I have, in truth, nothing to be defensive about. So, let me proceed with my story.

What the Cat-Goddess had me do, filled as I was with both enormous lust and enormous love, was to lick this God-Man in all his body. I licked his wounds, and licked and sucked his sexual organs. As I licked and sucked and felt and stroked, I was enraptured in joy and ecstasy. I felt Him come to life; I felt Him as man and as God in His organs and in His Being. My joy and desire and my lust knew no bounds. The Cat-Goddess drove me onwards, though I needed no prod. The Christ-God responded and came to life. Though I was dead, and in the land of the dead, I awakened a God, and I did this through a Goddess. If all this sounds strange, I can understand that you find it so.

When the God-Man came to life, he came off the cross and left me, saying, "I must be about My Father's business." I wept and wept and again slept. In my dreamless sleep I was at the bottom of all flesh and all soul: I knew what it was to long for soul, for flesh and for connection; for God. Desire alone was as nothing without love and union, and I wept.

When I awakened, I saw what resembled the God-Man but he seemed human to me, not a God. Here was a man, in middle life, whose face was strong, but lined with care. His deep, dark eyes were filled with intensity and compassion. He stroked my head and gave me water to drink. He told me that I had been in a state of delirium, or something very much like it for a very long time—he did not know himself for how long, since he, himself, had been in a near mad state. He thought it to be for over two years, in any case.

I was amazed to hear this, since for me, perhaps only two days, and not two years, had gone by. I tried to speak, to tell him of my astonishment and to ask him who he was, but I found that I could not utter a word. He saw my efforts and that they were in vain, and sadly put his hand on my lips, to calm my anxiety. He spoke: "I can see that, dazed as I was, I have been more conscious through all of our experiences than you have been. I think that I know why you cannot speak now. It is my fault, and I will tell you about it later on. Let me tell you, first, what I know, since I can speak and seem to remember what has happened. You were not speechless in the beginning and, in your delirium, you told me very much about yourself. I know about your Greek mother and Egyptian father, and I know about your nymphomania and hungers—indeed, I think that I know all about you, though you are not aware that you told me. But you spoke only for a time; for many, many months you have 'spoken' only with your eyes, your lips, your body, your hands. It began when you announced that the 'Cat-Goddess' was now going to act, and that the era of the Hawk-Headed God was coming to an end. It was during the 'Era of the Hawk-Headed God', if I may call it such, that you spoke deliriously of all your past and all your suffering. I tended you during this time and nursed you and fed you. That went on for many months. When the 'Era of the Cat-Headed Goddess' came to be, you stopped speaking and then began to touch me and fondle me and lick me and fill me with all manner of sexual delights. I was torn to bits by this–filled with both great joy and satisfaction and great guilt and anguish. During all this time, the only words that would pass your lips would be, 'Sweet Jesus.' I knew that you saw me that way, but I felt myself to be anything but a God–Man.

"Which leads me to speak about myself. I am a man, no longer young, who was a well-respected wise man among my people. They called me Rabbi and came to me, as if I were Solomon, full of wisdom. I read from the Great Book, and read it well, because I felt it deeply. It was from this Great Book that I read to you when you were in your 'Era of the Hawk-Headed God'. I am not sure if you understood me, but the sound of my voice, at least, seemed to calm you.

"As I say, I was known as a kind of Solomon among my people, but I felt like a hypocrite. With all my wisdom and knowledge of 'The Book', I was filled with vast and insensate sexual desire which overcame me. I am not of the view that having a desire is the same as fulfilling it, but I was so horrified by need for every kind of sexual perversity, that I wanted to die. It was not so much the sexuality which horrified me–I am not a prude–but my hypocrisy. I could not preach the Law and experience its opposite in my loins, without feeling the fraud.

"In my despair, I prayed to God for deliverance, and was sent a dream. I was told to go to Mitzraim in the west, and there to find a cave. In that cave I would meet a prophetess, a witch like she of Endor, who would show me the way out of my dilemma. Thereupon, in my dream, I had another dream; a dream within a dream, sayeth the old prophets, is the deeper wisdom of God. In this dream, I saw myself reading from the Good Book. A lovely young girl, looking just like yourself, sat listening to it in joy and appreciation. I went behind a wall and proceeded to masturbate myself in great desire, and great guilt. The girl came and did this for me, saying 'That (the Book) is good, and this (the penis) is good.' She did this so simply and lovingly that I was enchanted. End of dream.

"So, you see how it was that I set out, straightaway, for Mitzraim, and came to this cave. I had not been here for more than a day when you, the answer to my prayer, had arrived. I was immediately overcome with desire, but I had to restrain myself for many months, in order to minister to your needs. And now, for months, you have been ministering to mine, though you did not know it.

"Which brings me to my guilt towards you. You did not know what you were doing, I did. I was wracked with guilt and desire, and continually berating you in my agony. I blamed you, though I was guilty myself. At last, after all this time, I must admit my guilt, and accept it gladly. It was worth all the pleasure, and I accept it."

I looked at this man in wonder and in love. Here he was, berating himself, after having loved and cared for me when I needed it so badly. He had shown me love and compassion and constraint, when no other male had done so. That I could give him what he needed was no sacrifice on my part, it was exactly that which I needed. How could I put into words that I loved him?

How could I say anything? He said that it was his fault that I could not speak now. It was not his fault, it was the wish of the great Goddess. The Cat-Headed one, She without love, only passion; She who had hounded me forever without love, would She let me speak?

At that moment, I leaned forward to this Rabbi and whispered, "I love you." The Cat-Headed Goddess had let me speak. Then I and the Rabbi, in full consciousness and choice, made deep and tender and passionate love. As we made love, I had another vision, but this time clearly, and in no mad nor sick nor vague stupor.

What I saw was this: I saw the Cat-Headed Goddess unite with Christ, the God-Man; She licked and sucked and then He, too, united with Her. And this, while I and the Rabbi were as one.

A great peace overcame us and we slept long and peacefully. But my time with the great Gods of Egypt was not yet finished, nor was my consort.

The next day, I had a vision of a God of the same size as the Hawk-Headed One and the Cat-Headed One. This one had the head of a bull. The "Era of the Bull-Headed God" began. This Bull-Headed God spoke not a word. He pointed only to the place where my few belongings had lain since I first came to the cave, years before. At His bidding, I fished out a golden coin, the last remnant of my work as a prostitute.

I held the golden coin in my hand and offered it to the God. He did not take it. Instead, He reached up and seemed to remove His Bull Head, which I now saw as a golden mask of a bull. The God's real head was human and bore an amazing similarity to the Christ that I had seen earlier. Was this Egyptian God the same as the Christian one? Dim memories of stories I had heard as a child came back to me. Was this great God called Osiris? Was the Hawk-Headed One his son, Horus? Was the Cat-Headed One Isis? I did not know, for these impersonal, nameless Gods did not leave their calling cards with me, only the flesh and blood and vapors of their being!

In any event, this God gave me the golden mask of the bull and had me melt it down together with my golden coin. This seemed very strange to me. My companion and my love, the Rabbi, did not see the great Bull-Headed God–or if he did, he saw Him very differently from the way I did, but he seemed to know that we had a task to do together. We gathered all the wood that we could find and made an intense heat in a brick oven which we had constructed. From the God's unspoken instructions, the Rabbi and I made a mold of a bull-calf with a globe between its little horns. When the gold was melted, we poured it into this mold, let it cool. Soon we had a marvelous little golden calf with a golden ball between its horns. My Rabbi smiled when he saw it, but his smile changed to a fierceness I had never seen before when I told him that the God required us to bow down and worship before this golden calf. "I will not bow down and worship this golden calf!" he said. I had never seen such fierceness in him and was sore afraid, until I remembered one of the stories he read to me from his Great Book. Then I could laugh and say to him, lovingly, "No, no, good Rabbi, my love. You are not to bow down and worship this golden calf, you are to bow down and worship *before* him. That means that you have recognized his power!"

The Rabbi thought for a long time. He did not tell me his thoughts, but I imagine that he was working out for himself how he felt about gold, about flesh, about sex, about the animal. He said nothing, but he bowed down with me, saying to me: "I love you." We knelt for a long time, and then, with a gesture, the God bade us arise. He again had us melt down the gold of our little statue, and this made my Rabbi happy. Jews are nervous, I think, about graven images.

When the gold was fully melted, the God had us do a strange

thing—it was strange to me, at least, but not to my Rabbi. The God had us drink the gold. This we did, day by day, slowly, painfully, until we had consumed it all. The Rabbi smiled at this task and was at peace with his God and with the Egyptian Gods as well. He stroked my hair and said, "Oh, my little Mosina, now I know; now I know that you are indeed my witch, my priestess, of the spirit as well as the flesh. Now I have your gods inside me, and my God is not offended. I love thee."

With that speech, which I did not fully understand, he embraced me. I knew only that we were united forever in a bond which was unbreakable. I knew that spirit and flesh were one for me and that I had made him happy. It was enough. At this point, I did not know if my Rabbi were flesh and blood or spirit and he, I know, felt the same about me. I only knew that henceforth he would always be there if I wanted him, and that it was so for him, as well.

We knew, then, that we must part. He went back to his land and his people, and I returned, now twenty-one and truly a woman, to Alexandria.

V

At the age of twenty-one, after three years absence, I returned to the city of my birth, Alexandria. I felt that I had died and been reborn. In many ways it was true. My mother had long since given me up for dead and had deteriorated greatly. She had sought me everywhere, without avail, and longed for death herself. She was barely kept alive by those few friends of hers of the past, but with my homecoming, she, too, was reborn.

I recounted to her (and to no one else, for who else except my mother would believe me?) all my adventures, and she was dumbfounded. She murmured frequently, "miracle" or "wonder" and listened with rapt attention. The story gave her strength, and when she saw me healthy and well, she revived. I had changed markedly, of course, but all to the better. I once again had all the beauty of my childhood, and the bloom of my pubescence, but now I had the rich and full body of an experienced woman who knew herself, found herself beautiful and full of love. My hair had become more golden. Was this the result of drinking the gold, I wondered, or was it a consequence of being in that dark cave for three years? Almost all of my hair had fallen out when I was ill and working as a vessel for the animals, but now it had come back in even more luxuriant abundance. My figure was delicious to behold. Pardon me if I seem conceited. I do not feel self-satisfied. Rather, it was amazing, and a miracle to me.

I soon had many men seeking me out. No longer was even a word spoken about my sordid past as a nymphomaniac, and no questions were asked about where I had been for three years. I said nothing, but held my head high. Very soon, however, my belly began to swell, from the pregnancy sustained in the last month with my beloved Rabbi. I sent him a message via my soul that I was to have his child, and I received an answer that he was overjoyed. During that time, also, I nursed my mother back to health.

Soon, my child was born. He was a handsome lad, with wide open countenance and smiling mien. He was normal in every way, except in one particular: he was born deaf and dumb. At first, I was destroyed by this fact. I racked myself to find my guilt, but found no answer. I then shrieked at the Goddess, the Cat-Headed One, who once again, it seemed, had invaded me and done me damage. I then implored the Hawk-Headed One and the Bull-Headed One who had become human—I implored them to explain this to me and to cure my son if they could. These Gods appeared in a dream and said that they, the Egyptian Gods, were not to blame, that this was a visitation from the Greek Gods and the latter would contact me in due time.

I was placated by this news, though shaken in my happiness. I came down off of my high state and realized how much at the mercy of the Gods I still was. I waited. My son grew, and became more and more handsome. He was intelligent and brave and charming, in his way, but he did not speak. I grew less and less concerned about it, since he did not seem to mind it much and was a happy child.

I lived my own life in an ever more adventurous way. My beauty became known and I had lovers of every kind. Alexandria was a Mediterranean port with Greeks, Syrians, Lebanese, Jews, Italians, French, Spaniards, even Englishmen, and its life was sophisticated and luxurious among the upper classes. The poor—mostly Arabs—lived differently, but they seemed to enjoy the spectacle of this other life, as well. I soon became a part of the aristocratic life and had many rich and famous, as well as wise and powerful, lovers. I was much in demand and, within a few years, had my own salon. My life experience had made me wise to the ways of men, and my years in the cave (though known to none but my mother) made me wise in the way of the Gods. I was, thus, sought after, and would often think that this must be what my Rabbi had, in his way. I enjoyed this life, and even became a mistress of the King's son. This may shock you a little, for the King's son in reality, was none other than the son of my father by his wife of the arranged marriage. Yes, it was a sort of incest with my half-brother, but we Egyptians are not so shocked about brother-sister incest as, perhaps, Europeans are. Indeed, of old, the royalty was required to have this brother-sister marriage. In deference to modern times, we had a love affair, which was what we wished.

My mother had long since married happily. She had also met

and reconciled with my father, who was now King. It was a very sophisticated, exciting life. Only two things disturbed me. I sometimes wanted to be married, but knew that I could not, though I did not know why. The second thing that bothered me was the muteness of my son. Sometimes, when alone, I would commune, in my soul, with my Rabbi, and tell him of my sadnesses, and he would comfort me.

Thus did my life go on until my son was eighteen years old and I was a mature woman of thirty-nine. I was still beautiful and sought after, but I had no one to be a father to my son. I was now quite rich, so it was not poverty of which I was afraid. I once again wondered about the Greek Gods, and asked myself questions that I had not raised in many years. I was reminded of what the Egyptian Gods told me in my dream, and wondered why the Greek Gods had not visited me. I became aloof and finally, one night, after the celebration of our birthdays, I had the awaited dream. In this dream, I was instructed, by a bodyless voice, to proceed at once to Delphi, the place of my conception.

When I told my mother this, she was sore afraid, but she knew that I was touched by the Gods and that I must go. I bade goodbye to my friends, telling them that I had important business in my mother's birthplace—which I did—and tearfully kissed my son farewell. I told him, in the sign language in which we were both now so proficient, that I hoped that I would bring back good news for him. He assured me that he would be all right, with his friends and grandmother, and that I was to enjoy myself.

Within the week, I was at Delphi. I slept the night on the cold hard ground, near the stone of the Omphallos, as my mother had done, hoping to get a dream or instruction. No dream awoke me and no instruction came. Instead, in the middle of the night I was awakened by a young man who was trying to make love to me. The boy, about the same age as my son, had huge, dark eyes, black curly hair, and was incredibly handsome. He was fondling me everywhere in a greedy way. His hands went to my breasts and my vagina and his lips to mine as if he were ravenous. I laughed and calmed him. I was suddenly moved to take him to a nearby cave, which I found easily and then gave him all the love and passion that he required. I felt strangely maternal in all this, as well as passionate myself, and wondered what it was that these Greek Gods had in store for me.

We spent the night in love making, but my young lover said not a word. He made many sounds of love and passion, but they were grunts and sighs, no words. I remarked this, but said nothing. The next morning, I asked him about himself, and now I understood. The boy tried to speak, but could not. That is not quite accurate–he spoke but it was with an agony of stammering and stops and stuttering and explosions which drove him into peaks of fury and frustration and terror. I finally put my hands on his lips to stop him, and he bit me and then wept. He wept long and I comforted him.

When he was almost exhausted with weeping, he slowly and painfully stammered out his story, though now without the fury and frustration. He was born, just as my mother had been, on a small farm near Athens, but was the son of a Turkish father and an Armenian mother. The mother, of course, had been Christian, of the Armenian Church, and the father a Muslim. The parents had loved each other, but not only were their religions opposed, but their countries were mortal enemies as well. The boy had stuttered from his earliest years, and no one knew why. He had gone through such terrible torment because of this handicap that he had many times wanted to kill himself. At last, in exhaustion, he had prayed for deliverance to the God which was beyond nation and tribe religion. That night, he had a dream that instructed him, by voice, to go to Delphi and have a deep union with the priestess he would find there. He did not understand altogether what the voice had meant by "deep union", but when he arrived at Delphi and saw this beautiful and exciting woman lying on the ground, he grew full of desire and knew that the "deep union" must mean a sexual union. Which is why he made love to me. If I was not that priestess, please, I was not to be offended, but he was desperate.

Thus was his story. I was touched and amused by this sweet young boy and deeply moved by his suffering eyes, Armenian and Turkish at once. I had not the slightest idea as to how or why I was to be his priestess. I remembered, with pleasure, how I had once before been a priestess and now I trusted that guidance would come to me. I therefore told the boy all about myself, including my experience with the Rabbi, and I assured him that only my mother knew of this. I told him, too, about my son. After our full stories were related, we lay together and made love–something that we both enjoyed, and something I could give him, priestess or not, to soothe his tortured spirit.

I thought about how I could help him, as he slept afterwards. I thought I saw, above him, an image of a fiery warrior, a dragon slayer, belonging, no doubt, to that fierce Muslim spirit of his. I fancied, too, that I saw that meek and loving Christian-Armenian restrainer, showing pain at every hurt to every being everywhere, and I thought I understood. The spirit of the Christian God, with its forbearance, and the spirit of the Muslim God, with its fiery militancy, were torturing this boy. I had an inspiration. When he awakened, I asked him was he an educated boy, or was he an untutored peasant lad? He told me that he had been to school for only the rudiments of reading and writing and numbers. He knew nothing of the Greek heritage, nor history, and of religion he knew only the superstitions and the basic faith.

My inspiration was correct and I knew what I had to do. I took this boy out of the cave. I took him down into Athens and I made him a home. For many months I taught him myself. First, I read to him from the great Homer, of the Heroes of the Greeks: of Achilles, the Dioscuroi, and of Odysseus and the rest. I read to him, too, of Zeus and Poseidon and Hades; of Apollo and Hermes and Ares; of all the Gods of the Greeks, leaving Dionysos until the end. That fiery and watery and passionate God was, I knew, the answer to the youth's conflict between Christian water and Muslim fire. I read to him, too, from the Greek poets and philosophers. And I read of the Goddesses as well, for, thank Heaven, there is no Greek soul without the Goddess. I read and I taught. My charge devoured what I offered. In the teaching, I, myself, learned, for I had not been so well educated myself.

I did not only educate this boy's spirit. We made love and I taught him the secrets of Eros. Thus we lived for three years, and he grew and thrived. With each year, my charge changed. Gradually he began to speak without stammering. By little and little his words became clear. They had force and fire and substance. Soon, he knew as much or more than I did about both Logos and Eros, for I had given him all that I knew. I danced with him, and played music with him. I was his priestess and his teacher and his muse. We were very happy.

In the third year, I had a dream. In the dream, a voice said: "We are very pleased with our handmaiden. You have done all these things for this boy. You have passed our spirit on to him in body and in mind. You have done this out of love and care. Know, now, that Greek and Christian are united within you, just as Christian and Arab are united within him. You had spirit and flesh, now you have Soul. You are Psyche and Sybilla, the soul who speaks and mediates the Gods. And now you can know what was meant in the word, Nymphomaniac. Nympho is our Greek for bride and you are, in truth, a bride of the Gods. As bride of the Gods, you are also a bride of men. Go, Sybilla, bride of Gods and men, priestess of the soul, go and find your son healed."

The voice ended and I awakened with a great sense of peace and oneness. My charge looked like a young god. When I told him of my dream, he nodded. He spoke and said, "I have had a dream, too, but now I must be about my father's business." He smiled, and I smiled. We embraced and parted.

When I returned to Alexandria, I found that my son had recovered his speech and hearing, probably at the same moment in which I had my dream. We all were overjoyed, and did not know what to do. It was all too much joy to contain.

In nine months time, I gave birth to a daughter who was perfectly well and normal and happy. What then shall I say in words? At forty-four, just before my own menopause, I completed a circle. From my mother to myself to my daughter; a story of women and a story of men—and a story of Gods.

I suppose, ladies and gentlemen, you are wondering why I came here, being so happy and overjoyed with my life. Well, I said a prayer of thanksgiving to God for all that had happened to me and I wanted to be among those who had also been touched by God. Thereupon, I fell into a deep sleep and was transported here.

I have heard your stories, and know that I am in the right place. I, Sybilla, the Nymphomaniac, a bride of God and men, a priestess of the soul, belong among you. I see there, in the Tree, the sacred Phalli, breasts, and other Parts of the Body, and I see, too, the sacred God-Men. Best of all, I see a changing and revolving Pantheon, and. . . .what more can I say? I embrace you all.

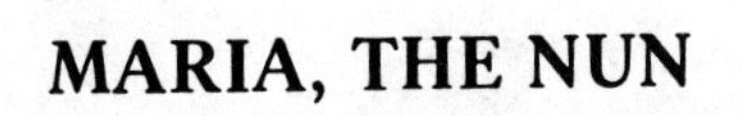

MARIA, THE NUN

MARIA, THE NUN

I

I am Maria. I am named Maria after Our Lady, Queen of the Angels, the Mother of God. It is a common name, I know, and also common in my family—for ours is a history of common people, although our origin is noble. We have this in common with Our Lady, do we not? Ordinary people with a noble origin?

We have always been priests and nuns. That may amuse you, to hear that one's ancestors have been priests and nuns—and, of course, I do not mean that quite so concretely. There has been a tradition within our family that at least one person of every generation is a priest or nun. Naturally, those who have given birth, the biological parents, have not been "religious," as we say—that is, committed to the religious life. Spiritual parenthood has been just as important in the history of my family.

This brings me to why I am here. My story, I think, concerns what I have found out a religious life can be in the twentieth century. Julia, like you, I am a child of this century, but I am by no means an atheist nor communist—even in the sense in which you have used them, though I can sympathize with your position. I am a fully committed Christian. From early life I was destined for and embraced the religious life in Roman Catholicism and gladly became a nun. You can call me Maria, the Nun, if you like, since you all seem to have titles. I have mostly been called Sister, and even Mother (I was, for a time, Mother Superior in a convent), but these titles do not mean very much to me. In a way, "Maria, the Nun" appeals to me since it is not very official. Nun, if I recall correctly from my education, is a derivative of "monk" and means rather "elders" or some such thing. The word is related, a priest once told me, to *nonne,* which means "whore". That does not disturb me (as it did not disturb you, Sybilla, but for different reasons). My story will make clear why it does not.

But before I tell my personal story, the recounting of my quest and problem, which seems to be the reason that we, strange bedfellows, are all gathered here—before I come to that, I would like to tell you of the origins of my family.

My ancestors have been in Spain for many hundreds of years. Our tradition is that we came to Spain shortly after the period of the Church Father, St. Augustine, who is said to have been distantly related to us. The family lived in North Africa before that. Our deepest tradition is that we were originally from Israel and, most importantly, were among the very first Christians. The story is—and I am inclined to believe it—that at the time of our Lord, the family was a more or less noble one. I say more or less since it was a Jewish family and there was not very much wealth or social status among the Jews during that period of their history. All the same, it is said that our family were among the first converts to our Lord, Jesus, and that, in particular, a mother and daughter witnessed not only the Crucifixion, but the consequences of the Resurrection. This mother and daughter, persecuted for being Christians, lost all the members of their family, as well as their wealth and social standing. They starved, became ill, and finally wandered into a great ditch where the lepers lived. After the Resurrection, the Lord appeared to them, and their illness was cured.

Ever since that time, our family has been Christian. We have been of all races, and even of diverse Christian creeds and sects, but we have been as one in our following of the Savior. There have been many religious among us—comprising at least one priest or nun in each generation since the beginning. For a very long time our family has been in Spain, where I was born. I am now in middle life, just forty, and I have two brothers, both older than myself.

My eldest brother is a priest and a monk, who lives far from the world of men, near a tiny monastery in North Africa. "Lives" perhaps, is too expansive a term, for he spends most of his time in silent contemplation in a cave at some distance from the monastery. Most of the time he is alone, occasionally returning to the monastery and the routine life of prayer and work with the brothers. I have not seen my brother for several years, nor do we correspond, but I know the makeup of his character and what he is about. He is really not of this world at all. His eyes are on eternity and fixed there. The things of this world, its problems, passions, loves, are of no interest to him. It is not that he is cold, or removed, or uncaring—all of which he, and I, would see as sins for a Christian. He has had such deep and compelling religious experiences that everything of this world pales in comparison. Nor, it seems, can he communicate these experiences. He is aware of his inability to do so, and thus, meditates and prays in his own way. He may be a saint, or he may simply be living a quiet Christian life. I only know that this is what he must do. His life poses one extreme of the "religious life" which appeals to me. I feel, though, as a person of the twentieth century, and thinking even of the twenty-first, that my brother is really living in an earlier age. I intend nothing disrespectful with this evaluation.

My second brother, just a little older than myself, is at the other extreme. He, too, is a priest, having become one early in life in contrast to my older brother who became a priest in his late thirties and after an adventurous and complex life. My younger brother is, in his way, as anomalous as my older brother, but of an opposite disposition. The younger, as soon as he could manage it, arranged to be assigned to Israel, where he is enormously active. He is not only a guide to the holy places, he is translating our Latin prayers into Hebrew for our Christians there, and travels all over the country on his motorbike, doing all that he can for both the Church and Israel. It is strange, in a way, since he is both a deeply committed Christian and a Zionist. Privately, he has confessed to me that he expects the Second Coming to occur again in Israel and "soon"—that is, within this century. He is not even certain if it has not already occurred. In any case, with his bushy black beard, black robes, robust body, and extraverted temperament, he is well known in Israel among Christians, Jews, and Muslims, and seems to be appreciated by all of them. So, you can see that my two brothers are really quite opposite.

Would you say that each of them presents a meaningful religious life for a Christian in the twentieth century? I mean, of course, Roman Catholic; I hope I do not offend Protestants or Orthodox. Yes, I suppose they do. But do they present a viable pattern of life for me? Should I follow one aspect of my nature and retire to a cave or convent where I can worship the Lord in quiet and peace, or should I actively fulfill God's love and go to the place where I, too, believe that the Second Coming will originate? What does it mean to be religious in our time? Before I try to answer that question, let me tell you a little more about myself.

I was born in Cordoba, in Southern Spain, not far from the old Synagogue, on the one hand, nor from the Great Mosque, on the other. As a child, I visited both of these "museum" pieces and the memory of them is fully engraved in my mind. The desecration of the mosque by that atrocious "church" in its center is, happily, going to be changed, but the symbolic fact of what my Church has done to other religions is not so easily repaired. The destructiveness and hypocrisy haunted me a great deal after I studied history outside of my own country and from a viewpoint other than that of the Church.

But I am leaping ahead of my story. I was born, as I said, in Cordoba, of a family noted for its "religiousness". My childhood was in no way different from that of other children in Cordoba except that, perhaps, we had rather more piety than most in a pious land. My father, however, was fairly well educated, and we were relatively free of the grossest prejudices and ignorance found among some people in my land. We had warmth and compassion, customs and rituals. Life was pleasant enough. I do not wish to dwell upon it. I do not share the view of some psychologists that one's childhood is decisive in the shaping of personality. It is important, no doubt, but my adult concerns after adult experiences and—finally—religious experiences, are what have most occupied me. If one answers that these are merely the result of patterns formed in childhood, I will not cavil, the Church believes that, too. I wish, however, to relate that which importantly concerns me. If I tell you that my hair was red, my eyes dark brown, and that I was a passionate, though moody child, does that add anything to my theme? I think not. Pardon my irritability; psychology and "psychologizing" have come near to wrecking religion. First you have Freud, who, with his stupidity, treats it all as "illusion", and then you have Jung, who wants to "psychologize" it all!

There! I have shown one of my irritations, and I know very well why it is so strong. It is simply because I, and the Church, must incorporate what psychology has learned—particularly from Freud and Jung—if it is going to survive. We know quite well that the Devils are most devilish when they tell the truth, and that is when we are most irritated by them. Yes, many of us know very well that Freud and Jung were not devils, but so it must seem to some of the "faithful"—who are, indeed, of little faith! Freud has shown us our hypocrisy and our foolishness, and that is always valuable, but Jung is even more devilish. He has gone deeper into God and Christianity than the contemporary Church has, and that, as we know, is unforgivable! So, we must, then, go deeper again, if our Church is to survive. Jung, after all, remained a Christian (though a Protestant), even though he incorporated science, psychology, and a dozen religions, besides alchemy and the occult. The deepest heretic is also the greatest Christian, and it remains for us, within the Church, to go as deep, if we wish her to survive.

I do not know if my views have come through clearly, but I hope that they have, for that is the main thing. You see, my life is really my search to serve. To serve is to serve God, and to serve God one must serve Man. But I am again getting ahead of my story. I just wanted to say that my personal life is not so interesting—what is more interesting is my search and my service. In that, ladies, I am more like the Knight, Arab, and Ronin, because my quest is greater than myself, but I am also like you, dear Sisters, since my search is not possible without *me,* and, in that—well, you will see.

Enough, now, of my introduction. I must get on with my story, and not trail in pieces of it here and there. I am a Spaniard, and not so systematic, and I hope that you will forgive me that. I trust that I will include all the parts.

II

My story—that is, the story of my "quest"—begins about five years ago, when I was thirty-five. I had been a nun for fifteen years and had even been Prioress of an Abbey for the previous year. I was, of course, too young to be a full "Mother Superior"—as they say—but I had been acting as such for the year, and was about to be officially so named. Through a series of events which seemed to be mere chance, but now, I feel, may have been divinely predestined, I was rejected for the post, and on grounds which were really idiotic. The rejection did not annoy me very much in my need for status and recognition (though that, I must confess, was always there), but I was disturbed more profoundly in other ways. I was deeply shaken and disappointed with the "elders", that is, the senior nuns and priests who made this decision. This is hard for me to explain and, I suppose, only you, Sir Ronin, will fully understand what I mean. To put it baldly, "How could those old fools, who needed me and what I was doing so much more than I needed them, how could they presume to judge me at all and find me wanting? They arrogantly thought they could judge a person's spiritual development. Did they think they were God?"

I suffered greatly from hurt and angry rebellious feelings, believing that I was committing an act of inner disobedience, based on spiritual pride. I went to confession, mortified myself with penances, fasts, and near starvation, but the hurt and anger did not leave me. I began to think the way Martin Luther did: if the terrible sin that I was experiencing was not leaving me, perhaps the Church itself was in error, for the hypocrisy that I saw in all these same nuns and priests was beyond any that I had seen before.

What should I do? Leave the Church? Submit? I could not submit, nor could I leave the Church to which I was deeply committed. Unlike Martin Luther, I also did not want to form a new Church or a new sect. Perhaps that is because I am a woman, but I also think that the time for new sects is passed, and that we need renewal from within. In this, I am a follower of the great St. Thomas More, who died for his Church, while he was fully aware of her need for renovation.

I went back to being an ordinary nun. This gave me the blessing of having more time at my disposal, since I had fewer duties than before.

Now I had to reflect more deeply. What did my disillusionment mean? Partly, I realized, I had expected my seniors to be fair and just, even if they could not be great. They had failed me, and I could not forgive them. Forgiveness. I could not do this, and therefore, I was lacking in love. They, of course, cared not at all for my forgiveness and would, no doubt, be derisive that I would see it is this way. I suspect that they felt that they had to forgive me! I had to laugh at that. All the same, I could not forgive, and that led me to something much greater. Behind this inability was my own feeling of forgiveness of God. Yes, forgiveness of God, in its deepest sense: I felt that God could not forgive me for my sins, and I could not forgive Him. That is not quite accurate; I had felt, for a long time, that my own lovelessness was unforgivable by God, but I had gradually felt that this was forgiven—at least as my own capacity for love was clearly growing. I could not forgive God, however, for all his sins. That, of course, is the greatest sin of all, and put me right up there with the Devil.

What were God's sins? Need I list them? The Inquisition for one. The death of so many innocents in two World Wars for another. The brutal deaths of his Chosen People. How could God countenance evil? Yes, I knew many of the answers to this question: God's ways are not ours; it is a mystery; those who died so brutally went straight to Heaven and the tormenters went to

Hell. All of these answers seemed rather childish to me and not sufficient. The injustice of God and His evil cast great doubt upon my Christianity. I found an acceptable Christian solution was much helped by this miraculous book of C. G. Jung, "Answer to Job." But, there was even more. I felt that the deepest sin of God was the sacrifice of His Son. How could a loving God–even if He had the darkness that was so obvious and that Jung wrote about–how could He sacrifice His Son for Man? It was the greatest sacrifice of all, it is true, for a father to sacrifice his only begotten son. Somehow, however, I could not accept that it was so self-sacrificing, really, and I saw that God was a hypocrite! God talked of His goodness, but was destructive and a hypocrite. You can imagine what that did to my Catholicism and my Christianity! The model was the hypocrisy of the elders. God supported them, and He, too, was a hypocrite! I choked on that–could not accept it. I wondered about my own hypocrisy, and found it painful but acceptable. I was well aware of Original Sin, and all my sins, and knew very well that I could never surmount them all, try as I might. I could accept and struggle with my own darkness, but I was not aware that God was struggling with His! Now I was dangerously near not only to no longer being a nun, but even close to leaving God's Church!

I was not panicked, but I was profoundly moved. I had to know about these things. I had to know what my vows of poverty, chastity, and obedience had to be now, in the twentieth century, and I had to know whether God was grappling with His darkness as well.

There was no one with whom I could discuss these things. I was not very learned in theology, and there may have been men in the Church who could answer my questions, but I doubted it. I was certain that there were many in the Church struggling just as I was. I had even met a number of wonderful men and women Catholics as deeply engaged as I in similar conflicts. It was precisely these people who helped me keep my confidence in the Church and in my hope that She would be renewed. The answers for me had to come from my own labors, I recognized. That the Elders failed me must have at least this meaning in it: I must battle it through myself.

I toiled with the dilemma as best I could. I no longer did penance, nor mortified myself, nor starved myself. I knew that the answers would not come this way. I felt that I could not, indeed, do it alone, and resolved to find a way of talking with my namesake, Mary, and asking her these questions.

Mary, after all, was quite human, had been both an ordinary wife and mother, as well as Wife and Mother of God. She had been almost quite human, but not quite. In any event, She was closer to us mortals, and now, when the Pope in Rome had proclaimed Her Assumption into Heaven—bodily—well, that was a prelude to a new Creation, was it not? Here I followed Jung: something was brewing in the Collective Unconscious and in Heaven itself. Perhaps the Second Coming was being prepared.

I, after all, was a nun, and I supposed that Mary would listen to me. I resolved to seek Her out, not as I and so many other Christians had done in the past, to get Her ear and Her blessing, but to have a talk with Her, a dialogue. I wanted to ask Her my questions.

My presumption astonished me, but the rightness of it impressed me even more. I was aware of many difficulties. On the one hand, it was right for twentieth century man to have his own, individual contact with God—or what was the point of all the development of individuality, and all the psychological achievement of Jung, for example—yet I was aware of what chaos there would be if we all followed only our image of God, and our own dialogue: the whole achievement of the Church, and its unity and wholeness would be destroyed. I had to risk it, but how did I know that I could have this kind of dialogue at all? That was the real presumption! It was hardly in my hands, now, was it? So, I resolved to find out if it was possible.

I thought, how does one go about this? According to Jung, one can just stay in one's own little room, really. Or one can go to the great places where the "God" has been manifested. I could not go, at the moment, to the places where Mary had "appeared" and had been adored, though I had been to many of them. I remembered very well, for example, my experiences at Lourdes. I had been there with the pilgrims and had experienced both sides of the Church: the pious, faithful and miraculously peaceful spirit of the people who come, and the noisy, fraudulent, exploitative spirit of the people in the town! Yes, I recalled my experience very well. I drank of the waters and felt happy. It was miracle enough that we all, diseased and healthy, drank and bathed in the same waters without infecting each other! I wonder why the scientists and others who investigate the miracles have never noticed that daily miracle. Yes, Mary was there—or I should say Marie, for thus is She called in that place—and on that spot where Her pagan ancestress, a Goddess, also lived. Could I now, in my little convent in Spain, could I now reach that Marie, that Mary, that Maria, who healed the sick and helped us all?

What about that Mary who "lived" in Einsiedeln in Switzerland, that Black Madonna, who is so lovely there and at her other places in Europe? What, too, about the new Apparitions at Garabandal in my own beloved Spain? Maria was beginning to be seen and heard more and more, all over the world. Would She come to me as well? Yes, I was sure that She would.

So, I went to my own little chapel of my own little church and I prayed. I prayed that She would come and speak with me. And She did. Be patient and you will hear what She told me.

III

I did not have long to wait. I did not have a great Vision, with a capital "V", but I do believe that I experienced certain things which will be of interest to you, especially if you are friendly to Christianity. So, without further ado, let me tell you what happened:

As I knelt in the chapel before a statue of the Blessed Mother, I began to smell a perfume, a feminine scent of flowers or powders. I laughed to myself. Was the Blessed Mother inclined to use perfume like an ordinary woman, something we nuns had long ago sacrificed? The pleasant smell subsided and gave way to a vision of what seemed like a playground. No, it was not quite that. What I saw was a teeter-totter—a board mounted on a fulcrum in the middle of a large expanse of green park. On this teeter-totter were two little girls. One child was blond and dressed in a deep blue frock. The other girl was black and clothed in a wine-red skirt. They were swinging up and down, gaily laughing, obviously enjoying their ascent and descent. I was infected with their jubilance. Just above them, not more than twenty feet in the air, there appeared an image of a large woman, dressed in the habit of a nun, though it was a deliciously deep blue color. Only her face was exposed, and it was white and pink and gay. She smiled as I looked at her astonished. This is what she said:

> "Maria, your mouth is open! Do not be afraid. You prayed and asked to speak with me, so here I am. It is not so difficult or serious or impossible. Here I am. And there, below, am I! I am that little blond girl and that little dark girl, that I am, too. Why does everyone always see me only as a Mother, kind and loving and forgiving? I am also like that!"

I was astonished. What was this vision? Was I really seeing the Blessed Virgin, or was I in the hands of some Devil teasing me? Before I could reconcile myself to what I was witnessing, the

Apparition continued:

"Yes, I have been and continue to be a child who likes to play, to have fun, to be gay. Is that so amazing? You are familiar with the child Jesus. Is it so impossible to imagine and recognize that His Mother was a child, too?"

I said nothing, but I wondered why it was that this Apparition was asking me to recognize Her. As if She needed my understanding and recognition, just as much as I needed Hers! As I thought this thought and looked up, She nodded vigorously, as if She had read my mind and agreed with it.

"Of course," She continued. "Naturally I need you, and I need all the other people as well. You are perfectly aware, by now, that God needs man to fulfill Himself and His own plan for salvation, and I, as both a wife of God, and a Mother of God, certainly need all the help that I can get. I will tell you a secret. The secret is that Everywoman is—or rather, can be—a Wife and Mother of God. Indeed—and now I tell you the whole and final secret and thus take away the mystery altogether, which is very bad psychology, no doubt, but very feminine, I suppose—the secret is that the Second Coming is really going to be the consequence of Everywoman's becoming the Wife and Mother of God. Not only that, but that the feminine soul of Everyman can also become the Wife and Mother of God. To the extent that that happens, and to the extent that they are all similar, only then will the general and collective and Christian Second Coming take place. Dear Maria, my namesake, I can tell you that this has already taken place with you and with many others. I suppose, though, you already glimpsed that!"

The Blessed Mother, if that is what She was, suddenly stopped speaking with me and fixed her attention on the two lovely little girls who were playing. I had to take in what She was saying. It seemed to make sense both in terms of what I knew psychologically and in terms of my religion: God had to incarnate in the souls of everyone, become totally man, and then we would have the Second Coming; indeed that *was* the Second Coming! Very simple, and very true, but was it heresy? I don't know. She seemed so simple and ordinary about it all, as if this were the most blatant and non-controversial item of general knowledge. I don't know if you all can believe it, Christian or not, but I know that I do.

I now turned my attention to the little girls.

The blond one was like an angel—sweet, charming, gay, much like the picture of the fairy princesses one saw as a child in the books. The dark one looked deep and passionate and intense, with eyes as dark and bottomless as Hell itself. Yet the depth was not negative—and I wondered again how we think of dark as bad. Was this a hint about the problem of evil, with which I was trying to get an answer from the Virgin? These two little girls were anything but evil and I had looked into the eyes of one and thought of Hell. Why? Because she was dark?. . . .At that moment, I heard the Virgin laugh again, and I looked up. I was startled to see Her open Her habit and take off Her nun's head-covering and reveal Herself stark naked! She had a lovely body, with hair as red as mine had been as a child!

"Maria," she said. "Your mouth is open again! What do you think? Do you suppose that the Virgin has no body? Yes, I know that there are those who would prefer it to be that way and even, for a time, it was right for me to act as if I had none. Even the nun's garb came to be understood that way, though we both know that originally it was just Everywoman's dress. I do have a body, you know, and I would say it is not too bad, is it? What do you suppose, could one have a baby without having a body?"

Now she laughed again, and I felt that perhaps I was being made a fool of. "No, no," said the Virgin, reading my thoughts, "I do not wish to make you feel foolish. I merely am trying to answer the questions which you have brought. I laugh, too, at all those who scoff at the idea of a Virgin having a child! That is easy! But having a child without having a body? Well! I am showing you spirit and flesh, light and dark, old and young, all of it is my nature. That is myself as a woman, chosen by God, who wished to unite with me. Is it not so, also, of God, Himself?"

At that point, I looked again at the teeter-totter. The little girls had now changed to grown-up women, but had maintained their original character–light and dark. I thought of Lourdes and of Einsiedeln, of White Madonna and Black Madonna, and I understood what Our Lady was saying about herself.

What of your Son, I thought. What of my original question about God sacrificing His Son, and being something of a hypocrite? I now recalled a dream which I had had some days before. In it, I was standing on a small hill overlooking a river valley, where many people were gathered. Many were below me and many were with me. I chanced to look off to my left, and there, in a pass among the hills some distance off, I saw a small group of men and women walking towards us. Light seemed to emanate from them. As they came closer, I could see that they had the equivalent of halos around them–not circles or plates of gold, but auras of golden light. Among them, and in their lead, I saw a man who was muscular and handsome, resembling a movie actor. To my astonishment, when He came closer, I saw that this was the figure of Christ. He was moving angrily into the world. All of us present understood, without words, that He was angry because He had been so misunderstood. I awakened with a start. Was this a mere wish-fulfillment of mine, or was this the new, risen Christ?

Again, Mary read my thoughts and nodded, before I put my question to Her directly. She was declaring that this was correct, I was on the right road to understanding. The Virgin was saying nothing less than that the flesh was to no longer be refused, rejected, held as dark or dangerous and diabolical, as in some Jansenist heresy. In the New Church, the body was to be welcomed. Was this not the point of the original "Incarnation" (becoming flesh)? Poverty, Chastity, Obedience could be understood as constrictions of matter, of the flesh, and, therefore, of the spirit which dwelt in matter. Thus, they needed to be seen afresh. God was becoming man, in every man, and, hence, a new freedom, a new authority from within, would lead to the experience of poverty, chastity and obedience in a new way.

Choose poverty: in the sense of not pursuing power nor wealth alone, which always constricts and demeans the spirit. But neither choose to deprive yourself of material blessings, which also constricts the spirit and makes it mean. Choose chastity: in the sense of purity. Respect and love the flesh as well as the spirit, and do not subject it to humiliating conditions such as poor health and excessive pain. Chastity is to be chosen. Chastity of the flesh is the love and purity of the flesh, to be sought and gained just as with the spirit! Choose obedience—the hardest of all. Obedience is submission, but to what? Submission to the dictates of God, who resides within the soul itself and takes precedence above all outer dictates. One follows the God within, but one is also responsible.

These thoughts were implied in what I was experiencing, yet the words were my own, not Hers. I knew that I would need to win these views as my own—it was not enough to merely experience them as an inner authority, which I was now seeing, paradoxically enough, as an "outer" vision. I would have to digest them.

All of this seemed so simple that it was very deceptive. Whether I remained a nun or not seemed quite secondary. If I could or they wanted me, very well; if not—if they could not accept my views—well then, I would leave. But nun I would remain, wedded to Christ, bride of God, and enduring the teeter-totter of my own light and dark feminine nature, of the Mary within. Not only within was She, not at all. She existed in all of us Christian women and we would all have to find our way to live Her totally and thus become "blessed" as She was blessed "in the beginning"—blessed in that the God-man wants to make us his bride and his mother. So be it.

IV

All was deceptively settled and deceptively simple. Somewhere I knew that it was too easy, but I felt that I had no real reason to be uneasy. That night, after a peaceful afternoon and the Vision in the chapel gradually faded from consciousness—that night I had a dream. Actually, I had two dreams, but the second one was more than a dream.

In the first dream, I saw myself lying down against what looked like a mountain, or at least a hillock of some sort. When I looked more closely, the hillock was meat. It was rich, full-bodied meat, of unknown animals, all ready to be eaten. I suddenly realized, in the dream, that unless this meat was to be eaten soon, it would all go bad and would start to decay. I awakened with a start.

Hardly was I awake—was it a dream again or was I fully awake?—it seemed to me more real than my waking consciousness—hardly was I awake, as I say, when I again saw the figure of the Virgin. But now She had a look on Her face which made my skin creep and my blood curdle in my veins. She looked like a witch—hardly better than some pagan Goddess, and a kind of Medusa. Yet, I knew Her to be the Virgin. She laughed at me and sneered:

"Yes, it is indeed I. Before yesterday you knew me only in one form. Yesterday you knew me in two. Today you will know me in three. For I, too, am complex. And now I will show you the dark truth! You, who ask about love, about poverty, chastity and obedience! You, who ask about forgiveness! What have you lived? You are a dried out old nun who knows nothing of love, of sin, of passion, of life! You sit asking intellectual questions as if these will solve the mystery of your feminine being. There is nothing so sickening as that! You are not worthy to be a nun, let alone a bride of God who hopes to give birth to the God-man. Get thee from the nunnery, and find out what it is to be a woman, and mortal, and loving, and of flesh!"

The Vision then vanished and I was left only with a horrible laughter ringing in my ears. That, I knew, was not a "vision" with a small "v". No, now I knew that the Virgin, the Madonna, that great and powerful creature who was also fully woman and ordinary—now I knew what She was like! For She had spoken the truth. I had entered the convent at the age of twenty and knew very little of life. Now, at thirty-five (this was, as I have said earlier, five years ago), I was already beginning to age and I could not say that I knew very much of life outside the convent. Inside, the women were as other women, but inclined to become as dried out as I was myself. I had long since stopped experiencing sexual desire, let alone love of a man. Indeed, the extent of my loving had been a kind of maternalism in regard to other nuns and in teaching children.

So now the Virgin had found me out. She knew. Now, too, I knew Her real nautre. I knew that the dark side which had sniffed of Hell had a reality to it, and I was grateful. I knew that the Virgin was like a Spaniard, and could be wild as a gypsy and as hateful and as occult. It was right that She should be so! It was right that I should be so, also. Was I going to be some pale lady who just sat and looked holy? I had no right to such hypocrisy!

Now, I understood the Virgin's not answering my question about hypocrisy—I had to understand my own first.

What was I do do? I had never really loved any man sexually. I was hardly stimulated by any man. . . .I began to feel pain. I was only too ready to agree that I was a dried out creature with no passion and no desire. How was it that I was so quick to admit that? I knew why the knowledge hurt deeply. In truth, I was a rather desirous, warm-blooded creature, but I was perverse. The men who had really excited me in my life had been those who were utterly not available to me. Dare I admit it? They had been my father and my two brothers! The darkest and most painful secret of my life was that as a child I had been sexually intimate with all three. I had successfully repressed these experiences until now!

Nor was this sexual intimacy the mere playfulness of children! I had played with my brothers when I was very little, but we had continued this practice in our adolescence. We were all mortified and chagrined, but could not help ourselves.

Finally, when I was eighteen, I went to my father in desperation. His answer was to be excited by me and to take me as well. He nearly died with guilt and chagrin, and I decided to enter the convent as soon as possible.

These terrible events were all "forgotten"—or so it seemed, until this night, these dreams, and this confrontation from the Virgin. I, too, was known as a virgin, but now I had to laugh, for I was no virgin. The Madonna could laugh at me, too.

But she did not laugh. It was more serious than that. She was judging me for my hypocrisy in *not* living, and in *not* sinning, rather than for my sins. She was very right to do so, for I was a prim, hypocritical fool! Now I could look at the elders and the other nuns and see them as dried out prunes. I knew that I must go and redeem myself, somehow, before I could be a proper vessel for the most High.

What should I do? I had really loved only those three men. My father, rest his soul and God forgive him, was dead. My brothers were far away—I knew in a moment what I had to do. I had to be in the flesh and make love with my brothers in such a way that I would *really* understand what the Virgin had meant; then I would know what "chastity" meant. I resolved to leave as soon as possible.

This was all quite mad and irrational and, I suppose, rather inexplicable. Perhaps it is even not understandable to you. I can only say that I see this task somewhat as you saw your problem with the hyena, Sir Arab, and, more closely to mine, your desire to ride the bull-ox and play the flute, Sir Ronin. But I am a woman, and we, of course, see it differently. I believe that Julia and Sybilla will understand without words. I shall not even try to explain, but I shall tell you what I did and what happened.

V

As soon as was possible, I obtained permission to leave the convent for an indefinite period. They knew full well that I might never come back, but relations were so strained that it was a relief for them to have me leave. I wrote to my brother in North Africa—the recluse and retiring mystic—informing him that I was coming. I did not even inquire or request permission from him, I simply acted.

When I arrived at his monastery, the brothers informed me that my brother had not dwelt with them for more than two years, but was out in the desert, some miles distant, living the life of an anchorite. Once a year he would come back to the monastery for a day or two, to renew his commitment to it, but, in point of fact he was living alone, tending a small garden, meditating and praying.

I walked out into the desert and followed the directions given by the monks. It took me two days, but I had no difficulty in finding my brother. When I did find him, he looked at me as if he were far away. It seemed to take him a long time even to recognize me. When, at last, he did, his face changed from its timelessness and distance to a pleasurable joy at seeing me. There was no feeling that I was intruding into his life. We shared his simple fare, along with some fine Spanish wines that I brought for him.

It was many years since we had seen each other, but for me all events in between were rather trivial compared with my recent experiences with the Virgin. I told him briefly of my disappointment with the elder nuns and the priests. He merely nodded, as if he well understood such things. He had not suffered any such fate, apparently—he was fond of and admired his brother monks—but he knew only too well how men were, including even religious men when they grew older and had "authority". It was partly to avoid such silliness that he had become an anchorite. He was afraid that he might follow a similar path and become as rigid and senile as they.

He listened attentively as I told him of my experience with the Virgin. He nodded repeatedly, but when I told him of my dream of the meat, Her appearance as a witch, and of my being reminded of our incest—then he paled, becoming thoughtful and remote. When I finished my story, including telling him about my plan to come to him, to redeem our love and to redeem and live the flesh—he looked at me as if I were not his sister, but some strange siren or witch who had the power to destroy him.

He waited a long time before he spoke. When he did, he spoke hesitatingly and from a faraway place, only gradually coming close to where I was. His answer was to tell me of his life in his twenties and thirties. I knew that he had a complex life with many experiences, but now I found that he had not only had many loves and many experiences, but that he had been a soldier and a detective and even a governor of a small province in Africa before he turned to the religious life. He, unlike I, had not felt great guilt for the sexuality between us. Rather, his guilt had been for his apparent incapacity to form enduring relationships. He loved deeply and passionately, but his love would soon die and he would seek others. He felt guilt for his fickleness. At last, he sought the religious life, and particularly, that of the contemplative, for there he would have to face his fickleness and could not run away to another relationship.

His life as a priest and as a monk had been very good, and he had been happy with his brother monks in the monastery. As he grew older, however, he had more and more experiences which took him away from "the world" and "life" altogether. At last, he felt that his fickleness was cured, but he preferred the life he was living. He did not know how he could help me, if I needed him, but he would try.

I shyly asked him if he felt desire for me now. He shook his head. This was a humiliation for me, but I knew that this was part of my task: I had to awaken desire, having earlier done everything I could to crush it.

This I did. I stayed out in that desert for two years, first consciously awakening my own and my brother's sexuality, and then proceeding to enjoy it. This was no "possession" by the Gods, but a conscious choice aiming at the differentiation and integration of desire. When my brother learned of my desire to spiritualize the flesh and materialize the spirit, and this in the most intimate of human relationships, he grew very excited. And this is what we did. We experimented with every form of sexuality, both physical and verbal, until we had the wonderful flowing union of two souls who are in perfect spiritual-physical communion. Only one thing we did not permit, and that was the flow of his semen in my vagina. It seemed important that I not become impregnated in the flesh, but that I be prepared for the impregnation by that Other. This sacrifice—in its deepest sense, not a "giving up," but a consecration, a consecration of the flesh to the spirit and the spirit to the flesh—this sacrifice was a mysterious assent to the law against adultery and a deepening of my understanding of chastity.

Perhaps you will not understand this, or, if you understand, you will not agree. I can only aver that this is true for me, and in full and honest obedience to an inner voice. I do not require your assent, and will not argue it. I can only say that chastity now means, to me, the purification of the spirit and the flesh, together.

These experiences deepened me greatly. I think—nay, I know, for I am being falsely modest—I know that they also deepened my brother. For he told me so. His visions now took on substance and form. He began to carve huge stones in the desert. He carved strange things, and wrote in languages not familiar to me, but he did so with great joy and happiness.

On my side, I was content to be with him, and to share our lives for that time. My dreams changed, and I noticed a deep filling in of all those places that had been vague for me. Sybilla, you will understand this.

After two years, my dreams and visions told me that we had completed our task and that I had to leave. We parted in great love and I felt as if I had actually internalized this mystical brother of mine in my own soul.

Immediately afterwards, I set off for the abode of my other brother—he who was as active in the world as my elder brother was in retreat. My activity in the inner life now was to give way to activity in the outer life.

I soon found my brother in Israel. His beard and eyes were as dark and fiery as ever, but his hair had thinned. Where my other brother had been light, this brother was dark. The opposites, indeed.

I knew that now the question of the flesh was no longer that of sexuality and differentiation, but one of giving and taking and spiritualizing. My brother's life was work and care, of the poor and sick and of the flock. He ministered not only to Christians, but to Moslems and Jews as well. I knew now what I had to do. I entered into his life of service as actively as I had previously pursued the life of religious union in the flesh. I did so with joy and alacrity. There was so much to do that one was never finished—so many to care for, feed, succor, comfort, teach. There grew up between my brother and myself a warmth, a comraderie and an affection which went far beyond both the fraternal tie of the flesh or the common work. We could express affection for each other freely.

I spoke early to him about our previous sexual experiences, but now we felt no need for each other in this way. So the warmth and affection and closeness were enough.

Here, again, I lived for two years, and I felt both redeemed and redeeming. There had been a true work of redemption. Now my younger brother was inside me. The spirit "within" and "without" were part of me. We said goodbye in love and joy and I returned to my convent.

VI

It was one year ago that I returned to the convent in Spain. I felt that I had to recover myself in my totality: I had to find myself and decide how I was going to live for the remainder of my life.

The life in the convent was the same as ever—the routine was the same and the people were the same. If this was "community"—then I was sorely mistaken in my aspirations. I knew that I had my self within, and that I would be a nun for the rest of my life no matter what I did outwardly—even if I married. That is to say, I was a nun "inside" and committed to the service of God no matter what outer life I led. I knew that, but I lacked a real community, and this nunnery was not such a one.

"What was the religious life of the twentieth and twenty-first centuries?" I had wanted to know four years earlier. I did not know the answer to that, but I knew that I needed both my inner life and community, and that I had to serve God both within and without.

I had also struggled with the question of the "forgiveness of God." Here, too, I had no ultimate solution, but I felt that I understood in a much deeper way. God had sacrificed his Son for Man. I had mistakenly felt that God was doing mankind a "favor" and was, therefore, a condescending hypocrite, since He needed man as much as man needed God. Now I understood that God fully realized that He had sacrificed His Son for His own sake—He needed to know what it meant to be fully Man, to experience His Humanity in its bitter wholeness, and that now man would be ready to experience his own Divinity. That was the task for the next century, and that was what our religious life was meant to be. I understood this "sacrifice" in terms of my own sacrifice with my brothers: I committed the heinous sin of incest, and consciously: I did so to "chastise" my flesh, that is to make it clean and redeemed. It became chaste not in the denial, but in the fulfillment. Total fulfillment in the flesh was not what I was seeking, it was the union of flesh and spirit, in order to make my body and soul a home for God. And this I did accomplish.

My second brother taught me sacrifice in a different way: to serve men and women and children, regardless of sect, belief, in terms of what they need: body, soul and spirit. That is the sacrifice that leads to fulfillment, and that is the "imitatio

Christi." I felt more deeply and totally Christian than ever and these ideas, born of my own experience and not of dogma alone, convinced me of it. I felt, however, that my views would not be accepted and I had to acknowledge this probability.

This awareness led me to the deepest sacrifice of all: I had to keep my "truth" to myself, knowing that it was deeply Christian, and that the outer "truth" of my Church was no longer viable. I was Christian, but had no Community. God and I had "forgiven" each other, but neither the God which I longed to serve nor I could quite live in the present world. The old God was "dead"—the new one not yet allowed to "live".

These were my thoughts and these my concerns and longings for many months. I prayed again to the Virgin. Once again, in the little chapel, I had a vision. I saw the lovely little teeter-totter on the green field that I had seen almost five years before. On each end, I saw again the pretty little blond one and the pretty little black one, each with her dress of deep blue and wine-red. The girls changed back and forth from children to women, and they playfully and happily went up and down. As I looked at them, I realized that these "daughters" of the Virgin, were also the girls in myself and they had been "lived" and fulfilled in relation to my brothers. At that moment I had a second vision: I saw my two brothers walking on this same green field. They were carrying a wooden plank. They carried the plank directly to where the girls were and placed it, cross-wise, on the teeter-totter of the girls. Then each brother sat at opposite ends of their own plank.

Wonder of wonders: the teeter-totters made a cross! North and South, the light and dark girls. East and West: the light and dark brothers. They went up and down, all of them, child and adult, and the sight filled me with great joy.

As the brothers and daughters played and went up and down on this teeter-totter, singing in the happiest way, I became aware of a change in the center, where the two boards joined. Out of the center there formed a circular red and blue rose in which I saw the Blessed Virgin, who had spoken to me and sent me on my quest before. She ascended above the teeter-totter and the rose, just as She had years before when She showed me the two girls. Now She looked at me in a joyous and happy way. Without words She communicated to me that this cross, this union of daughters and brothers, was to be my own, my own cross on earth, and that She would be with me, personally, in the red and blue rose. But She had also, and here She rubbed Her belly, to be about Her Husband's and Son's business and was thus, Ascending. She was to participate in the Second Coming, in Herself, in me, and for Mankind.

I understood: I had my cross, with its trinity of Daughter, Brother, Mother. The Rose-Self in the center was ascending to Heaven, to join with the pair of Father-Son. A new Father-Son-Holy Spirit would become fully manifest in the world in the Second Coming. I knelt and my heart burst with love.

Thus it was that I came here, O Brothers and Sisters. For on yonder tree is not only my own little cross, with its rose in the center, both red and blue, but that larger Cross to which mine is connected. On that Tree is my symbol, which is a reality to me. This is where I am, and I embrace you all.

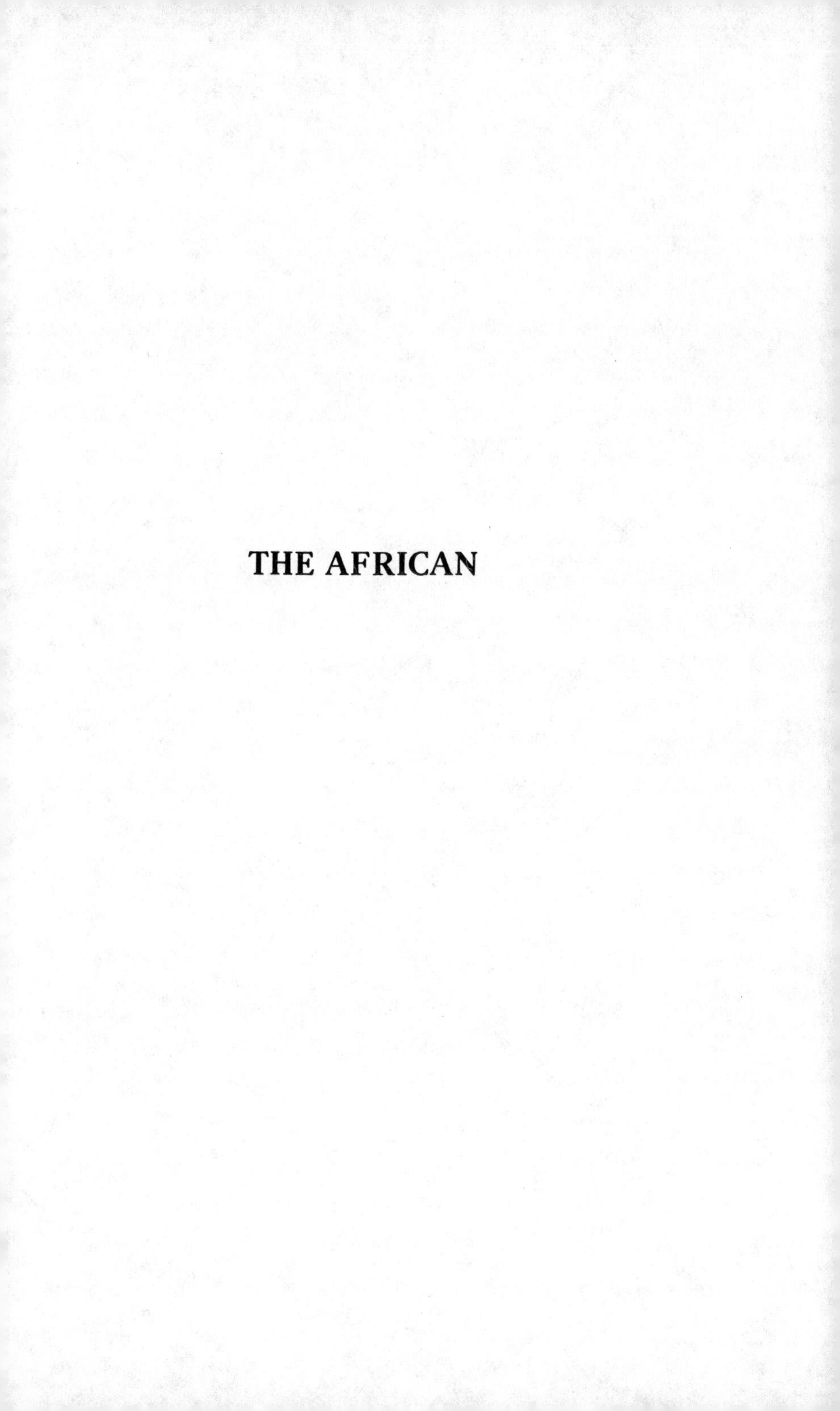

THE AFRICAN

THE AFRICAN

I

How do you do? My name is Joe Solomon, though you can call me "The African" if you like. The men among you seem to have a title rather than a name. I can go along with that. I suppose, in a way, I prefer it, since my name is a peculiar one for a person like me—black and born in Detroit, Michigan, U.S.A.

You will ask, "Then why do you call yourself 'The African', and why a name like Solomon?" I will try to explain. The full explanation, I think, can come only out of my story, but I will give a brief and more superficial account first.

I was born, as I said, in Detroit, Michigan, in 1932, just after Franklin D. Roosevelt was elected president. My parents were relatively well-to-do people for Negroes in Detroit, since they were both school teachers. In Depression days, school teachers did very well, financially, compared to other people, and I was their only child. My parents were good, hard-working, honest, middle class, Baptist, Negro people wanting to get ahead. Just like most other people in the U.S.A. and like those that Ebony magazine would point to with pride. They were also very good to me and eager that I "rise" even higher than they. I am sorry, in a way, that I have been a disappointment to them, but I trust that I haven't hurt them too much either. My parents, and their parents, were ordinary working people from Chicago. The unusual members of my family (and this is where the name comes from) were my great-grandparents. My great-grandfather was a white Jew from a prominent family of bankers who had made it big, just like the Yankee traders. He married my great-grandmother, who was a beautiful singer and one of the first Negroes to succeed on the American stage.

Great-grandfather Solomon, and his wife, (don't laugh) Sheba, were disowned by both families, but they had a fine time in life, apparently. They left little money to their children, and thus won only grudging appreciation from them. My great-grandparents were a scandal to both sides of the family.

By the time the story got to me, it had snowballed in exaggeration until the pair seemed like the only important people in the U.S. at the time, or, at least, were familiar with all the "important" people. Their status and privilege were admired, but their going against convention was not. Understandably, it took two generations to get "square" again. My parents, as I have indicated, were neutral in judgment, but inclined to exaggerate those people. In any case, we still had the name, Solomon.

In point of fact, the name is not so uncommon, after all. In the Army (I spent two years as a soldier during the Korean War), I even met a man who was called—really—King Solomon. No, he was not Negro (as you might guess, especially if you are prejudiced), and not even Jewish. He was from a southern white, Protestant family. I never asked how he got that name, but there it was.

Anyway, the name Solomon goes back only a hundred or so

years in my family. Before that it was some damn slave name, I suppose, and God only knows what our real names were when they dragged us over in the 17th or 18th century. Though whites find meaningfulness in a name as a point of identity, for blacks this is somewhat questionable. I suppose I belong to both, really. You might, in truth, call me the Afro-American, but I find that pretentious these days.

You can see that I have a "thing" about names, but this is not because I was called "nigger" as a child, nor "coon", nor any of the other terms of abuse that "whitey" likes, except by other Negroes or by white friends. This may surprise you, but white friends might call me "nigger" in affectionate hostility for some stereotyped behavior or attitude on my part, just as I might call them "kike", or "wop". So, it wasn't the term, or even the criticism and demeaning judgment that hurt. What hurts with those terms is the lack of personal connection, the lack of personal care. I wish some of the dense politicians would see that. No matter, though, I am not interested in politics very much. I am here to tell you my story. You will see, in time, why I choose the name "African."

Let me tell you, first, more about my life, before my "story" got started. I grew up in Detroit, as I have said, in a rather undistinguished way, except that our family had more money than most. I liked sports, I was very good in school, I had many friends, and we had a good time. I read a lot, and thought about being a writer, but I was not too serious about it. What distinguished me from my friends at that time (besides the peculiar name) was that I was deeply involved in music and played the piano rather well. Most kids took lessons on one instrument or another, but soon stopped. I, however, continued with my lessons for about five years and continued to play on my own. There was no question of a special talent for music, though my ear was good and my pleasure in playing, enormous. I thought, for a time, that I might even have a career in music, but that little flame was gently blown out by my teacher who said that I was good and that I knew enough to appreciate music, but that I would never do much better than be a piano teacher like himself and there were better ways to earn a living! In music, pleasure was to be preferred to self-support. I treasured that bent old man, and I am grateful to him yet.

I grew up, went to school, suffered very little, hardly knew "what it meant to be a Negro" until the race riots during World War II. Naturally, I knew about how black people were oppressed, abused, treated like less than human beings. I read about that and saw glimpses of it, but this was all second-hand, nothing that I experienced personally. During the riots, I was shocked by what I saw in the faces of whites and Negroes alike. I began to know first-hand what that kind of hatred was all about. All the same, life was all right. I went through school, and even graduated from college by the time I was twenty years old.

Two years in the Army, during the Korean War, taught me a good deal more about prejudice, attitudes, and life in the U.S. It was funny—I felt more or less at home in America, but realized that the other Americans did not really accept us. We black people were not just immigrants like all the others—there was something else. I thought about the question a lot, but could not find an answer. Other Negroes had ideas about the subject, but their answers did not satisfy me.

In any case, when I was discharged from service, I sought to continue my education (to my parent's delight) using the G.I. Bill. Not knowing what I wanted to be, except that I wanted "to be," I took off for Europe, and, of course, France—one place in white civilization where the black man really feels equal and individual.

I had a splendid time there. I studied at the University with the idea of perhaps becoming a writer, but that was just because one had to "be" something. I was really studying life: art, music, girls, cafes, wine, people. It was the best education that I had received. Talk was intense, hours long, life alive. After three years, when my G.I. Bill was over and I had no money to support my education, I chose to stay on. My parents were satisfied that even though I was no longer pursuing a degree (though they would have preferred it), I was seriously trying to become a writer, and a writer needed experience above all. They agreed to help support me by sending me a little money every month.

I tried to live on the little money I had and did fairly well. I also worked seriously at being a writer, out of guilt, perhaps. My attempts were only passable, and I realized that I had no great talent at that either.

By the time I was twenty-eight, I was growing frightened. My internalized "parents" were at me, from the inside, wondering what I was "going to be", how I was going to support myself, when I was going to be married. In one way, I wanted all those things, but in another way, I was both happy with the way that I was, and also, even if not fully happy, still not willing to get into that "straight" life.

I suddenly realized that I was trying to live the life of my great-grandparents—music, studies, and unconventionality. I also realized that it was getting to be a bit fake for me. I was no longer quite the young and gay and interesting American Negro with the funny Jewish name. But I did not know, really, who I was.

The question started to panic me and I consulted a friend who was a first class psychologist. We talked together for a number of days about it, and he inquired about my dreams. I do not recall just what dreams I had that impressed him, but he was of the opinion that psychotherapy would not be valuable for me, at this time, nor would it be a good idea to go back home and find my place there. He said that his impression from the dreams was that I ought to go to Africa to find out who I was. This was no romantic idea on his part—indeed, he felt a bit fraudulent giving that bit of advice—but that was the intuitive impression that he got from my dreams.

As soon as he said that, I felt the truth of it in my guts. I told my friend my reaction, and we congratulated each other for coming to the right solution. Well, not a solution really, but a way of getting at the solution.

I resolved to leave for Africa as soon as I could. I wrote to my parents about my resolve and my need. They were ambivalent, but agreed to send me a few dollars every month for one more year. By the age of thirty, they said, I would have to fend for myself. They felt that this would be best for me. I had to admit that they were probably right, but I did not guarantee how long it would take.

Just before my twenty-ninth birthday, I set sail for Africa.

I sailed from Marseilles to Oran, Algeria. The plan I had formulated for myself was to travel slowly and leisurely overland from Algeria south and west to South Africa, and then make my way back up from the Cape, east and north to Egypt. Travelling slowly, and for a year, with my bicycle, on foot or on an occasional train, would be cheap enough and slow enough for me to see and experience whatever it was that I needed to experience. But fate was to have it otherwise. I arrived in Oran, and went to the American Express office (to get my first check), when I found a telegram stating that my father was very ill and would I please come home at once.

I was struck by this peculiar turn of fate, but accepted it and quickly took a plane for the States.

It was strange for me to return to the place of my birth. The United States seemed like an alien land to me—loud, noisy, aggressive, materialistic. I suppose that I was seeing it from the viewpoint of a European at that time. But I was seeing something else, too. I thought that most of the white people were very ugly. They looked crude, mercenary, angry, and stupid. The black people looked more beautiful. They looked as if they had more pride and self-respect than when I had left years before. Yet I also saw traces of explosive violence in them.

The main thing, though, was the illness of my father. He had suffered a heart attack and was near death. He was quite weak and pale. He also looked very little on that bed. I remembered him as a much bigger man. I do not know if I had "grown" in the meantime. My parents were very glad to have me back at home, and, I must admit, I was glad to see them.

Though it was feared he would die, my father very slowly came back to health. There was something hearty and unfinished in him, and he recovered. He had to live a more quiet life, however, and I was needed to stay. I do not know, exactly, why I was needed—for emotional support, I suppose—but I accepted the situation all the same. I lived with my parents, and took a job as a school teacher. For some reason, my knowledge of French and my having lived in Europe for several years gave me a special aura for both Negroes and whites which enabled me to get a teaching job in a junior high school quite easily.

For two years I tried hard to fit into the American scene. I worked, earned my living, and was kind to my parents. I dated and was considered quite a catch. I also dated white girls, for the color lines were already loosening then. I enjoyed myself, but it all seemed pallid, unreal. Below the surface, I felt the seeds of violence and revolt around me.

I had never, as I said, felt any special hatred toward white people, but now I felt such feelings brewing within me. I began to experience what others of my acquaintance had experienced—wishing to kill the first white man I saw, hating his very existence. I was also getting suspicious, irritable, and I easily exploded into anger. I did not know what this was all about. I had never had a big problem with rage. I had never been afraid of my anger and could express it easily enough, but now I was growing frightened of it, and noticed that others were alarmed, as well.

My suspicion and uneasiness were increasing, rather than subsiding, and I did not know what to do. I knew that I was resentful that I had not had my chance to go to Africa, but I felt that I would some day, and that my rage and irritation and suspicion were attributable to something else.

I started to listen to various black cultists, one of whom saw the white man as a Devil. He had worked out a theory about this matter and I began to believe it myself. When this happened, I realized that I was caught in a kind of profound, but (to me) crazy event taking place in America and that this was very bad for me. I knew that if I could ever help my people at all, and even try to stay reasonably sound in what was coming—I visualized revolution, violence, great changes—then I had to be at least right with myself. My conviction was very strong, and I went to my parents with this. They thought that I was a bit crazy for having this view, but they loved me and trusted me enough to let me go. We knew that my father might die while I was gone, but the two years that we had spent together was already a bonus, an act of grace. I also proved myself as a "square"—having worked hard, earned good money, and saved a great deal of it. I proved that I was not just a rootless wanderer or youth who could not find himself. It was true, deep down, that I could not find myself, but at least I could "make it" on the American scene, and this seemed to be enough.

I had saved enough money in my two years of work to be able to live and travel in Africa for as long as I needed to, and with this I was finally able to resume the voyage that I had planned two years before. I was now thirty-one, not married, and not sure who I was. I left for Africa less happy than I was two years before, but with more calmness and more awareness of my need.

II

"What do I need?" I thought to myself, as I spent the long hours alone on the ship that was taking me to North Africa. I had intentionally taken a slow freighter, in order to gather my thoughts and prepare myself for my encounter. I did not know what my need was. I vaguely felt the necessity to cope with my anger and rage; I wanted to find my own identity, but I felt very self-conscious about that. A "search for on one's identity" was rather like being an "Afro-American"—there was something fake, fashionable, and self-conscious about it all. I decided, therefore, to find out what the land of my ancestors was all about. That open-ended expectation freed me, and I landed, once again, in Oran, rather lightheartedly.

It was fortunate that I had this attitude, because it allowed me to be genuinely open to what I experienced in Africa.

Over the months, I walked and bicycled from North Africa south along the west coast, inland, back to the coast, all the way to South Africa, and then back up through the east coast to Ethiopia. This tour took me upwards of a year and my impressions and adventures were many. I need not tell of my adventures, or my love affairs (if you can call it that), because this is not what I wish to relate to you. Rather, I want to give you some strange reactions: I did not feel that I had "come home." No, I felt more of a foreigner and stranger in Africa than I had either in France or in the U.S.A. I felt very warmly towards my black brothers in Africa. I saw, at last, how many different races and tribes and types we were, and how foolish the white man was to group us into one big image in his mind. I saw, of course, the very tall and the pigmy, the light skinned and the dark skinned, the red headed and black headed, the kinky hair and the straight. I saw, too, many different tribal types. I knew that the true reality of Africa was the tribe. All these nations, all these new nationalisms were as nothing compared to the tribe—and so many tribes.

I felt warmly, as I have said, toward my African brothers, knew that they had a long and interesting past, a creative development ahead of them, but I was a stranger all the same. The whites that I saw irritated me very much. They were so often ugly and righteous and terrible, especially in South Africa and other racist places. The less said about that, the better. It is obvious that such nonsense will soon leave the world, in one way or another. I am inclined to believe that there will be a lot of violence and bloodshed, but that terrible white bigotry will go.

Lest I seem too one-sided, I must tell you of one insight I had. I saw that my black brothers were not just the put-upon ones. I became acutely and painfully aware that my black brothers were the ones who sold their own people in the slave trade that brought us all to that miserable life in the States—and that we are not guiltless.

But such insights are not new and, though I had a fine time and learned a lot, I was hardly more than a tourist, really. By the time I arrived in Addis Ababa, I wondered if I had really needed to come to Africa at all. There was a certain emptiness in me and I had a feeling of thinness. What do I mean by that? I mean that I was beginning to live my own drama. I could see myself, back in Detroit, telling everyone about my adventures and my view of Africa. I could see myself being important and a man of both wisdom and experience. I got sick at myself. I was already not only playing a role, but playing a role of playing a role in my own mind. Was that all this trip was for?

I got more and more depressed and drank more than usual. One night, I was invited to a party where, in my strange hunger and emptiness, I got quite drunk and was alternately sentimental and irritable about both Africa and the U.S. My hosts were accepting people, and tried to humor me. My real anger, however, began to emerge and some of the people grew frightened. I seemed to touch a layer of rage—of rage at America, at whites, at Negroes, at God Himself, which was way out of proportion to anything that I had really seen or experienced myself. I was shocked at myself, apologized—hard as it was—and retreated out to the balcony.

Within a few moments, I was joined by one of the guests whom I had not noticed before. She was a handsome woman, with great bearing and a delicious looking figure. Her bright red dress made her look a bit like a whore, but she was far from that. She had enormous dignity and presence and, while deeply at home in her body, was far from being an "easy mark" or "for sale."

She seemed to have compassion for both my chagrin and anger, and took me aside. She had brought coffee and waited, patiently, while I drank and got a firmer hold on myself.

"You are right about your anger, you know," she said. I looked at her in amazement and somewhat quizzically at the same time. "The emotion is right," she continued, "but you are directing it to the wrong people. That bunch in there," she indicated with a nod of her head, which was half-way between contempt and an amused acceptance, "those people won't be of any help to you in dealing with it. Anyway, I don't think people can help you with it at all. My friend, it is your guts and bones and blood that are speaking in that rage and you can't get an answer there, at that level, from these people. They are all trying to get ahead, just like your Baptist friends in the U.S.A. They are just as square and bourgeois, even if they are Ethiopian, or Senegalese, or Nigerian. You saw—the cities are just like cities of Europe and America. If we still have some nature here, it is because we are slower and old fashioned, but it is all moving in the same direction." Now she started to get angry herself and spoke only partly to me, I thought, but also to herself:

"It is better for you to talk to the animals, and the plants, and the stones. They will know what your rage is all about. They will give you the Africa that you are looking for! That is what we need. That is what they took away when they took all those millions of black brothers and sisters off to that land. They took away our freedom, which is an enormous crime, but they also took us away from our animals and our plants and our stones. Those of us they didn't take away, they perverted with their terrible religions which hate animals and trees and stones! That is why you hate, and that is why I hate, too! You they took away, me they left, but they perverted us both!"

I looked at this lady in astonishment. Her words were speaking to something in me which rose up and nodded. I involuntarily let out a "yeah" which sounded like the response of those same Baptist Holy Rollers I had seen as a child. The lady laughed.

"How is it that you know about America and about these things?" I asked.

"I have been there," she replied. She went on to tell me a story to which I listened in amazement.

Her name—and you will not believe this, but it's true—her name was Sheba. She was born in Addis Ababa of a rather well-to-do family. Because of the wealth of her family, she had been able to study in Europe and also travel in the United States. Though only twenty-seven, she was already a trained anthropologist, with a knowledge not only of ethnology, but also of the biological fields, as well. But she brushed her learning aside as so much unnecessary garbage. No, that was not quite it. She did not see it as garbage—she saw some of it as valuable, but she objected to the over-valuation of the intellect and confessed her fear that the Africans might take the same route.

What astonished me most was her story of her ancestors. She was named Sheba after the original Queen of Sheba, who, of course, was the hereditary Queen of Ethiopia, and whose royal line emerged out of the union with King Solomon. Not only was my lady—and now I call her "my lady" since I felt that she almost belonged to me, and also as if she were the lady I served as a Knight (you will understand that, Sir Knight)—not only was my lady named Sheba, but she was part of that royal line. For many generations, part of her family had been practicing Jews—they were of the famous "Black Jews" of Ethiopia. Sheba's great-grandparents were such, and it was only her grandparents who had converted to Christianity. I was more astonished by Sheba than by anything else that I had experienced in Africa. I felt an enormous sense of the uncanny, and of the pre-destined. Here was my soul-mate. When I told her of my own background, of great-grandfather Solomon, and his singer-wife, Sheba, she nodded, as if that all made sense to her.

I looked at her with joy. My hunger and emptiness were beginning to vanish. Here was the meaning of my trip to Africa! I was meant to meet her, to love her, to wed her and bring her back to the States. She was rich and smart and beautiful and was my soul-mate. I was inordinately lucky.

I started to tell her this, to tell her of my joy, and my embarrassment at my good fortune. I stammered, but got it out. She smiled a little, but then got irritated and even stamped her foot.

"Are you annoyed with me?" I asked, wondering if I was too joyously mercenary over her money and she was mad about that.

"Angry? Of course I am angry! Here you take all that time and energy and trouble to come to Africa to find your soul. You are in despair after more than a year. You are enraged and empty. Suddenly, you meet the girl who seems to be your soul-mate. She tells you a few things, and you are ready to go back home and be a bourgeois yourself! Angry, that is putting it mildly! Are we poor women doomed to be the only ones who really care about the spirit, who seek to expand it, to ground it with a firm base, to devote ourselves to it? Was all this quest of yours just a sham?"

At first I was sheepish, and felt like a little boy chided by his mother for stealing cookies before dinner time. I shook this off, and spoke: "You are right, Sheba, I do seem to 'sell out' for comfort and pleasure the first chance I get. That is a failing of mine. But your pulling of rank, of acting as if only you and other women like you are really tending the flame of the spirit—all of that is not only inhuman, it is also a bit of a bore!"

Sheba tossed her head at me and walked off. I walked after her and took her by the shoulders: "Stop this impudent, inflated behavior! I told you you were right about my 'selling out', but don't rub it in! You acknowledged my rage was right, but in the wrong place. Look, I acknowledge your pride is right, but it, too, is in the wrong place. Don't use it to put me down!"

Sheba softened and gave me a smile which I felt from my eyes to my ankles. Those soft brown eyes which had both fire and water in them—I could wander there forever!

Sheba brought me back to my task. I saw that I did have a tendency to get lost—either in the material world of pleasure or the spiritual world of dreams, and that I needed her to keep me on the right path. She said that she meant every word that she had said, that both of us, she and I, had to get back to the African world of the animals, of the plants and of the stones. We had to get back there literally, and talk to them literally.

I looked at her as if she were mad. With her Ph.D. and all that, she was quite insane. "No one talks to animals and plants and stones, except madmen," I said.

"Madmen," she replied, "and our ancestors, who were far from mad." She asked me if I had seen the Bushmen in my travels. I said that I had. She told me that the Bushmen, the oldest and most "primitive" tribe in Africa, were also probably the best people. They, at least, still talked to animals and plants and stones. I countered that they had stories where this occurred, but they did not actually do so now. Sheba acknowledged that this was true, but that *we*, she and I, were going to talk to the animals and plants and stones directly.

Now I was less certain that my discovery of Sheba was so wonderful. Had I fallen in with a crazy woman? Or—and this was the same thing, only on the inside—was I a bit insane myself? My elation wore off considerably and I was tempted to go away and be alone until I could get a better perspective. My other feeling, however, was simply a desire to go to bed with this luscious creature, and so I started to make a pass at her—as the saying used to go. She blocked it, saying simply, "Not yet." I knew very well that she was not being coy, and that she felt the "task" of which she spoke was really more important than an easy union between us. Again I felt "primitive", but this time I made no speech to restore my pride. I simply went to my room, knowing that I had to come to another attitude in this strange encounter.

III

I awakened in the morning with a sense of determination. Sheba was right about me, but I was not going to let that woman run my life. I had hoped for, and half-expected, a dream to help me, but I did not remember any. I made my way downstairs to breakfast, and there she was. She was bright and happy, wearing that fine red dress and waiting for me to hurry and start our journey. I was puzzled by her change in mood, but let it go. I did not want to get involved in another dialogue in which only misunderstandings would result, more hurt, more rage, and no solution. Right now it was important to get to that something to which she referred and which I, too, needed very much.

I sat and drank my coffee in silence, staring into its darkness and blackness. I gradually felt relief from my tension of anger, frustration, and unknowingness. The darkness and blackness seemed to calm me. I was silent and Sheba did not try to invade my privacy. I slipped into the darkness of the coffee and was lost. . . .I have no idea how long I was in there, when I heard her gentle voice, "Shall we go now?" I say "gentle voice". It was certainly not gentle the previous night, but now it was soft, warm, rich and deep, like that black coffee into which I peered and from which I drank. I looked up and into her eyes, as black and deep and warm as the coffee. They were alive, active and demanding; they were loving and frightening.

I answered, "I am ready." Off we went, not knowing exactly where this adventure would take me, but feeling very much like some Knight with his Lady, out to fight dragons or find the Grail. I laughed to myself—a Black Knight! Not just some white knight with a black suit of armor, but a Knight black on the inside! You will understand that, Sir Knight. It is something like being a Jewish Knight, isn't it? But you, of course, really were one. I was just feeling like one.

What do you suppose happened? Where do you suppose my Lady led this Black Knight? You know where? To the zoo! To the zoo, mind you! That was where my dragon battle was going to be? A zoo? And, mind you, a zoo in Africa! That was too much, and I sat down and laughed and laughed. I did not know if I was a Knight, or Don Quixote, or just a foolish nigger from the U.S. pretending that he was not Uncle Tom. I laughed until the tears came down my face. I laughed and finally stopped, but a sense of amusement stayed with me. I knew that I would not likely get caught up in a role again, as I feared only a short time before. It is true that I did not exactly find out my identity in its entirety, but I knew that I was no Knight! I beg your pardon, Sir Knight, I mean no disrespect.

I looked up at Sheba, who was waiting patiently, arms akimbo. Did I say patiently? Well, not exactly: she looked exasperated with me again. "Well," I asked, "what is it now?"

"Your moods, and your vacillation," she said. "Your moods and vacillation make me angry, despairing, and I don't know what. Yet, that is the very thing about which I am speaking and have spoken. You have lost your sense of being a man-animal, like other animals, and I can't really blame you for it. 'They' have done it to you. But come now, we must get about our meeting with the animals. Do not laugh because it is a zoo. Do you think, in your state, with all your superficial civilization, do you think that you would be up to meeting animals outside of a zoo? Do you think that you would be able to communicate with, relate to, handle a free animal? Hah! The thought both amuses me and fills me with disgust for the impossibility of this. We have to start with the zoo, because that is the only place where you—and I, I must confess (I do forget that I need it, too, it is easier to put it all on you)—can begin to find them again."

I calmed down now, and we walked over to the cage of gorillas. They were kept reasonably well, though I saw much better zoos back in the U.S. People here, just like everywhere, were amused at the caperings of the chimpanzees and monkeys, but I was attracted to a large gorilla who was off to one side in a large cage. He was half-squatting, half-standing near the wire mesh in front of the cage. I came up close, within just a foot or so, and looked at him. He turned to look at me, and we gazed in each others eyes.

My God, it was awful! I could not bear it. At first I was frightened, as if to look so deeply and directly at the ape was a violation of a deep taboo. I was looking at the gorilla as if we were brothers, not as if he were some object to be peered at, or some pet. No, he was a brother! I could not sustain it, because he was greater and deeper and more real and more total than I. I put my face in my hands, overwhelmed with emotion, and ashamed for not being able to control it.

"Look at him," I heard Sheba saying. "He looks like us, doesn't he? He has so much of the human being. Of all our races. He is dark like us, but he is thin-lipped like a Scandinavian, and flat-nosed, like an Oriental, and bushy-browed, like a Mediterranean, and his eyes are black and deep like ours. Yes, he is our brother, and our ancestor was even more like him than we are. . . ."

"Shush," I said, for her words were beginning to sound like a lecture from some anthropology class. I was looking directly at this gorilla and no longer felt sad, nor sheepish, nor the taboo. I no longer felt the need of her mediation. I said, "sh", but touched her lightly, to show that I was not rejecting her. I wanted to talk to this gorilla myself.

I felt that we did talk. I looked long into his eyes, and he into mine. I believe that he told me very much, though neither of us used any words. If I tell you that we silently stood there for a very long time, in which I was in deep communication with him; if I tell you that I lost track of how long, lost track of the surrounding world; if I say the experience was as this moment; if I tell you that what finally broke it was the. . . .But no, that is, I suppose, hard to believe, and a long story in itself. I have no words for this, really, but I suggest that you all go to the zoo one day and look at the animals in a new way, if you can. Look at them as the brothers and sisters that they are, if you can bear it. If you did, then you would weep and moan that your brothers are in cages. You would weep for yourself, too, for you have put them there; and you have put your inner animal in a cage, too.

Enough, no lecture from me. I will just tell you the facts of what happened, and let you draw your own conclusions. I stayed a long time in front of that cage, as I have said, and got a deep dark message of no words. . . .

We came back to the zoo that night, when no one was there, when the animals had their own dialogue among themselves. It was frightening to hear all the animals coming alive, forgetting their sluggishness. They are lethargic enough in normal daytime life in the jungle when not looking for food. Captivity increased this languor. The animals, as I have said, came alive and were calling out in all their variety. We were awed and frightened by the sounds.

The wing of a peacock brushed us. He wandered freely, of course, not inside a cage, and I shivered at his touch. I looked then at that gorgeous creature. Here, in the half-light of evening, his feathers seemed luminescent and like an ultra-violet lamp. Strange, isn't it, that I have to use mechanical analogies to describe what is quite ordinary in nature? Sheba was right, indeed. I looked at the peacock and was struck with this many-eyed wonder. All those eyes, which see nothing. Was that darkness of eye in the ape of the same unseeingness? Had I deceived myself and simply read into that poor gorilla all that I learned and felt in my encounter that morning?

We soon came to the gorilla cage, as we had planned, and we were frightened half out of our wits now. Our plan had been to free the gorilla. I was shaking and even Sheba realized how foolish she had been. But we could not back out. We had vowed it. I decided that I was not going to free the gorilla, since that would be a threat to others. Instead, I would risk my new found connection with the animal by going into his cage. We waited, hiding in the shadows, until the gorillas were fed. It was easy to get inside the cage, after the keeper had left, since we saw that one door was kept locked only with a series of wooden hinges which could easily be moved.

Cautioning Sheba to wait outside, I went into the cage. The gorilla seemed startled to have me there, but went on with his eating. I waited until he had finished, and sat down beside him. I was quite close and could smell all the animal smell. It was not very pleasant, which I attributed to his being locked up. All the same, I got quite close and again looked into the eyes of brother ape. Now, all was not well. The ape looked at me, then away, angrily. I realized suddenly that I had to listen to my own instinct, and I quickly ran out of the cage. Not a moment too soon, for the ape threw himself against the door just as I did so. I sighed and breathed easier, but I had my message. I had to listen to my own instinct, and not trust even my brother ape. When I told Sheba this, she laughed. She was pleased, but I saw something strange come over her face. Before I realized quite what was happening, Sheba opened the door to the cage and went inside herself.

If I tell you that I watched horrified, you can believe me. She walked up to the ape and embraced him. She fell into his arms as if he were some huge football player wearing a fur coat. She was not only fearless, but looked as if she were utterly happy to be there. I stood there paralyzed. At first I thought that I should rescue her, but realized that she not only went in there of her own free will, but was enjoying herself!

Hardly had I grown accustomed to what was happening in that cage—a woman embracing an ape—when I became aware that the gorilla was getting an erection. A dread and disgust filled me, as well as anger. Is this the basic fear between man and animal, man and man, race and race? Is this the origin of the prejudice? I didn't know. But I did know that I was no gorilla, and that ape, after all, was just being an animal! Before I knew it, the gorilla had torn off some of Sheba's clothes. She was on her knees and he was penetrating her. I didn't know how to react. I was angry, and felt that this gorilla was taking my property. I was ready to knock his head off. I was also afraid that he would knock my head off if I interfered. I then realized something which made me breathe more easily: the ape was just being an ape, true to his nature. I often felt like that myself, without having the guts to fulfill my desires much of the time. With that realization, I looked into Sheba's eyes and saw that she was not being raped, or hurt at all. Her eyes were glazed and unseeing. I was again shocked and horrified. Now she was an animal altogether, and lost to me. I shouted at her to look at me. I stood there, looking deeply into her eyes, as that poor gorilla was doing what he felt quite natural in doing. I stayed with her in silent union throughout her. . . .what shall I say. . . .agony, ecstasy? Let me just say that it was a mystery and as wordless as when I looked into the eyes of the ape. When it was over, I went inside the cage, and gently lifted her up. I carried her out, almost nodding to my brother inside. I closed the door of the cage and took Sheba home. I had been privileged to witness a mystery.

IV

The day following our encounter with the gorilla, I went to the zoo, bought the creature who had initiated both Sheba and myself, and had him sent to one of those great animal preserves. I am grateful, and pride myself as an African, that there are great natural parks protected by man where the animals can pursue their natural destiny. I am glad that they are protected from man and that man is protected from them. I am also glad that man can go there and visit if he is respectful enough, and brave enough and connected enough. Some day there will be no more cages, for any of us.

I do not want to lecture, as Sheba does, but want to get on with my story. It so happens that we followed our gorilla. We did not banish him to some Rousseau-like place, but we knew that we needed to go to where the animals lived. We had been initiated, but now we had to find ourselves, find our own human animal which had been so sorely treated by the white man and his religions, and by us as well. So we went to one of the large animal preserves where we stayed many, many months.

We did not try a kind of back-to-nature movement, because we knew very well that we can never be Bushmen again, and can never "return" to the primitive way. We also knew that we would not want to—for part of nature is hunger and violence, fear and brutality and coarseness. We knew only that we wanted to find our human animal. And this we did. We had a jeep and a tent, and much of the other helps that civilization offers, but we slept under the stars. We camped, and we walked, we breathed fresh air and we ate food that we brought and game that we shot. I did not feel like a butcher when I shot game. I shot for food and I do eat meat. Other animals eat meat, too, do they not? But I shot with feeling for my animal brother, and I murmured a prayer for us both when I killed him.

We felt the wildness of nature, and its tenderness, too. We had to be careful with the animals, but not because they were dangerous. No, that is what man fears, because he is afraid of his own animals. We had to be careful in order to stay close to animals at all. Movements would startle them and they would run away. We had to grow quiet and watchful and gentle. That is what the animals taught us. But we also grew hard and careful and strong—in looking out for ourselves. It is difficult for me to describe all the things that we learned. Do you know why? It is not because they are inexpressible. I have already told you about things, such as the mystery, which are, indeed, inexpressible. I cannot describe them to you, because I have not yet finished my education. Though I am no longer living in that forest, that marvelous primeval preserve, I am still learning to become the human animal that I once was, and that we all were, until the Fall. I mean the Fall, both historically and personally. I come ever closer to being that full human animal, but I still have a long way to go. That is why I cannot express it well enough.

I would like to tell you how I learned pride and independence from the lion, how I achieved a great vision from the hawks, how I assimilated tenderness and sensitivity from the deer of all types that abound –I would like to tell you all this. You know, I did learn much, but not as much as I would like. For my illness was deep, and the history of my being separated from myself was long. I also do not wish to embarrass myself and bore you with a tale of my accomplishments. Not that I learned humility from the animals, no. They have it, but I did not learn it there–for I had already been humiliated enough, or do you not think so?

What I do want to tell you about now is the plants.

When Sheba and I were living in the forest, in the jungle of the animal preserve, I felt the need to get closer to the plants, just as she had said. I had noticed that we had changed considerably from just being near the animals, and I was beginning to take to heart what she said also about the plants. But how do you get closer to a plant? I asked myself. You can get poetic, I supposed, by pretending the plant is human, or has a soul, or some such thing. I could recall my college classes in psychology, where they complained that people read their own emotions into animals, and the professors called this anthropomorphism. What would they call it if you did this with plants? Those psychologists did not understand animals, anyway, I now knew for myself. They were of the type that Sheba had talked about—who abetted our estrangement from our inner animal—so why listen to that kind of "whitey" at all? I had to find out for myself. That is, Sheba and I had to.

So I asked Sheba. I said to her that she had been pretty glib before in talking about getting in touch with the nature of Africa, with the animals and plants and stones, now just how did she plan on getting in touch with these plants?

She had to admit that she didn't know how to do this either. Well, then, the thing to do would be to look at them and see what could happen. I remembered something about phenomenology and that being the most honest method, after all. Sheba agreed. So we both set down to look at plants.

Perversity of perversity, the first thing that came to me was that we had to leave the forest and go back to the city. I needed to look at the plants, not here in their wildness, but as they were in city life. I had to start with where I was, and not in this highly self-conscious stupid way. Sheba and I had come to the jungle because we had to, and we had to bring back the gorilla. It would be too grandiose to start here with the plants! Sheba agreed, so we went back to the city. I settled for a little vase with two roses! That was the place to start, a little vase with two roses, a red one and a white one.

This seemed to satisfy Sheba very well. I sat and looked at the roses. They both smelled exactly the same—good. I touched them and they felt exactly the same. They were soft and pleasant, and painful where the thorns were. Their shapes were not very different from each other. Only in color did they differ. I was tempted to get philosophical about that, but I didn't. The difference in color did not lead me, luckily, to speculate about race problems.

I did awaken to color. And beauty. But when I started to go into that—no, that wasn't it either. At least not yet. That was not the message that plants had to offer me at this time.

Then I got it! It was food. That is what plants had to tell me. That gorilla had taught me about sex, and only then could I learn about other instincts from animals. Now I was trying to learn about beauty, when I did not even know about food and hunger! I laughed and turned to Sheba. I told her what I realized, and she nodded grimly.

"Yes," she said. "With all our talk, neither of us has ever been really hungry. Neither of us has had to starve or go without food very much."

I responded, "Where I come from most people have to watch their food-intake and go on diets! I have heard of plenty of hungry colored people, but I haven't met them. I know that they exist, but I wasn't one of them."

So, it was food and hunger that plants had something to teach me about! I looked again. They live on air and water. They live only on air and water and a man can live on them! How can that be? Oh, sure they get nourishment from the soil, don't they? Mother earth provides all the things that they need. That is why they nestle their roots deeper into her, getting all that rich, dark, black goodness out of her, while they stretch strongly into the air and show all their wonderful shapes and colors. Yes, now I was getting the picture. Mother earth is a great, black African Goddess. She is big and juicy and rich and feeds her plant children on all good things. Just by being there.

Now I was ready to go back to the forest with Sheba. I saw, now, what the plants were all about and now I could go back to Mother Africa and enjoy that big, black Goddess in all her richness and variety and goodness, in all her plants. But I did not have to go to the forest for that, did I? No, I could go to the market just as well. There is little more colorful and joyous and rich and satisfying than an African market. I suppose the market place is attractive in most parts of the world, where the people come to buy and sell all their beautiful plants and to talk and to have fun. But I did not want to go to the market. Nor did I want to be a farmer. I knew that I needed to be, just as you needed to learn that, Ronin. But I needed to learn something else, as well.

It was hunger. So I fasted.

I fasted for one day, two days, three days. I even tempered my intake of water, so that I would feel what it was like to be a parched plant and wait long for the water. I then drank it in great gulps and found myself greedy and too "animalistic". Notice I said too animalistic and not too animal—there is a big difference. Then I took it in with small sips, like a small animal, or like the plants do themselves. Now I could taste the coolness and freshness of the water. I could sense its goodness and knew that I could not live without it. I could feel my cells, the little units of my body, responding to this water. After four days and five days, I knew what it was to live on air and water. I was as if emptied out. I no longer felt even hunger pains. I only felt weak.

Sheba had been doing the same and I realized that we had gone too far. I suddenly got my rage back, and said, "I am no flower, I am a human being! My hungers are not to be a rose petal! I am not airy and soft, nor thorny and hard—I am flesh and bone." "But", thought I, "it is not right to return to the meat of the animals. There is something yet I need to learn."

We ate, Sheba and I, after that, but only of plants. We had salads and vegetables. We enjoyed them very much. We found that we could be vegetarians if we wished. We tasted of fruits and vegetables and found them fulfilling. I realized, however, that I was missing something. I turned once more to the plants and saw their beauty. Their colors. There were so many colors. I knew that the colors were like art—it was for itself. Sometimes the colors communicated—to other plants or to me. But the plant showed its colors because it had them. It had to do just that. The beauty was in showing its own colors.

That phrase turned over and over in my mind: "The beauty is in showing one's own colors." That was the message from the plants, but there was more. I knew about my deeper hunger: I longed to show my own colors and connect with the colors of others. That was what I wanted. The only trouble in that role-playing horror of mine was that I did not reveal my true colors. Naturally I wanted to show my colors, like a rose or peacock, but they had to be my own. It is harder for a man to find and show his own true colors, just as it is hard for him to find and show his own beauty.

Then I thought: It is not my own beauty of color that I seek, but that of another. It is empty and hollow to be alone in one's colors—the colors have to be shared. I turned once again to Sheba. I had been so caught up in my own thoughts, my own search, that I no longer adored her as I had at the outset. Where was this gorgeous creature? Where was this lovely one who had set me on the right path and who accompanied me throughout it? Was she not my rose, my flower, the gorgeous one?

I looked at her, and she looked at me, and smiled. The smile was a joyous one, an understanding one, and for the first time, playful. We connected. In laughter. In. . . .what can I say? That we had taken ourselves too seriously? Perhaps. Now we played, like children, and animals, and plants. For plants play, too, you know. Or have you not seen them nodding and tossing in the wind? Letting their pollen go where it will? So did Sheba and I play. Like two animals or two plants.

V

Stones. How do you get to know stones? And not only stones, but metals and stars. Because that is what I was after. I knew that I had to get to know matter more intimately, more deeply. I had to know it, but to know it in an intimate fashion, from its inner quality, and not from a classification system.

I had often held stones. I had often stared at the stars. I had even played and experimented with the metals in my chemistry classes in high school and college. I even knew a bit about the alchemists, from my psychology friend in France. But what did I know? I knew nothing. I had acquaintance or knowledge "about", as William James said, but not that intimate knowledge "of". The way they said it in the Bible: to know as Abraham "knew" Sarah—intimately, deeply, wholly. That is the way I needed to know. That is the message that Sheba got across to me. But here was a place that I had to go myself. It was as if she already knew about these things, at least some of it. If I went with her to these places, these stoney places, I would always be a fool or a child. I would have to go there by myself, and only later go there with her. My intuition already leaped ahead—as it was only too ready to do—but I restrained it and said "Wait, you are all right, but you must wait."

So I walked alone in the forest. I picked up a rock, and thought of the times in my life that I had found a stone which was meaningful, which gave me peace, using it as a fetish just like my ancestors. But I didn't much look at the stones; no, I always let them send me back into myself. That is to say, the outer stone only led me to the inner stone. This introversion was nice, and pleasant, but somehow it was a failure. I could not get at the sensations of the outer, concrete stone in that way. I turned again to the stone. I looked at it—long, carefully, hard. I started to draw it, but felt sheepish about that. . . .I lay down and spent the day in dreamy wonder. There was no way to get to the stone.

Night came. I looked at the stars. Beautiful. But the same. Music of the spheres? Gorgeous notes? Yes, in my head, but not from those stars. I waited, emptily. At last I got the idea, and I laughed. Here I was trying to be alone and come to something which I could not do by myself. I was, indeed, too childish and foolish. To grasp and comprehend as an adult where I was a child—that was childish. I accepted my childlikeness and rejected my childishness. I went, hat in hand, to Sheba.

"Sheba," I said, "teach me about the stones, and the metals, and the stars. I am a child, in need of instruction about these things. I cannot run when I do not know how to walk. Teach me, Sheba!"

At that moment, a violent feeling overcame me and I was flooded with tears. I did not know why. Then it came to me. One ancestor, long ago, from the Solomon side, taught the other ancestor, from the Sheba side. Now, it was reversed: In teaching me, Sheba was teaching Solomon. I stammered these words out to Sheba, and felt them deeply. She nodded, as if it were an obvious thing to her. Again I felt foolish and childish, and had to accept it as so. Sheba had first been with me in my feeling, but then she grew annoyed with what looked like sentimentality.

Now the whole problem shifted away from the stones and metals and stars to the problem of vanity and sentimentality. We had been there before, but it was her pride. Now it was mine—and her coldness.

"But that *is* the stone," she said.

"What?" I asked.

"The hardness and the coldness—that is in the stone."

My intuition leaped again. "Of course, just as the alchemists said!"

"No, no, no!" she said, angrily. "Please, do not leap, or jump, or think! Stay still. Stay with *it,* the stone. No ideas, no possibilities. Nay, not even any feelings. Just *it,* the stone. In its hardness and coldness. And its vanity. For it is not touched, even though it is touched. It is utterly with itself. Here, hold it."

I took it in my hand. I held it. I felt its hardness, and coldness. I felt its imperturbability. It would not be moved, even though moved. It would not be touched, even though touched. I laughed. The paradox was only a play on words. Was it only that? Let me think: To be moved and touched, those were the feelings, vulnerable, and stones were very vulnerable to that. But only inner stones, not outer ones. The outside ones were movable and touchable but not in feelings. Where then was the vanity and sentimentality? Where, too, was that oneness, that one world of within and without that Sheba had promised we would find?

Sheba knew my thoughts and nodded. Her pride was gone. She was with me, for she also knew not. We were together in our unknowingness. I held the stone and gave it to her. She held it and passed it back. It was hotter in the grasp. I felt her heat and warmth. I felt the wetness of her hand in the stone. It excited me. I longed to hold her, but I restrained myself. It had to wait—until I felt the mystery of the stone.

The mystery of the stone is upon me: Sheba, I love you. You it is who are the stone. You it is who tantalizes me and torments me and seduces me and haunts me with a sweet pain that can only be relieved by you.

I long to touch your softness. I feel it. It is round and soft and ringed with soft down. Oh, how I feel it. My back aches as the pleasure of it runs up my spine. My fingers—they twitch. My fingers, they are too weak to contain the pleasure and the immensity of it.

Oh, Sheba, I feel your wetness. The dew of your flower penetrates me. Do I dare taste it? I do. What is it? A peach, an orange? No, it has its own taste, deep and heavy and rich, like. . . .yes. They have called it honey, but honey is named after it, and not the other way 'round.

Oh, Sol, I love you. You it is who are the sun and I the moon. I grasp your manhood and I turn into softness and wetness and hardness. I am no stone, I am flesh and a bit of bone. I ring my hands upon it. I cover the sack with kisses, for it contains the eggs of eternity. I am lost in your forest and rest my cheek upon its jungle dampness. I gasp, for I am lost in its wonder and die from an excess of Paradise.

Sheba, teach me to love. Teach me as your ancestress taught mine. Say. . . .I feel that Solomon with me. I feel him as Solomon and Solo-man. Man alone, and Seuleiman, Black Power and Black Prophet. He lives in me, as She lives in Thee. Teach me, Sheba. Teach me, Black Moon! I have seen. . . .I see your round breasts, who look at me in mocking and beckoning. I lunge toward them and tremble in my desire. I want not their rich milk within, be it ever so white or ever so black. I want only their soft, moist dampness. For I am dry as any stone.

Oh, Sol, Black Sun. Son of the Prophet, and Solo-Man. Teller of dreams and interpreter thereof. I will teach thee to love and you will teach me to see. Help me to see that which I do not see. For thus did our ancestors entwine each other. You are the stone, and dry. . . .but dry as the sun, whose hot flames sear away the dampness of my ignorance.

Sheba, I sniff thee. My nose doth follow the contour of thy back. I sniff down to the base of your spine, and lo! I am an animal! I am a wise dog who sniffs his mistress bitch and knows her state in a moment. I am he who sniffs the backside and can tell all about her unknowingness. And I take joy therein. Your odor is as so many petals of the rose. But dank rose, grown in hothouse and fertilized with all manner of deep, dark and rich secrets. I sniff thee and enclose thee, and with my tongue I rim your world of darkness. This mystery, for all to laugh. For all to laugh and declare me base and foolish. But in this mystery, I rim the world and know the darkest darks and lightest lights of that Goddess. For I have seen God, and She is Black. She is Black, but Comely, as my Ancestor said, for he, too, knew, but he spoke only for the wise to know.

Oh, Sol, oh, Joseph, for now you are the teller of my dreams, and the taster of my soul. For it is you, indeed, who knows. They know not, and they think not, and they test not. I am raised, oh daughters of Jerusalem, for my love, he has ennobled me among women.

Sheba, come to me. I embrace thee.

Joseph, I come and thee entwine. I give thee the apple as of old, but now we taste and know and we do not run! We do not cry and we do not weep, for we taste and know that we taste. We know that The Dark God wills it and She lives in that deep, dark, damp earth from which the Tree grows. There is no Tree, no World, and no Paradise without Her.

Sheba, my moon and my queen, we are as one, and I faint with sweet passion and tender desire. Nay, I faint not, I die.

Joseph, my love and my being more than I am myself, we are as one, and I die.

The two are one and they sink into the earth. The voice you now hear is neither the I of Joseph Solomon, nor the I of Sheba, the Queen. It is a third I, yea even a third eye. That is the voice, now, of I who speak. I am the objective I who sees with the eye of heaven and the eye of hell. The bird above looks down and sees, and the bird below looks up and smells. This is what is seen and smelled:

The two are one and they sink, in death, into the great stinking vagina of mother Earth. The smell is rotten as the rotting flesh settles into Her depths. First the worms come and the crawling things, dark and feces-eating, then white frogs who live in the midst of it and gaze with one blind eye into the horror of life and death. That is why they croak, and that is why the words are the same.

Do you know the smell of sick armpits? Excrement from chickens? Vomit after a day in unaired beds? Paris pissoir? Abbatoirs? Decaying food?

All these are only smells, and you can add your own private hell of smells. But smells are hells only briefly. One either goes away, or the nose, great adaptive organ that it is, turns an insensitive hair to it and rejects it. Smell hells are brief. Taste hells are even briefer: just spit it out, you know. Even if some Big Brother conceives a new torture of taste, one can swallow, and taste is over.

Where, then, is the hellish hell? We know: in the heart. In the sensation of despair, of humiliation, of love lost; being rejected; of hungers unfulfilled or fed with the wrong food. The foods of the heart and senses are goaded and glutted and deceived. Add separation and loneliness. Magic words of hell. Broken heart. Visual. A sensation. Pain everlasting.

But, at last, hell goes, too. Then there is silence. Peace. No movement. Not even the stone.

Who is it, then, who speaks? It is I, the I who was there before Joseph and Sheba, and who is fulfilled therein. Who is it, then, who asks? It is the Joseph and the Sheba who were there before they were there. Do you understand? Yes, of course you do. Just as you understand that two can be one and one can be two, and what is there came into being because.

Death is real, and so is rebirth. They begin and end with I Love You.

I am the Resurrection and the Light. I am that He-She who was there in the beginning and will be there at the end. But think not that being before Joseph and Sheba and after Joseph and Sheba that I am more immortal than they. For without them I am nothing, and without me they are only fantasies and figments. Thus it is that one becomes two, and the two go back into the one. If you understand me not, you die.

VI

So, my friends, to continue my story, I, Joseph Solomon, black man from Detroit, Michigan, U.S.A., had a great mystical experience in the middle of darkest Africa, which was not dark at all. When Sheba and I awoke out of our dark and dreamless sleep which was like a death, we looked at each other and wondered. It was as if we had died and been reborn. She was beautiful and radiant and smiling and rich and luscious, and. . . .and I? I knew who I was. The Black Power of that African Earth was all in me and around me. I, Joseph Solomon, heir of the Great Solomon and Sheba, of the Kingdoms of the Spirit and of the Flesh, of the Heavens and the Earth, I, an African man, had my bride and my happiness.

I knew that I had to go back to my birth-land, to Detroit, Michigan, U.S.A., and that now I would find my place there. I knew that the great God, that He-She of the African Veldt and the Stars would sing and guide me, and that Sheba and I would help to bring a new vision.

We took ship and sailed away. We sailed to the land where I was born. One night, I stood on deck of this great African ship, and looked up into its crucifixion-masts and beyond, to the great stars which wheeled and tossed above. One night, as I say, I looked and looked, and then I found myself here, among you. I do not know if I dreamed it all and this is my reality. I do not even know if I am dreamed, rather than the dreamer! But, my friends, I know what I experience. I have experienced your stories, and I have experienced my story.

I see your Tree, Sir Knight, and I have your Vision of the Brotherhood of Man and God. Look there, upon that Tree. Look at the fruit of the Great Black Goddess, Mother Earth, the African Queen who loves us and nourishes us and engulfs us with Her Beauty when we live, and receives us when we die. Oh, that Tree of Life, I see Her there, within. She is below and within it. Do you see Her? That great Black Mother of us all? Do you see Her? Black Power of Love; Love in Life and Death. Oh White and Brown and Yellow, embrace me as I embrace Thee, for I am Black like She!

Look again, for I see another thing upon that tree. Can you see it? I see a great hermaphrodite, a He-She of King-Queen, and I know that it is a Solomon-Sheba, a Sun-Moon. Look there, He holds a goblet, a grail with great snakes, three in number. Look there, She holds one snake, all entwined. The He-She is bedecked with wings, and stands upon a moon. Nearby stands a death tree with heads for fruit, and a bird doth gape. See you it? Nay, it matters not, for some may see it, some not. What matters is that you see your own, and you, great friends, have shown me your visions as I have shown you mine.

It is given to me to say that we have come together to share our visions and make a new one for us all. Nay, it is not so, for the Tree can hold all our visions, can she not? Yea, verily, until the Coming, which may be soon upon us. So join hands and sing, for we shall overcome and be as one!

MAYA, THE YOGINI

MAYA, THE YOGINI

I

My name is Maya. I was born in the city of Calcutta, the state of Bengal, and the nation of India forty years ago. I might pridefully add that I come from a long line of gurus and that I am, of course, of the Brahmin caste. In these days of Independence, after the British Raj and when the world itself may be nearing an end, such pride may be rather irrelevant. It is also not entirely true, since my heritage is mixed. My father was an English army officer who had a torrid and romantic love affair with my mother in the 1920's, when the whole world was beginning to shift on its foundations. The man was honorable enough and wanted to marry my mother, but this was not permitted by her parents. She was married, instead, to a decent and equally honorable storekeeper, for whom she was a feather in his merchant caste's cap. Since my father was dark and my own features are quite Indian, my step-father became my only father, as far as the world was concerned. I suppose that this was an advance for the time; in an earlier era they might have stoned or burned my mother and I would not have been born at all, or else been tossed upon a dung heap.

I tell you these details because my peculiar background does have relevance to my story, which will gradually unveil itself. Straightaway, however, you can see that my origins are not entirely conventional, though I was raised in a more or less usual fashion for Hindu girls of my time and of my class and station. I married at 14, had one child each year until I was 19, busied myself at home with my husband and family, enjoyed the social life of the post-war years, was excited by the turbulence of political activity and our new independence. I had several lovers, which is not so out of the ordinary any more, as you might think, but my real unconventionality began just three years ago.

My children had grown and the last of them had married and established her own family. At thirty-seven, I was still attractive, had led a life which was both active and reflective, and I was by no means ready for old age, nor to die on a bier with my husband. I loved him dearly, this man ten years older than myself, but he was not my entire life. Obviously. For some time I realized that I needed to retreat from the world, perhaps follow the path of my ancestors who had been gurus. The men of my family had either pursued a life of meditation or had sought enlightenment in the usual Indian way when reaching middle age. It was still uncustomary, though possible, for a woman to seek a guru but something in me rebelled at that. Here, perhaps, was an independent spirit of my English father, asserting itself against the Indian elders who had deprived him of his love. This thought, however, is more likely to be a romantic cover-up for the fact that women everywhere have changed; we are no longer so willing to be disciples or slaves to men, even if they are gurus. I, as a modern woman, simply did not want to submit my spirit to a man. If I could have met a guru who would be willing to share a spiritual relationship with me, to seek together into the reaches of the unknown world of the gods, I would have been delighted. But I did not know any Indian men who would either desire this or be capable of it. Gurus there were aplenty, but they would want their submission—especially if they would even deign to grant their time and presence to a mere woman. Besides that, most of the gurus I knew about were rather corrupt and not worth submitting to!

Yet, I needed to retreat, to achieve enlightenment. What was I do do? I had read somewhere that the Masters of old had said that all two-footed creatures of the world could be enlightened, and that the best guru was Shiva himself. One did not need a concrete guru in the flesh; it was the spirit of Shiva, in any case, which came to the good guru. I felt that this piece of wisdom might be right, and, in any case, it suited me. I resolved to go off by myself and meditate. I would live simply and pray that the good lord Shiva would guide me.

My family, of course, thought I was quite mad when I told them of my plan, but they were used to my being independent in other ways and when I assured them that I would return if the procedure were too uncomfortable (I was no ascetic!) and that I would write regularly to them. The night that I got their blessing, I dreamed that the Lord Shiva came to me and instructed me to take with me, into my wilderness, the pictures of the Kundalini Yoga. I awakened delighted; Lord Shiva was with me! I knew the pictures only casually, but was convinced that I had a guide with me and that my desire to be a Yogini on my own was meeting with divine approval.

Thus it was that I began my meditative experiences as a Yogini three years ago, and that is the substance of my story—what happened in that meditative retreat.

I went to a mountain cabin, far from the bustle of Calcutta life, but close enough to civilization to buy for myself the few necessities that I would need from time to time. I knew that I was there to be alone, and to come to an inner enlightenment, but I had no need for the disciplines of the flesh that some men seem to require.

After a few days of accustoming myself to a certain quietness and the calming of my wandering mind, I sat down with my first picture of the Kundalini series. I prayed to Shiva to be my serpent Kundalini, to guide me and inspire me in the way that he, in his wisdom, would know that I needed. I submerged myself into *dhyana* and allowed myself to be thought, rather than to think. "Oh, Shiva," I prayed, "Let it be you that work in me; you it is who will both coil and uncoil the Kundalini; you it is who will be both enlightener and enlightened, for I am as nought, a mere point on the needle of eternity." I then could look at the first picture, the *Muladhara*.

I sat and stared at this first picture. I studied and looked and reflected for one day, two days, three days. Nothing but stale bread seemed to come from it. I knew that the center the picture connected with was located between anus and genitals. I knew that this mandala was of the earth, that the elephant symbolized everyday reality. I was aware that the four red petals enclosing the center contained the kundalini, "luminous as lightning, shining in the hollow of this lotus like a chain of brilliant lights." That center, basic for smell and speech, contained the material energy of the universe. I knew that coping with this chakra would bring mastery of desire, of envy, of anger, and of passion. All this I knew—from reading. I peered at the picture: elephant, yellow, Child Brahma, Shakti goddess, snake coiled about the lingam. I looked and I studied, but I knew nothing.

Despair was my lot. I had come for nought. I had come to find myself, to meditate and to reach the heights and depths of the yogins, of my ancestors, but I was a foolish, conceited woman who sat only in her ignorance, with stupid books and more stupid pictures. I could not do it.

I sat despaired. I wept upon the page of the picture. I slept. I fasted. Then it happened.

How can I tell you how it began? It is with me yet, and it makes me tremble in fear and wonder. I meditated upon this center near my own anus. I called repeatedly upon Shiva, the great Lord, to aid me. Then I heard a great cackle. It was not the Lord Shiva who came to me! It was not Krishna. No, it was not any male God at all! Out of the depths of my own darkness and ignorance, desire and despair, came a cackle of the great Goddess who was a woman like myself! She was no ordinary woman, this Goddess. Oh, no! She combined the hells of the four thousand aeons. She was Kali Durga, but She gave me no name!

She cackled and spoke:

"So, little woman! So, petulant, demanding little thing! You seek the highest powers! You seek to become as great as the Gods, let alone those yogins who have fasted and torn themselves to pieces to flee from their ignorance. And you expect to find it by yourself, in a moment, with just a book and a few pictures! You are, indeed, beyond yourself.

"I would laugh at you and tear you to pieces if I did not have my own reasons for letting you live in sanity and go on. Indeed, it is a pain to my heart that I am required by my own need to attend to such foolish mortals as yourself. I would be quite contented to let you pass ten thousand more rebirths without achieving enlightenment were it not for my own need."

"What is your need, great Goddess?" said I. I know not wherefrom I had the courage to so address Her, especially after Her initial bitter and explosive and frightening outburst. But I did, all the same, and She answered.

"My need is also the need of my great Lord Shiva, though He does not know it and will not admit it. He has given unto me the secret which He cannot admit even unto Himself."

"What is this secret, great Goddess?" I asked, growing a little annoyed at Her for not coming out with what She had in mind.

"The secret, little one," She continued, "is that the great Lord Shiva needs a change in His consort. He needs Her to be a Sister, an equal, a co-creator of the universe, a manager of the kalpas. Not only does He need Her so, but He needs Her, too, to be a Queen-Sister to His creations, just as He aims to be a King-Brother to His. This is His need for the new aeon. He hardly knows it yet, Himself, but has given it to me to be known. I am His willing and loving consort who will be with Him and bind Him and embrace Him and create with Him. I cannot do this alone, but have need of you, and millions like you. Do not wax rhapsodic at this revelation for I must tell you that this comingling with creatureliness, this becoming sister to my creatures, this elevation on their part and going down on my part is no pure joy to me. I do welcome the elevation of the feminine, however, and of women, for it is a sweet desire that this be true. You, little sister, are chosen just because you come here alone, will not bow down to the gods and to your men. You, just because of your rebellious spirit, your courage, your conceit and your foolish desire, you are chosen to be aided, whereas others, content in their status and achievements, are not. Thus, little one, you secretly partake of my own being."

At this moment, the picture came to life. Now I saw with my eyes; before this I had only heard the words. I saw the child Brahma dispelling fear with his four arms; I saw the goddess Shakti, in Her redness and four-armed dancing wonder. There were the spear, the staff, the sword and the drinking cup. There, too, was the happy elephant, with six tusks. As suddenly as it had come to life, however, it all vanished.

I sat fixedly for a long time. There was no question about the reality of my experience, but I felt cheated, somehow. The Goddess had deemed me worthy, for whatever reason, to talk to me and to show Herself to me. I was part of a Divine plan which was nothing less than a new development, a re-incarnation of the great Gods. I was chosen as a woman, just because of my independence and. . . .well, it was all true and wonderful, but, somehow, not real enough. Not real enough? I asked myself. Why?. . . .I felt unchanged. Where was the mastery of anger and desire, of passion and envy? It seemed to be all words, even though I was granted a vision of the image of the Goddess. Was I just the usual stupid female who does not trust words? Then I thought: "No, I am not stupid, but it is true that I have only experienced it in words; I have not yet felt it in my body, in my senses, in my true being as a woman! If the great Lord Shiva wills it and if the Great Shakti wishes it, too, then they must find a way for me to experience them! I refuse, as one who values the flesh, to subject myself to those silly, self-punishing antics of the gurus!"

With that, I obstinately tossed my head. I was silent for a moment, but then laughed. I was quite alone in my eloquent sovereignty, and, in truth, I was only partly convincing to myself. I was autonomous all right, but lonely. I had to admit, ruefully, out of my feminine being, that I longed for company. But I stuck to my independence and stayed on in my little cabin.

Days and weeks passed, as I felt the loneliness. I saw not a soul. I ate modestly, walked about the mountain, and waited. There was nothing more for me to do.

One day, when I felt that this whole experience was simply going to trickle away into a kind of "holiday at the mountains," I heard a whisper in my ear. The hiss of the Kundalini serpent came as a woman. "Walk!" she said. I walked, in my imagination, up a hill to a large building. Fantasy it was, but as real as I am. The building was a temple, of beautiful design, upon which were painted and etched, in bas reliefs, all kinds of sexual intimacies between men and women. I went inside this building and wandered about in it. There were beds and couches and tables, but no one was present. Then a woman came toward me. She seemed undistinguished in appearance, but there was something special about her which I could not fathom. She told me, in a matter of fact manner, that she was a priestess of this temple and that this was a place where men were kept to be of service to women. Women could come and go as they pleased and could gratify any and every sexual hunger that they might have, but the men kept here were bound and immobilized—physically or spiritually or both. These men could do nothing other than what the women wished.

Astonished, I asked how this came to be. I was told that many years ago, in this region, the women did all the work and the men just sat about and talked. Sexually, too, the women were more or less at the convenience of the men. Then, the women discovered gold, and the men took credit for it. They used the gold to establish trade and to grow rich. After a time, they had so much gold that the wives no longer needed to work. Some grew fat and lazy. Others became restless. All the important women of the community began coming up to this mountain, but the men neither noticed nor cared what was going on up there. In truth, on this mountain, the great Goddess had established a temple wherein women could gratify all sexual desire. The men there were generally handsome and of good physical condition, though not always. Old men were there as waiters and retainers, obsequious and silly. The Goddess had arranged matters whereby no man could come to the temple unless summoned, and no man could avoid coming when so ordered. The mystery of the place was that the men, although tyrannized and kept as slaves and playthings, also wanted to stay there, in service of the Goddess. The men so selected, it seems, were the special ones, the better ones, but by no means the socially successful men of the community, though some of them were there, as well.

I was astonished at this story, and wondered why the great Goddess planned and maintained this situation. I was horrified, but also sexually stimulated. I wondered if I, too, could have my desires satisfied. The priestess seemed to know my thoughts at once, for she came out of her blandness and laughed. "Go, my child," she said. "Enjoy yourself, for here women are free and can come and go as they wish. Only the men are bound. They are here because they must be and because they wish it!" Having concluded her story, the priestess walked silently away.

I now began to explore the building to see what kind of activities were taking place. In one room, I saw a woman repeatedly whipping a number of men who could do nothing but cower and wince in pain. In another cubicle, a woman was being licked and sucked upon by several men. In a third room, a woman copulated repeatedly with a long line of men, perhaps fifty in number. All these sights both fascinated and repelled me. I smelled the odor of privies. I began to wonder what sort of sexual hunger I had that might be satisfied, when I spied a man tied to a stone column. As I got closer, I saw that he was European, and very handsome. He vaguely reminded me of pictures of my father, though he seemed, also, to be at least half of our own nation, resembling my husband and one of my lovers. Yet, he was none of these, and a stranger to me.

I went up to him and looked at his sad, deep eyes. I was touched by his suffering. He looked at me with a strange mixture of fear, anger, and desire. When he did so, I was absolutely electrified, for here were mirrored the emotions that I had felt so frequently in my life and in just such a combination. I had experienced great sexual desire and fear of both the desire and the possibility of its fulfillment. My desires were often of the kind that are frowned upon. Yet I had also felt great anger that my desire was not being fulfilled, or only fulfilled at great cost to myself in pain and guilt. I was instantly drawn to this man, who mirrored my feelings and conflicts. Despite the intensity of his eyes, he seemed half dead, as if he had been whipped and used repeatedly by many women. He said nothing.

I dropped to my knees and began to lick and suck at his exposed genitals. I was fulfilling both my own need, and I think, his as well. For there was love in me, and with love all things are possible, and all dilemmas are resolved—or so I thought at that point in my life. As I indulged my desire, the man came to life, and I saw that he was like a God. I saw him as Shiva himself, yet a mortal like my father, husband, lover. My lover-God had come to life, but he was trapped in this place. I could come and go as I wished, but the man of my soul was trapped here by the great Goddess. How could I free him, make him the willing consort of my soul, I wondered? Was the Goddess so full of revenge, for all Her rejections and past hurts, that She would not let this be? Or would it be, as I had known and experienced and feared from men, that once free and independent, he would leave me? Men do leave us for others, do they not? For another woman or for some beckoning demon of fame and fortune?

I was confronted with an age-old woman's dilemma. Indeed, I felt the agony of the Goddess, Herself! That is why She had him trapped here, to keep him for Herself! What a despicable woman She was, just like the rest of us! Yet, he wanted to be here, the priestess had said. He must not want to leave Her, as well. He, therefore, must also be undergoing suffering, like me, in order to transform himself. He was chosen by the Goddess, after all, and She is not such a fool as to choose just anyone. She told me, I recalled, that She was serving Her consort, the Great Shiva, who needed Her equality and sisterhood. Then I realized something: this man, this God before me, had reminded me of father, husband, and lover, all of whom had been authorities for me, not really equals like a brother. Was the man of my soul undergoing the trials of the Goddess in order to come down, to become my equal and friend? Was he being transformed from his mightiness and superiority? Yes, Yes, Yes! At once I knew that my own independence, rebelliousness, superiority of spirit were incarnated in this man, and that he too was being groomed to serve the Goddess.

Oh, how I loved him, and how I felt the meaningful love of the Goddess! She was terrible in Her form and in Her spirit, but She was grand and loving, and in the service of love, as well. Yes, here my man was being transformed, as was my spirit at the very same time.

I clutched my man to my bosom. I sucked upon him and upon his spirit and made it my own. I felt his suffering as my own. I felt as one with him in that terrible union of fear and anger and passion. And I knew at that moment and for all eternity that the union of fear and passion and anger is of the great Goddess, that it is Her gift of this conflicted rack to help us find that love. I understood that She undergoes this suffering Herself in the name of Her own great love for Her consort. All this I knew in a moment. Even now, I thrill to this knowledge. I may lose it, in my moments of despair and lostness and meaninglessness and unlovingness, but it comes back as I am there in living memory. I am, once again, locked in embrace with the man of my soul—He who is my spirit, my consort, and my king—sharing the sweet-bitter agony of fear, anger, desire, and transformed by love. At the moment that I first experienced this union, Great Shiva was also freed from His imprisonment, and I felt the Kundalini rise up from the region of my anus. The smell of privies was replaced by the sweet smell of flowers.

II

Less than a month passed before I was once again thrown from my perch of joy and self-satisfaction. After two weeks, I had already looked at the second Chakra, the Svadhisthana. I had seen its six vermillion petals, the white water within, and inside that, the terrible Makara fish with the great mouth. I knew that Vishnu, the Protector, lived here, too, but felt Him small in the lap of the Bindu. In this Chakra, above all, dwells the Shakti, Rakini, with Her four hands and three eyes and fierce fangs. Frightening were Her spear and drum and battle-axe. More frightening still were the stream of blood running from Her nostril, and Her wild, mad eyes. That face, together with the terrible Leviathan-like fish Makara, made me shiver.

My book said of this Chakra: "He who meditates upon this stainless Lotus is freed immediately from all his enemies (the six passions of lust, anger, greed, delusion, pride and envy)." These words gave me little solace. I did not gladly meditate upon this lotus. I would gladly have rested content with the freeing from ignorance that I had achieved with the first Chakra, Muladhara. But I was not to be so lucky as to escape. After three weeks, I began to feel the repeated need to empty my bladder. It was quite unusual for me, but I needed to urinate many times a day. I then realized that the Svadisthana Chakra is located above the genitals, and that the kidneys are related to it. What was in that dark water, I wondered? With a shiver of fear, I said a silent prayer to Vishnu, the Protector, and proceeded to meditate upon this Chakra.

I did not have long to wait. The Shakti-Rakini made Herself manifest and I cried out in terror and horror. She gobbled white rice ravenously, despite the continual pouring of blood from Her nostril. It reddened the rice, but She heeded it not. The Makara fish appeared and changed into a hundred wild animals which raced by me as I stood perfectly motionless. It stopped and transformed into a demon which approached me. I became so frightened that I could hardly breathe. I was as if in a terrible nightmare from which I tried to awaken. There was nothing for it but to look deeply at the face of this demon, but I could not. My breath faded and I fainted.

When I recovered, I looked about me, and saw that everything was the same. Even the page of the picture was unchanged. Perhaps it was only an overwrought imagination, I thought. But the pain in my belly, my feeling of weakness and a shivering fright made me think otherwise. An awareness was dawning upon me. With the Muladhara, I was privileged to unite with the God, Brahma, and to free Him from the imprisoning grasp of the Great Goddess. Now, I had to meet Her again, to face the Mistress of the temple, with whose priestess I had talked. I had to confront the Goddess, and free *myself* from Her terrible grasp.

At that moment, I felt the sharp talons of Her vulture-like claws. I chose to look into Her horrible face, to peer unflinchingly at the blood and into those mad eyes. I fainted once again. Who can look into the eyes of the Goddess and see therein the lust and greed and anger and delusion and pride and envy and still remain conscious? Who can do that? Surely not I.

I wept and wept. I was abased. I was frightened. I was horrified. I was rent asunder and felt split into a million pieces. There flashed before my eyes the vision of every greedy act of my life. I tasted the bitterness of my own failures and hatreds. I tasted my own briny tears. The water ran out of me. Worst of all was the wordless rending asunder that I felt. No words had I. No answers. Only pain and delusion and fear and ignorance.

"Oh, Goddess," I prayed, "Why do you torment men so? Why do you turn them into demons for Your sake? Why?" My belly ached. I felt repeated pressure to relieve myself. No answer came, only pressure of water—tears and urine, urine and tears.

After a time, the water stopped, and there was stillness. Just stillness. No answers, no change, no redeeming thoughts. But stillness was preferable to the horror. I resolved to stay with this stillness, and did so for a long time. There was something peaceful in the silence. Was this an answer to greed and lust and pride and envy and delusion? No. This was an answer only to the mad lovelessness of the Goddess. It was surely no use to confront Her with any of these things. It was like blaming Nature, with its evolutionary processes, for its lovelessness. There is love: I had learned that with the Muladhara. I knew now that there also existed an opposite to Love. What was that? Raw power? Yes. Selfish "mineness"? Yes. Power and greed and lust and envy and pride and anger, all blamed on another. Blamed on us by the Goddess and by us on the Goddess. Enough. Enough of my words. I will be silent. Once I have spoken in complaint. Twice have I spoken in prayer. Now I will cover my mouth. I will be still.

I sat in stillness for many days. I began to understand how it was that my ancestors the yogins could sit for hours and days, utterly alone and silent. It was not a stuporous condition, but a state of total wordlessness and movinglessness. After a very long time of the agony of the stillness, I began to weep. The tears came gently from my eyes, but it brought release from the pain, the tension, the stillness. There were no sobs, nothing to change the soundlessness, yet the movement of the water seemed to break the quiet as well. As if one can hear the flow of tears.

I smiled. Imagine, "to hear the flow of tears." That made me smile. I noticed that I previously had not paid attention to the sounds in the mandalas, which seemed rather meaningless to me.

Now I guessed that the sounds had an abstruse meaning, like "to hear the flow of tears." I left that paradox, not wanting to break myself into pieces again, and allowed myself to breathe freely and happily. I soon fell into a deeper reverie.

I found myself transported into space—or so it seemed. There was water above, through which I went, as well as the water of the oceans below. You in the West, do you not have such a statement in your Bible of "waters of the firmament" above and below? I am not sure if that is what is meant, but this is what I experienced. I knew that I was about to take an astral voyage.

I soon found myself on a planet which I could not fathom. It was dark and the earth was black. The ground was rocky and there seemed to be little or no vegetation. I wandered about in the very dim light, which came from a source I could not divine. I knew I was on a planet, but I did not know which one it was. Was it Chandra (or the Moon, as you call it), or was it Mangala (Mars)? The barren nature and the rocky ground suggested both of these. Then I came across a tree. It was a seemingly ordinary tree in shape and size, like one of your elms, perhaps. But the leaves, the leaves! They were shimmering yellow. It may not be unusual for there to be yellow leaves, but here was a black tree with shimmering yellow leaves which appeared to shed light from a source within the leaves themselves!

I stood looking at this strange tree, when suddenly a most lovely young girl came close to me and smiled warmly! I looked at her rather astonished, as you can imagine, but she smiled once again and placed her arm on mine.

"Fear not, Maya" she said, and I wondered how she knew my name. "Fear not," she repeated. She said not another word but communicated to me silently, as if by telepathy. She informed me that this planet was, as I had guessed, Mangala (Mars) and that she was from Shukra (Venus). Mangala was, indeed, barren, though it had once had a very great civilization. This civilization was destroyed by the ever-recurring wars that it had suffered. These wars, in turn, were caused by both the people and the atmosphere of the planet, which was heavy and crass. The people were healthy, aggressive, and positively physical in nature, but this vital essence was overly enhanced by the electric thickness of the atmosphere. The two fed off each other and caused destruction. The beautiful tree that I was now looking at was one of the black trees of Shukra, of which there were many. It was planted here, as the first of its kind after the catastrophe. The atmosphere of Venus-Shukra was very different from Mangala-Mars, though not opposite to it. These trees were being introduced to Mangala-Mars to help change the atmosphere, and then a new civilization would develop, even greater than those which existed before.

I took in this strange idea that people and atmosphere were dependent upon each other. I knew, of course, that the atmosphere could affect people, but the other way about? That was strange. And yet, it seemed possible and reasonable to me. We do affect our atmosphere physically, do we not? Why not psychically?

I closed my eyes and was led by my new friend to the planet Venus-Shukra. We went through a very hot and gaseous atmosphere in which I thought I would die. At the last moment—if one can speak of time in the ordinary sense in such astral voyaging—the poisonous and destructive vapors gave way to a hard earth which opened up to receive us. We continued to fall for a long time, as if magnetically attracted toward the center of this planet. Finally, we landed but it was not on solid ground at all. The earth—if one may if one may call the strange substance on which we stood "the earth"—swayed as if it were an ocean. My thoughts quickly went to the western myths, of sea-born, foam-born, wave-born Aphrodite, the Venus of the Greeks. I had read of the wave-floating earth of Venus, as written by an Englishman. The Greeks and Englishman were right about Venus, but why was Venus–Shukra bringing to mind these western associations? Then I remembered. My natural father, after all, was an Englishman, and a soldier (Mars) who risked all for love (Venus). I smiled, for I was his daughter, was I not?

Be that as it may, here I was deep within the planet of Venus itself, finding it hollow like a cave, with no sun nor moon. Instead there was a glow of mellow light, now red, now yellow, now blue, now green, a changing rainbow of colors, but so subtle and diffuse that the eye was not aware of the changes, unless it focused upon them. Yes, this was very different from Mars–Mangala! I remembered a scrap of knowledge from Hindu astrology: Shukra's color was that of the rainbow! Now I understood what that meant: the light of the atmosphere changed like a rainbow. This surely would be something that would be worthwhile to transfer to Mangala. My friend easily divined my thoughts and nodded to me. I realized that the black tree with the yellow leaves, giving a light from within, was the first of many trees to be transferred from Shukra to Mangala. Eventually there would be many, many such trees. I realized, too, as I looked about Shukra, that there were so many varieties of tree that the eye could not comprehend them, but what they had in common were leaves of all shades of the rainbow. Most remarkably, all these leaves—red, green, yellow, blue—all had a luminous glow which came from within the leaves themselves. I realized that one day Mangala would have such trees and that the atmosphere would change to these various colors. How then, I thought, would this go with Sun and moons, which Mars had? Here was a mystery which seemed deep and problematic, though I knew not why.

I looked again at my friend for an answer. She said nothing, but I had an inkling of the meaning nonetheless. Something about the union of the diffuse, rainbow-light of Shukra and the solar light of Mangala, piercing and direct—the union of these two would be a marriage of Gods. Indeed, I had the distinct impression that this had already occurred in the pleromatic world of the Gods, and that the realization would gradually take place on the planets. I was vouchsafed a glimpse of coming events, but I did not know what form it would take, nor why I was given that glimpse.

I looked again at my friend, and I saw something very strange: one eye seemed alternately gay and happy, and then sad and tearful. While these changes were going on, the other eye changed from being wild and fearsome, to being still, deep and fathomless! Two eyes: four conditions. The opposites were not happy-sad, on the one hand, nor still-fierce on the other; no. Happy-sad made one union, while still-fierce made another, and the pairs were opposite. More than that: I was in the presence of the Goddess Venus—Shukra-Shakti Herself! Here, my guide, this ordinary girl, who had seemed sweet and benevolent and in deep communication with me, She was the Goddess and was showing me Her vision: Her two eyes and four conditions. I laughed now, for I understood. My Goddess was showing me and choosing me, just as She had said and promised in the Muladhara. It takes two eyes for the perception of depth, after all, and now She was showing me that happy-sad as one eye, and still-fierce as the other eye, together made a pair and a foursome which gave her perception of depth! All my pains and changes and feelings, and angers, and fiercenesses were attributable to the Goddess! I fell at Her feet, embracing Her ankles and Her knees. She lifted me up and kissed me. I knew that I was free of the Goddess, as I wished, but free because I accepted Her, loved Her, submitted to Her. Most deeply of all, I understood her! I danced with joy. Suddenly, I found myself once again on earth, beside my cabin in the mountains of Bengal.

During the following days, I pondered and turned over in my mind the opposites: happy-still; sad-fierce. The words and the states gave some sense to my feelings, but I was not satisfied. How, I wondered, did all those feeling states in the atmospheric rainbow of the Venus-Shukra unite with the Sun and moons of Mars-Mangala-Kuja? And how was that warrior planet, so masculine and vital, going to change? This I needed to know, or else I would not be able to free myself from the Chakra. At once I realized that I needed to be freed not from the Goddess, but from Svadhisthana Chakra! To be freed, I had to further overcome my darkness and ignorance.

The Goddess had explained much to me, about the atmosphere and the planets and the feelings and the unions. But I had to know more before I could proceed to the next Chakra. Who would tell me? The Goddess had unceremoniously deposited me back upon my meditative doorstep. To whom could I turn? I thought for a time, and then it came to me: Vishnu, the Protector, of course! Did he not live in this same mandala of Svadhisthana? Would not this great Lord, who had appeared so often when the world was threatened by evil powers, would He not incarnate Himself again?

"Oh, Vishnu," I prayed, "Oh, savior of humanity. You have become an avatar for humanity's sake so many times; You, who have been both Krishna playing the flute over the mountains and our hero Rama; You, Vishnu, incarnate yourself for me. Perhaps I ask too much for myself. I know that my need is to free myself from this place of ignorance. I know that what I need to know, of the marriage of Shukra and Mangala, of rainbow and sun-darkness, and what emerges therefrom is as nothing to You. I should pray, I know, for a greater boon from You: to be savior of mankind. That we all pray for. But you do not answer us yet. So then, Vishnu, perhaps You will vouchsafe your maidservant a vision, an answer to her question?"

I received no answer to my prayer. Unlike the time when I began my meditations, when I sought the guidance of Shiva, the great Guru who is beyond all gurus, I had no answer to my prayer. That is, I had no answer that I expected! I waited a few moments, and then I heard a laugh.

This time it was no female cackle, such as the great Goddess gave me. No, it was a very male laugh. It is hard for me to explain, for the laugh had humor and benevolence in it, along with sneering and harshness. I heard the laugh, but I saw no person. I knew, however, just as I had known with the Goddess, that I was in the presence of the God. He was Vishnu, the Protector, and Mangala-Kuja at the same time.

I was not transported from the spot, nor was I moved at all. No, I sat absolutely still, in my lotus position, and felt the world around me change: the heavens opened up and became as if swallowed by the great fish Makara, and there was only darkness and a very dim light. Through the dimness I saw the planet Mars—Mangala—Kuja come hurtling toward me as if it were some great spacecraft. It hurtled so close and was going so fast that I instinctively held up my hands over my face as if to ward off the blow. How foolish our inadequate little defensive instincts are; as if my little arms could protect my vulnerable body from the great planet.

The hurtling stopped and now I was audience to a spectacle of the planet itself. How can I describe this to you? It was as if I were observing a history of the planet in time, and as if all of it were going on simultaneously. Time was being visually portrayed, serially, in terms of events, and simultaneously, taking place in different parts of the planet. And I was aware of it all at once. I had only to cast my eye on this place or that, and I would see it all. The word "all" is the right one, for it is a totality which is a totality all the time. The part, at the same time, is the whole. Is that confusing? I imagine so, for it confuses me as well, and I still do not rightly grasp it all.

What I saw might be termed "A Natural History of Aggression." The first part showed the battling and devouring of animals who were instinctive enemies: cat and mouse; fox and goose; lion and deer, and so on. In each case, the battle was for good, or for territorial defense, or for sexual partners, or for leadership. It was horrible and natural. Then there were scenes of men, and it was the same. Civilization after civilization, the heights of achievement were increased and the destruction augmented. I saw civilizations rise to great peaks and, like Atlantis and Lemuria, go down under waters of Malekaric destructiveness. I watched all this with a cold eye, as if I, myself, were the Sun of Mars-Mangala-Kuja, looking down upon it. But, as our sun is not cold, perhaps the analogy is better with the moons, those two moons of the planet. They, indeed, are cold. But no, it was a combination of both: I looked with the coolness of the two moons as two eyes, and with the clarity of the sun, but without its warmth. I saw coldly, without fire nor feeling nor horror, nor agony, nor even pleasure. As I looked with these two cold eyes of two cold moons and with this one bright eye which saw all without warmth, I saw the continuing development of the "natural history of aggression," as I have said. The light grew dimmer as I looked, until I saw the planet devastated by its aggression. I watched as the people grew more and more aware of what was happening. I saw them withdraw from the cold moons and clear sun and retreat into the depths of the planet, to build their cities and their civilizations away from these cold eyes. All became barren outside, and the life that went on inside the planet was not available for me to see. Now events were occurring in the time-scale I had experienced when brought there by the Goddess: I saw a great black tree being planted, and on this tree were beautiful yellow leaves. As I watched, I saw more trees being planted, just as the Goddess had informed me. Before long–it could not have been more than fifteen or twenty million years–many, many trees were planted, and the cold dim atmosphere began changing. There seemed to be a strange union going on. During what seemed to be the middle of the day, the bright sun had full command and cast its clear light on all sides. In morning and evening, the rainbow light had its sway and gorgeous colors filled the sky. At night, all was dark, except that one moon shown, and the other broke up into thousands and millions of particles that became stars.

With this union of the atmospheres, of Venus and Mars, of Shukra and Mangala, the people came out from under the earth of the planets and began to communicate with one another. One knew that things were happening: the cold-eyed aggression of the one was transformed with the feelings of the rainbowed other. And the simple continuity of trees which shine with an inner light was joined with the greater light of the one Sun. Whereas before this Sun was simply a cold orb, seeing all, now it was filled with heat and light and warmth and fire and passion.

Numbers appeared in the sky: The two plus two, of the two eyes of the Goddess, mingled with the one plus two of the sun and moons of the God. It was a strange sight: two and four of the Goddess; one and two of the God. They united in equally strange ways. The two of the Goddess merged with the two of the God, making four. There was the One of the God, the Two of the God and Goddess, the Three of the God (with his own one sun plus two moons) and the Four of the Goddess (with Her two plus two). Together they were as One and Ten, for they sum to ten and are as One, are they not? In the Heavens and in the Waters and on the Earth, there were united in embrace, Shiva and Shakti, Vishnu and Lakshmi, God and Goddess. And I was freed from the bonds of Svadhisthana.

III

Many days went by, but I did not feel the joy and freedom of enlightenment which I had felt after I had escaped the bonds of the Muladhara. Had I really freed myself from Svadhisthana? Was my vision, my astral voyaging, only a dream, only a self-deception, only an illusion? I smiled ruefully, for my name meant "illusion" and, it was true, I could hardly tell if I, myself, existed. How could I know? I had seen, I had heard, but—and now I knew that a part of me was not freed from Svadhisthana—I had not tasted. And taste was the very center, the very purpose and point of that Chakra! The Tattva of taste was not dissolved.

So, I was not free. I noticed that again, as had been happening every day for some time—one eye began tearing. It was strange. I was not really sad, and only one eye wept. I reached up and with my finger took a tear and tasted it. It was salty. I reached down and took some of my urine. It was bitter. I laughed. Yes, now I tasted: the salt of wisdom and the bitterness of my lack of enlightenment! I was freed from Svadhisthana, all right, but I was still only half, and cool, and not. . .

Enough. Whatever I was lacking had to be redeemed as I proceeded. I had been through the earth of Muladhara, the water of Svadhistahana, and now I needed to face the fire of Manipura. It was just this fire, this heat of tapas which would transform my meditation into the freedom that I desired. It was good; now I would continue my *dhyana.*

I fixed my attention on the Manipura, the "plenitude of jewels" which was at the navel. I looked carefully at the picture. Facing me was a central crucible of red fire, triangular in shape. I looked at its three handles, the swastikas. Inside the fire was the Ram sacred to Agni. There, I knew, was a central place. I also looked outside the triangle, and saw the God Rudra, the Destroyer, seated upon the bull. I saw, too, the Shakti Lakini, blue and three-faced with three eyes in each. She had four arms, fierce teeth, and chewed rice mixed with meat and blood. Rudra was white, smeared with ashes. They both made the signs dispelling fear and granting boons, but their visage said otherwise. Only the outside of the Mandala, with its ten blue petals, seemed to suggest peace.

These were the Gods ruling the Chakra: the Destroyers! Dare I descend into the heat and fire? I had read somewhere that the fire-walkers were those who had mastered this Chakra. But who could go into the fires of hell and emerge unscathed? Not I. I said this with full knowledge of my limitations even in terms of self-mastery—I did not even think about the desirability or meaningfulness of walking on coals concretely.

It was many days before I could directly view the task of this Chakra. It seemed that I had already been through so much, why should I expose myself to the fire and pain of the Destroyers? At last, however, I could set myself apart from these Gods, and look, even so, into the burning crucible and fires. I waited, and the vision began to form for me. I felt the heat rise and fill my eyes with the colors that are meant for the Gods.

Now I saw them there: Rudra, pure vermillion, white with ashes, gross and barbaric, on his unattractive bull; the Shakti Lakini, blue and vicious, with bloody mouth. It was then that words began to form within me. I am moved to call them a prayer, since they are addressed to the Gods, but I had never so spoken to the Gods in this way, and you might even find me rather blasphemous in my statements. In hopes that you will understand, and—dare I say it—even share the sentiments with me, I will relate what words formed in me:

"Rudra, Great Destroyer! I do not count you Great. As I contemplate my navel, I sense a sickness and nausea within my belly which leads me to want to throw up the pain and rancor and resentment which lies within me! And it is You whom I hate. You and Your rotten Consort. Look at You. I see in You every tiny little tyrant, every fat Rajah and vicious potentate who has burdened and drained and deprived my people of their joy, of their material blessings, of their livelihood, while You sit in Your fat splendor, unmindful of their suffering. What care you? You care only for the sacrifices which are given to You. You care only for the sweet scent of the smoky spirit of the animal as it rises up to Your wicked nostrils. Yes, Ram sacrifice you wish, as well as Goat, or Lamb. It is as nothing to You. You care not that the animal eats when it is hungry, makes love when it wishes, fights only for its security or food—all these natural and good things are as nothing to You. For You care not about Ram or Lamb, unless it is of use to You. You care not about Man, unless he is of use to You. You care only for gifts and sacrifices, and that Man sing Your praises! Yes, now I will tell You, and make no more cowed response to Your threats. For what can You do to me? Kill me? That is no great threat. For I tell You that I despise You! You, God, I despise You, and curse You! I am no atheist who foolishly believes that he can dismiss You. No, it is much worse; I know that You exist, just as these petty tyrants, and hypocritical leaders exist. They exist just as You exist, and they serve You. And they make us all serve You, do they not? Well, I will not serve You willingly, though bow to You I must. I know that I am impotent to overthrow You. I know that I can only rant and rave and groan and weep, though You can and will have Your way.

"And You, Great Shakti Lakini! Neither do I count You Great, though You, too, are the Destroyer. What are You, with Your three eyes and three heads and bloody mouth, only out for itself! Your Consort and Lord is after Power, at least, though He gets it in his devious, bitter, mean and skulking ways. You do not seek even that! You want only to devour poor souls. You want only to torment us, feed upon us, drive us into all sorts of temptations and experiences and emotions, and then it is You that feed, unmindful of the feelings of others, unmindful of their pain. You simply keep the whole bloody mess of life going, get Your bounty of flesh and rice and blood—and mankind weeps and groans. What is worse, You incarnate Yourself in us, and get off freely! Oh, how I despise You!

"These are my prayers to You, You Gods, You Destroyers! I heave up my pain and my wrath and my bitterness. Eat, therefore, of this pile of vomitted words which are my prayers to You!"

My words reduced my nausea and I felt a brief respite of the pain in my belly and pressing on my navel. But the Gods neither moved, nor made any sign at all that they had heard me. Not even a sneer from Rudra, nor a cackle from Lakini! Rudra merely sat, pompous and self-satisfied, on his gross bull; Lakini devoured her meat and rice like a vulture or hyena.

I sat and looked at them and sighed. What was this? Why did my efforts have no effect? Was this only egotism and self-centeredness? Did I just see there, in these Destroyer Gods, my own power and hunger and selfishness, which were not apparent to me within myself? No, I would not fall into that trap for myself, for I had often been there; it is easy for me to simply say, "Oh, yes, that is my own darkness and evil." The Gods love us to do that, do they not? They love to indulge every whim and get their sacrifices from man and then have man feel the guilt and pain and agony and suffering. Lastly, if man takes the burden on himself, he is the sacrifice for their grievous behavior! Yes, they want their Ram-Lamb sacrifice, do they not?

Now I remembered a ritual at the temple of Kali in my fair city of Calcutta. I recalled the sacrifice of the Goat, and his one eye staring wildly and painfully up at me. A sacrifice to that Kali who needed to be cut up in many pieces and spread over the entire land! But we can cut Her up no more, for She can re-unite Herself easily. It is illusion to think that we can destroy the Terrible Mother! Why then, I thought, do they want sacrifices and prayers and praise? They seem to need that from us. And this poor goat? This poor Ram or Lamb, with his eye staring up? Then I thought in satisfaction: Yes, that is it! That is it! It came to me in a flash of lightning, like the energy of the Kundalini itself! I spoke in words of declaration, not prayer:

"There, Great Goddess Lakini! Look at that Ram, with his One Eye showing. Look at that animal creature! He, in his littleness, in his naturalness, in his goodness, knows more than You, with Your Three Faces and Three Eyes in each. For your Threeness is as nothing! You see all, have all power, but You are incomplete! And I, as a woman, know what it is to suffer from incompleteness. You are only moving and dynamic and changing and devouring, no rest. Your three faces need a fourth face, and your three times three eyes need a fourth and tenth. It is the Ram's face, and the Lamb's eye, and the Goat's being that You want. Without that, You are incomplete! You need that natural animal to satisfy You all the time. Praise us, Mankind, for you need us to offer these sacrifices to You! Without us, You simply do not have Your totality!

"And You, Great God Rudra! In your impotent and little fury! You get all Your power from the Bull, and You do not know it. You have everything, but You do not know it! The One-Eyed Ram-Lamb-Goat sees more clearly than You, with Your Two. Look, tyrant, look! You are a lesser animal than the Ram! For he, at least, is pure animal and can be nothing other than pious in following his nature. You, great Monster of a God, act worse than any animal, yet claim and show a human face as well!

"Well, you Gods! I reject You and despise You, and now let me hold up a mirror to You and show You how You look!"

With that, I took the Eye of the Ram and held it up to the Gods so that they could see therein the vision of themselves. Until this point, both Gods seemed quite oblivious of me and rather uninterested in anything that I had to say. I did not even know if they heard what I said. Nonetheless, I offered the Ram-Lamb-Goat eye up as a mirror, as an angry and vengeful and superior kind of sacrifice. I then became aware that They—these great and powerful and awful Gods—were interested and moving towards me. Now it was I who sneered, and I who laughed and cackled at them! For I had the mirror eye, the one thing that these vicious, uncaring, monstrous Gods needed—the capacity to look at themselves! I had it from the spontaneous nature of the Ram-Lamb-Goat himself, and from my own nature. So, now, I held up this Eye, and they looked.

The Shakti-Lakini looked and saw the horror of Her three faces and three eyes in each. She retched at Her blue color, and grew ill at the sight of the blood and meat in Her mouth and, I presume, at Her greed. She fell back in horror, it seemed, and gave the Eye to Her Consort.

Rudra looked and saw His ugliness! He saw the grossness of His being, His pomposity, His self-centeredness, His power-seeking, all of which really showed His impotence! He then looked at me, His little nothing of a female being, and at his Consort. He awakened to the fact that She had more power than He and that I had more insight. He shrieked in agony!

The Two Gods clawed at themselves. I showed them the great burning vat of fire, with the swastika handles. They shied back in fear, but I reached out and pushed them in! What joy and vengeance, that those who had kept men in the heat of ovens of pain and desire and having to sacrifice for the Gods, that these Gods should now suffer as men have suffered! I shouted aloud, for I understood a deep truth: It was not man alone who needed to be transformed, but the Gods needed this! The Gods, in their lack of insight and consciousness of what it is to be a Human Being, needed to be burned and transformed in that self-same fire!

I sat before that crucible of fire and looked at the red, boiling, bubbling mass of thick liquid. It was like fire and blood at the same time. I was still, without pain and without passion. I was even without thought. I said only, "Let them stay in their broth, for they so willed it and wanted it."

With that, I took the Eye of the Ram-Lamb-Goat and swallowed it. I felt as if the eye went quickly and easily down my throat and into my belly, to lodge beneath my navel. I then imagined that it looked up at me from the opening in my navel, and I looked down at it. And then I laughed! I laughed and laughed and laughed! It was no sneering laugh, as that of Rudra; it was no cackling laugh of horrible glee at another's suffering, as that of the Shakti; it was no giggle of a girl. At that moment, despite my years and despite my having had husband, lovers, children, much experience in my life—at that moment, I became a woman! I became a woman in the spirit! I laughed with joy and with self-insight and I laughed also at myself and my own pretentiousness. As I laughed and felt myself to be a woman in the spirit, by one of those meaningful moments in which Nature and Spirit, Man and the Gods, are one, I began to menstruate. The blood flowed freely and warmly, and I felt its rich, fiery quality pulse through me. I put my finger in it and tasted it, and I found the blood tasty and good! I felt at One with my Sister, the Shakti, for I, too, could look at myself, my animal nature and laugh!

Then I thought of Rudra, puffed up and pompous, like the silly tyrant He was, and I laughed once more. I laughed, for this is what I, too, saw in the mirror of the Eye of the Ram-Lamb-Goat. This natural creature, without conceit, without selfishness, without even consciousness of itself, this creature's eye showed me my terrible vanity and pride. I saw myself full of ego and pomposity, searching after praise. I laughed and laughed and laughed. I did not sneer at myself for these things. For this is what it meant, I knew, to be both an animal and a God! We, poor human creatures, were in-between! I knew, once again, all that I had known from the Gods in the Muladhara and Svadhisthana, but now I knew it in a different way. How can I say it, better than I have already? I cannot. Know only that the Gods need to be praised, the animals need to be praised, and Mankind needs to be praised, for we are all One!

With those words of laughter and joy, I saw the Great Rudra and I saw the Great Shakti Lakini rise out of the boiling red fire and blood of the crucible. They rose up as if transformed into jewelled, golden statues which emanated a glow from within. They were still and lifeless like statues, yet they had a numinous luminescence.I had an inkling of what it meant, but I cannot put it into words, lest I, too, become only a destroyer with words.

But now I could see that which I could not see before. These same great Destroyer Gods, were also moving, changing, Creator Gods. "Oh, my Gods!" I said, and I fell to the ground in utter awe and wonder: The Creator Gods and the Destroyer Gods are One! I saw then the motioning of the one hand in each God, which said, "Fear not." For with one hand they destroyed, but they also, as it is written, "dispelled fear and granted boons."

This great vision was too much for me and I held my hands over my face. I felt the warmth of my own blood, and I felt tears rising and blood rising, from the lower regions of genitals and navel upward. The Kundalini was rising. I was freed from Manipura, and the plenitude of jewels therein.

IV

Anahata, the "charming" lotus. "Charming" perhaps, because of its gorgeous reds and oranges and vermillions, of the "shining colour of the Bandhuka flower." No other Chakra, for example, says a commentator, has the "rays of the Sun on its filaments." They are like twelve soft leaves which give off a lovely light. Charming, yes. But what does it mean? Does it mean that he who achieves liberation with this Chakra shall be warm and friendly and give off a sweet light? And be charming? Yes, perhaps so. For at the very end of the verses, it is said that the Yogi will be "dearer than the dearest to women." As a woman, I understand that he will be gentle and loving. Yes, that would be nice. I would like to be that way, too.

What I really want is Anahata, the "Unattackable." Ah, that would be the redemption and liberation which I would seek. Imagine, no longer being at the mercy of the violent winds which sweep one. No longer at the mercy of the others who can split one in pieces with their *avidya* and desire and unconsciousness! Imagine! Would that be possible? That is what the verses claim. The commentator says: "He is able at will to enter the enemy's fort or citadel (Durga), even though guarded and rendered difficult of access. And he gains power by which he may render himself invisible, and fly across the sky." Yes, I understand that poetic language. To me, it means that the Enlightened One can enter the Self of another, can connect and understand him, even if the other is guarded and defensive. He must do so by intuitive means. The Enlightened One can also "render himself invisible"—that is, he can hide in his own "citadel", inside his own Self—and can "fly across the sky." I suppose that means that he can vanish into his own or the general spiritual atmosphere and thus be safe. Yes, I do believe that I understand this. I am even rather flattered that I can translate the poetry of the old Guru Masters of hundreds of years ago and understand it with my modern, post-independence mind!

But to achieve it; ah, that is another matter. How I have learned that to know only with the mind is to be possessed only by Shiva!

How I have learned that to know only with the body is to be possessed by Shakti! The Form and the Power; both are always present. How can they be united? Here is where I must find out.

Let me look at the Lotus. All around are the beautiful orange and red and vermillion leaves, each with a letter. I had not attended to the letters of the lotuses before. Just like a woman, I suppose. But now the letters are not just letters; within this lotus is heard the sound of the Shabda Brahman, "the sound which issues without the striking of any two things together." That is the sound, the "Om," the Mantra which even caused a new religion to develop. The sound that issues without the striking of any two things is, indeed, the primordial sound of the universe, the tone of all creation. It is said by another commentator that many varieties of this sound can be heard: the sound of a swarm of bees; a waterfall; high humming of a holy man; roaring of the sea; ringing of a bell; rustling of tiny silver chains; flute notes; shrill, high whistling; the sound of a drum; distant thunder. All magnificent sounds, and I think that I know what is meant. Is it not like the Buddhist's "Sound of one hand clapping?" Yes, yes, and this may be a "Buddhist Chakra" for other reasons, for there is another little lotus beneath this large Anahata lotus. That little lotus has eight red petals, and inside it there is not only the great Kalpa-tree, the wishing tree, but the Ishta-deva with an awning, and trees laden with flowers, fruits and sweet-voiced birds. That little "mental-chakra" is, no doubt, the place of the Buddha. I sense that he sat under his Bo Tree, which was, on earth, the same as the Heavenly Kalpa Tree, and that he faced all the devas and demons as they swirled at him. It is certain that he proved his "Anahata"—his unattackableness—and was enlightened. For all his fruits and all the fruits of those that followed surely came from his Bo and—in sooth—from the great Kalpa Tree in Heaven. This is, indeed, a Buddhist Chakra!

But look inside the Lotus of Anahata. There is the Vayu-Mandala, a smoky-colored, six-cornered one. Grey as a mass of smoke is it, and in the shape of interlocking triangles, male (apex upwards) and female (apex downwards). In the West one calls this the Star of David, or, perhaps, the Seal of Solomon, the union of Macrocosm and Microcosm. So, a Jewish symbol, too! Well, could it be that there meet Hindu, Buddhist, and Jew? Yes, it could be. For here, it is said, the great Jivatma, the Atman, the Self, makes its appearance. The union of the opposites, the end of division and enemies. A fitting place for the union of the highest and where at least three religions can meet.

What does it mean that the smoky region, with its six-pointed star is here? Let me read further. Inside the smoky region is a Shakti-Trikona, a female triangle which is like "ten million flashes of lightning" and is a Shiva Linga of shining gold. Here, too, is the half-moon, the crescent which might join the Muslims to us.

What does all of this mean? It means nothing less than that the core of one's being, the spark of the divine, which flows "like the steady tapering flame of a lamp" is inside the smoky-grey citadel of protection. It is a fire which is safely lit and never goes out, for it is in the region of protection. Oh, to have this flame which can be blown by the winds of heavenly desire and joy and not have it go out! Oh, to have it protected by the union of the Male and Female. Could one but have that citadel in which it is safe! And oh, to have the lovely outer perimeter of reds, to show to the world! Oh, Shiva, Oh, Shakti, let this be so for me!

There is more. There, in the Lotus dwells also a lovely black antelope or gazelle. It is light and graceful, fleet and fugitive. Perhaps it is the instinct that one needs to know danger, to run when there is trouble. Yes, to flee within oneself to the smoky union of the citadel and its ever-burning flame within, to the great sound of Om, and stillness. I can almost taste it! But this is the region of touch, and the tattva is of touch and motion—I must feel it and touch it.

Still more. For this is the region of the Heart, is it not? And the heart is in the region of lungs, of the Air. In this Chakra, after Earth, Water, and Fire, is the region of Air. The Heart, has feeling, and Air, has the spirit. Here I shall no longer be perpetually hurt or misunderstood! Nay, not so. I shall surely still be misunderstood, but I can protect myself in my citadel. I shall know my heart, and feel my flame and be able to go out to another, but to stay within my own chest, my own treasure, as well. For here, too, it is said, that the one who meditates herein will be smiled upon by Lakshmi, that benefactress who gives wealth and prosperity. What greater wealth and prosperity than to have safe and sacred one's inner treasure of one's Self? Yes, I hunger after it.

Finally, let me look at the Shiva and the Shakti who dwell in this Lotus. There they are, in their little mandalas. The verses say that here is Shiva-Hamsa, of the Sun, and He is also Shiva-Isha, with three eyes. He is "lustrous like the Sun, and his two hands make the gestures which grant boons and dispel the fears of the three worlds." He lives in the "Abode of Mercy" and is described as "wearing a jeweled necklet and chain of gems around his neck, and bells on his toes, and also clad in silken raiment." A commentator says of him: "The beautiful One possessed of the soft radiance of ten million moons, and shining with the radiance of his matted hair." Ah, how he has changed from the previous Chakra! What a great Sun-Shiva is He, benevolent and granting boons and dispelling fears!

I look to the Shakti. What say the verses of Her?

"Here dwells Kakini, who in colour is golden like unto new lightning, exhilarated and suspicious; three-eyed and the benefactress of all. She wears all kinds of ornaments, and in Her four hands She carries the noose and the skull, and makes the sign of blessing and the sign which dispels fear. Her heart is softened with the drinking of nectar."

"Her heart is softened with the drinking of nectar." Oh, would that were true! One commentator said that "Her heart is made joyous by the drinking of rice-wine." That may be. It is hard for those of us who have suffered from Her to see and experience Her "Heart softened." Yet, here it is so. For it is in the heart region, is it not? The Shakti must surely have transformed in between, has She not? Yes. But here, too, it is said that She is dressed in the skin of the black antelope. So surely She is now covered with the sensitivity of the animal and its darkness. Perhaps she has gained from my encounter with Her and my showing Her the eye of the Goat, in the Manipura.

So, there it all is. All that is necessary is for me to feel, to touch, to bring it into my own being. I left out only one tattva; the penis is the organ of action, the tattva to be dissolved herein. All is there: Heart, air, mind, spark, flame, penis, Self, mandala, citadel, leaves, sounds, Om, sweetness, protection. Wholeness. I see all, but do not have it. Let me pray again to the God and Goddess. Let me pray to their union, to the One who will protect it like a flame amidst all attack.

I pray to thee, oh Shiva-Shakti. I pray to the One who combines flame and citadel, and You, who dwell in Heaven and in my Heart, You who already have the Kalpa-Tree which goes beyond what one wishes, You know what it is that I want and need. I pray in silence.

I stayed with my prayer for many days. I knew clearly what I needed to achieve. I knew clearly—with my head. But what good was it, to know with the head, when above all, one needed to experience it, to possess it, in the heart. The heart, this unattackable citadel. To have it in the head was to be only with Shiva.

Now I knew: Shakti was of the world. Here was I, upon my quiet mountain, retreating from the world in which Shakti had her sway. Surely She could reach me here with Her passion and desires, but here, with the Eternal, with the Formless Forms, here I was safe from Shakti as She could present Herself in the form of other human beings and animals. No sooner did I become aware of this, than I knew that the test of my citadel (if in truth I had it) would come from meeting other souls and not being destroyed by them, or undermined by them. I could not do it alone, here upon my mountain. I needed the encounter with my fellow creatures.

The same morning when I recognized this fact, there came to me, for the first time, a visitor. It was not that my cabin in the mountains was so isolated. No. I needed to walk only an hour to come to a village where I could purchase food and other necessities. My nearest neighbors, farmers, were no more than minutes away. My isolation was self-chosen and enjoyed, but, as I had assured my family, I was no recluse nor hermit, and certainly not a self-torturer. Yet no one had yet been curious enough or interested enough to come and see the strange lady who was living alone in the cabin. My neighbors had left me pretty much alone. So, as I say, it is peculiar, but by no means strange to the ways of the Gods, that the day that I recognized my need to find and test the citadel in myself in relation to my fellow creatures—that same day should be the first that a visitor should seek me out.

It is more astonishing yet that this same visitor should be a foreigner. For the lady who came to me was Greek. She had been visiting my family in Calcutta, having been a friend of my sister many years ago when they were in school in England. She had a dream. She dreamed that a kind and benevolent woman had visited her and told her to come to me. She was told by this woman that I, Maya, was a special sort of woman, singled out by the Goddess Shakti. She said that I was especially courageous to go off alone, to face the Gods alone, and to attempt what all the Gurus had attempted. I was foolhardy to do this alone—as a woman and without a guide—but was also to be congratulated for this. The Greek lady was to convey this message to me. Why was the Greek lady singled out to do this, she asked? Because she, too, had been courageous and insightful, and was also a seeker and a modern woman, but she was a medium and, in particular, she was a medium of the Goddess' love.

When the Greek lady told me this, I was astonished. I was suspicious, but I was moved. Tears began to fall from one eye. At last, I was receiving the love of the Goddess, and this lady was Her mediatrix. I listened and took it in. I thanked her. I did not know if this were a Deva or not. Then I knew: The demons can come with love or destruction. They can come with insight or with darkness. They can come from men or from the Gods. I did not know for certain, but I had to listen to that within me which told me. This "something", this inner flame told me in a quiet manner that what the Greek lady said was true. For the Greek lady also added that I should just be about my business and be modest. The modesty meant "being about my business" and not a false humility. I laughed, for only a Greek, after all, can speak with authority about Pride. That is their greatest problem, is it not? Modesty: to be about one's business, and only one's own business. A lovely definition. It was true. The Goddess acknowledged that the flame existed. The flame was burning inside me, and the Goddess acknowledged it. I laughed again.

After that, the people came. First came a friend who said that I should be back at home taking care of my family. Then came a man who thought I should be serving his particular cause. Then came a seducer. They came in variety. What I felt forming in me, in reality, was a deep inner flame. This great warm and tender Sun, giving off a glow of crescent Moon. Around it was the smoky Star of David. I knew that this smoky mandala was my citadel and my fort. Here was the three-sided union of God and Goddess: they were united in the smoke of my emotion. Whenever my emotion was aroused, there was the union of God and Goddess. The smoke was that airy spirit and that effect of the inner flame: that dark and volatile "something" that was the product of flame and matter and air. The airy region of my lungs enclosing the fiery center of my heart. The emotion was my citadel: when aroused; the smoke appeared. I could either express my emotion—a way of saying "Who goes there?" and wait to see if it were friend or foe—or listen to my antelope and flee back inside, without a word. The antelope, with its horns, could defend itself, or flee. But the smoke, beloved smoke! There was a dark grey, murky and potent citadel! There, oh union of Goddess and God, in emotion You are to be my fort and protection! But I must not forget those reddish little leaves, those outer edges of my lotus, which delicately and feelingly exist, as well. For how can I reach into the fort of another without these delicate vermillion leaves? Yes, I need them very much. Yet I must not cry when I do not have them. I must not punish myself when I feel no warmth nor delicacy moving outwards. At such moments, my own citadel needs attention. My emotion tells me that, does it not? Yes, I no longer need to be a sacrifice for the Gods. I was such a one many times, but no longer. The Muladhara has taught me that!

When I realized that I no longer needed to be a sacrifice for the Gods, that I was no longer a Lamb, nor Ram, nor Goat, I felt that I, myself, must go back into the world. I realized that many times in my life I had offered myself as a sacrifice for the greed or lust or power of another—just because of my own need to be of service to the Gods, and to be a sacrifice. Now I needed to find out if I could be in relation to my fellows without being this unconscious martyr.

I went into the world and watched carefully for my reaction to others and them to me. Many were glad to see me, since I had been away so long, but I realized that most people were busy taking care of their own needs and their own little worlds which were just as rich and busy and difficult for them as mine was to me. Now I listened to the antelope within me. I was like a careful animal observing and listening, and bounding away to my inner citadel or even physically away when there was too much danger of being assaulted. To my surprise, it worked well! My citadel was strong.

I went back and forth between my cabin in the mountains and my life in the world, for I knew that I had to have my Anahata, my citadel and my union and my strength and totality, in both worlds. Otherwise I would just be a fraud! I knew that I was a person who served the Goddess, not just the God, for I needed love and my relationships with people every bit as much as I needed to transform and be transformed by the Gods in my solitude. The Gods, after all, are to be found among us, are they not, and not just within us?

But, in the world I experienced much pain and fear, for my sensitivity had been increased by my meditations. Alone I experienced pain and fear as well, in addition to loneliness, uncertainty, despair, guilt, and so many of the other dark emotions which tended to make my light, my inner sun, go out.

Finally, I sat alone in my mountain cabin. I knew that I had my mandala, my Anahata continued, but still I did not see the face of the Goddess soften. I did not experience "Her heart softened with the drinking of nectar."

I sat in silence, in my lotus position. I sat in silence, determined, like the Buddha, not to be moved until the Gods really granted me the boons that their gestures had promised.

I now sat in the open, exposed to the elements. It was not that I was like the ancient gurus, proving my invulnerability to elements of heat, air, water, earth, or fire. No, it was merely that I felt the need to be exposed—not as a test. It is hard for me to explain. I felt stronger, was healthy and needed to be out in the elements. Know, only, that it was not a test, nor a challenge, but an openness.

Thus I sat for three days and nights. I think it was three days; I lost track after the first day. I was not troubled by the cold nor by the wind, nor by the rain, or heat. This, I think, was because I was so deeply immersed in my inner search and waiting. It was a passive search and an active waiting. It was just so. I had said my prayers—the Gods knew what I needed.

The third day, just when the sun was at its highest, the God appeared to move. The great Shiva-Isha smiled, or so it seemed to me. He pronounced the syllable Om and moved out of the great Throne in the firmament which He occupied. He came toward me and embraced me. As He embraced me, I felt an intense thrill which made me tingle as I never had before. My fingers trembled rapidly and my skin crawled. I moved and began a strange dance which I did not understand. Every pore of my body was undulating and vibrating at an enormously quick pace, yet my larger moments seemed to be slow and deliberate. I was like a great dancer, I am sure, though no one but the Gods was there to observe it. I had never danced in this way before nor since! It was a dance of and by the Gods that was miraculous. I danced, as I have said, with very fast movements of fingers and toes and pores and skin, but slow and deliberate motions of hands and arms and head, at the same time. My feet made a mandala. They formed the pattern of the whole Anahata, the gentle leaves, the smoky Star. For the last was left the central flame, the inner sun, the inner Shiva-Hamsa. At that point, my dance stopped and the syllables of word-music which accompanied me stopped as well.

Shiva-Isha smiled again. He lifted me, as if I had the weight of a small stone, and put me beside the pattern that my feet had traced. He then took a great stone lingam and placed it in the center, where the central flame was to be. At the same moment, he touched my chest and I felt as if a phallus were growing out of it. I looked down. It was no phallus, but the flaming power of the lingam was pulsating inside my heart.

At the same moment that I felt the flame in my heart, the stone lingam on the mandala spontaneously burst into flame. It was a miraculous sight! I felt the flame within and viewed the flame without. The winds blew, but the flame did not go out. My passion blew, but the flame did not go out.

Then Shiva-Isha became as one with Shiva-Hamsa, and I knew that the God without was the same as the God within, the Suns were the same. To my surprise, a gentle wind came, the sun went behind the clouds, the flaming lingam went out, and I felt my heart-flame stop. All was silent for several moments. It was as if death had filled the air. And then, just as it had gently gone out, behind the clouds and stilled, the flaming fire of the lingam, the sun, the candle in my heart, re-ignited. All was warm and light again. The God said nothing, but He smiled again. When He smiled, I was reminded of a dream I had when a great Guru, the outstanding one of my time, had died. In the dream there was a birthday cake, with many candles—about as many as had filled the years of the Guru. The candles were lit, and a gentle wind blew them out. In the next instant, the candles lit themselves again. I saw the Guru smile and I knew that there was immortality. The words of my dream came back to me now: "The flame goes out; but it comes on again!"

The warmth and wonder filled me all that day and into the night. It had rained a little, but the wetness merely added pleasure to the sensations playing upon my skin. At night, a crescent moon appeared. At what I would guess to be the midnight point, the witching hour, I saw the face of Shakti-Kakini in the moon. Her hands held the noose and the skull, and Her face was hard. I looked on in sorrow. Words formed in me:

"Oh, Goddess. I fear neither death nor silence. I long for peace, for softening. Would that nectar would soften Your heart as well. But I submit to You, and bow my head." As I bowed, the Goddess came down from the moon. She was like a little child in my arms and suckled at my breast. I do not know if there was, indeed, milk in me, but it felt so. The fluid which came out seemed like milk and semen and wine, all at once. I laughed, for I thought of myself as a strange sort of creature: a manufacturer of good things for the Gods. My gifts flowed freely from me to the Goddess, as it had flowed freely from the God to me. The Goddess was then back on her throne in heaven, gorgeous in Her golden beauty, with the many ornaments. I was stunned at Her glory, but She laughed and did the dance of the mandala which I had performed before. She danced with a grace and charm which was exhilarating and calming at the same time. I knew that the Goddess had been within me when I danced. The Goddess smiled again, and seemed to leap into the Anahata mandala.

She jumped to the "mental chakra" beneath, and clothed herself in the tree, the great Kalpa-Tree. I knew that She was showing me that She and the Tree were One. Then She hopped, as if it were a child's game, playfully, into the spot on the larger Mandala where Her image would appear. She made a crescent sign over the flame, and playfully did the same in my heart. The crescent moon over the fire—play and exhiliration and joy—is that what She meant? She nodded. These words came to me: "Play and Flow, Flow and Play." They conveyed the thought that Life was a woman's game, with play and flow of mother milk, and semen, and wine. We live it and suffer it and both give and take of it; it is all of and by the Goddess. The Fire is of the God, but the glow is of the Goddess.

I joined in the Dance of the Goddess. She and I were One. My eyes flowed and Her eyes flowed and the liquids flowed from everywhere. We danced, She and I, the Dance of Life, with great intensity and speed, and with great calm and deliberateness. We danced as the flame moved us, for now I knew what it meant to be "Unattackable." Anahata and I were One, and our Hearts were softened.

V

The joy and exhilaration which came from being freed from the bonds of Anahata, the liberation I felt in my achievement of my "citadel", did not last long. I went back into my life in Calcutta, to test my new-found condition and, within a very short time, the flame of the candle went out.

This is how it happened. One day, I chanced to meet a cousin that I had not seen for very many years. She was the daughter of my step-father's brother and we had never gotten on well together. As we greeted each other, she said, "You look just like your mother!" This annoyed me, though I thought—and said—"You look just like your mother." In truth I despised her mother. There had been something of a family feud throughout my childhood years, my own mother taking a bad beating emotionally from my father's relatives. Well, in short order, we were in painful talk. I am not sure what happened, but in retrospect I saw that I had fallen back into my childhood and had lost myself. I was reacting as a child to the aunt that I had despised, and also reacting from my mother's troubles with that family, not my own. The same was true when my cousin spoke badly about my father. It was true, what she said, but I grew angry and threw it back at her. I was again carrying the unexpressed animosity between the brothers never shown openly. This exchange overwrought me very much. I sheepishly felt that I had lost Anahata, and the heart of the Goddess was not softened. All the same, I returned to my cousin the next day and repaired the damage that had taken place. I told her what I thought had happened, and was able to listen to her views. It was better between us, more human, and I immediately felt the flame inside my citadel rekindle.

I returned to my mountain retreat in a chastened frame of mind. What was this strange wound which was so easily opened? Why was I so vulnerable to this dark act of the Goddess? How was it that I could cope at the vast cosmic level of the Goddess and failed rather miserably in my own childhood family? These rueful questions were with me, as I returned to my meditations. I felt that the "softening" had occurred, but there was something more that I needed to know from the Goddess, something that was not clear to me. It was with this attitude that I approached the next chakra, *Vishuddha.*

I reflected upon the meaning of Vishuddha, "Purification." Curious that purity should be beyond "unattackable." But this was surely true. There was still something impure in my mandala, was there not? My reaction to my cousin had proven it. Here, perhaps, my further liberation would include a purification.

I looked at the Lotus: A smoky purple with sixteen petals, each one carrying a vowel in crimson, of the Sanskrit language. Quite right, I thought, purple, the royal, religious color—blend of blue and red, perhaps it is beyond the smoky Anahata with its reds! All the vowels are here in crimson—this is the center of sound, speech, and hearing. These tattvas will be resolved herein it is said. The word, the word, the pure reality of the word, which is beyond the reality of the senses!

I looked further. Within the lotus is a circular mandala, "white like the full moon." Within that is the white elephant. A great and rare purification of the animal—the elephant has become white. I recalled a saying of a sage: at Vishuddha, one comes to the reality of the soul. Here what was started at Muladhara—with its "root support" of the elephant and square—comes the final transformation from the reality of everyday life (which is, in truth, illusory), to the reality of the soul. In Vishuddha we find "purification," the white elephant and the circle, more perfect forms. Grey changing to white, square to circle. Now, then, I could expect to find the reality of the soul.

Here, too, within the circular mandala of the moon was the Bija of Ambara. This reminded me that Ambara, the Ethereal region, made this Chakra a place of Akasha, of Ether, and the element herein was Ether. From Earth in Muladhara, through Water, Fire and Air, I now came to Ether. What was Ether, after all? I did not know. I knew only that its center was in the throat, and my throat was sore. I smiled. For my meditations always kept me close to my bodily centers, even though I did not follow the Masters exactly. I felt that the mightiest Guru, Shiva, was still with me.

I must still describe the Shiva and Shakti of the lotus. Herein, the Shiva is Sada-Shiva, the Beneficent One. He is snow white, three-eyed, five-faced, with ten beautiful arms and clothed in a tiger's skin. Here He is also "She" for He is Androgyne. In addition to His great male half on a lion seat, there is, too, "The Eternal Gauri", His other half, "the Mother of the Universe." I pondered. The unity has occurred, for here the Great God is united with His Goddess: He is white and silver, She is golden.

In addition to the Androgyne form, there is also another Shakti in the "lap" of the mandala. She is the Shakti Shakini, clad in yellow and carrying the noose, the goad, the "sign of the book" and she makes the Jnanamudra, by touching a thumb and first finger and placing them over the heart.

Such is the simple lotus. Simpler than before with only four verses describing it. Let it only be added that the Sadhaka, the meditator who attains the purification of this lotus, achieves, among other things, a vision of "the three periods" (past, present, and future), subjection of the inner senses, and becomes free from disease and sorrow. Above all, peace. Yes, that would be nice, thought I.

So, I meditated upon this Chakra. I felt the pain in my throat and fixed my eyes upon the image itself. My eyes fixed themselves upon the Shakti Shakini. I felt strangely sad, but was warmed by the goodly yellow color of Her garment. I looked ruefully at Her four arms, and ruefully understood that the noose and the goad were still very much there. I was continually goaded by my need for Nirvana, for Enlightenment, and my neck was much in the "noose". I was still very much tied to the process of the work, the yoke of the yoga. No wonder my throat was sore.

I nodded my head and saw the Goddess smile, ever so faintly. She took one of Her arms and made the Jnanamudra on my own heart, as if she already recognized that I had achieved the Anahata, and she was verifying it.

She nodded at my understanding, and showed me her other hand. There was a fluttering, for this was a beginning of the "sign of the book." Now the Shakti Shakini became very white, like light itself, and Her hand beckoned me to follow Her. My eyes did so and saw Her fade into the region which was not a place but a state. I saw clearly a lovely building, situated in a natural forest of great beauty. My eyes followed Her inside this building and I saw therein many, many books. She took down one book and nodded at me once again. At that moment, the petals of the mandala, with all its vowels, began fluttering, and I knew, too, that the whiteness and the region were of Akasha, the Ether. The petals leaped about and formed the vowels of Akasha. It was given to me to understand that the books were the records of Akasha, the library of the placeless state of Ether where all the deeds of one's past lives were kept. I realized that the Shakti Shakini kept the record of my previous lives. Each book contained the story of each of the lives. Some books were thick, some were thin. Some were gorgeous and had lush, golden bindings. Others were spare and drab. Still others were not of paper at all, but were picture books of animals or plants. There were numberless books. Not exactly numberless, for they were finite, but very many. I realized that I had lived many, many lives in many eons, and that here were kept the records of all of those lives. The record was kept for me to see, if I wished, or for another, if he was so inclined. But there was no record keeper. We all have our own libraries, or records of Akasha, in that Ethereal place which is no place, and we have merely to go there, when we are ready, through that Vishuddic center which lives in our own throats. For it tells us of the transmigrations of the soul.

I looked at some of the books of my previous lives. In my last one, I was a recluse philosopher in a Scandinavian land. I had dwelt long and deeply upon anxiety and despair and upon the meaning of God, but I had been afraid of women and had despised them. This was partly because I was abandoned in childhood by my mother, but this was also a consequence of unredeemed karma from previous lives.

In the lifetime before that, I had been a poet in England—a wild and romantic figure who had loved the ladies gaily and had hurt many a heart. My natural father of my present incarnation had been my son in that life, and I had left him to pursue an idealistic cause in Greece. There I died in violence. I realized that I had not done right by my son in that incarnation, nor by my natural father—the same person—in this incarnation, and that I must go and seek him out in England and make peace with him before I died. I saw, too, that the Greek lady who had been a friend of my sister had also been Greek at that time, and that we had a passionate love relation. It was a true love, hence her help for me at this time.

In the previous three lives, I had been a woman, an ordinary woman living in various parts of Asia. In China, I had suffered very much, losing several children in famines and wars. Two incarnations before that, in India, were not especially notable. These lives, as shown by the thinness and drabness of the books, were ones of karmic "ordinariness"—apparently teaching me to be prepared for the "specialness" of my past two lives.

Before those lives, I had been a temple courtesan in India, a prostitute in Greece and North Africa, a Catholic priest (austere and removed) in Germany, and variously a tradesman, farmer, wife of tradesmen and farmers in both Europe and Asia. The main tenor of my lives as they presented themselves, was a struggle between male and female, spirit and flesh, idealism and materialism, love and self-sacrifice—all destined to lead me to my task in the present. But before I come to what my task in the present was, I must say that I saw into further books, where there were pictures—no words. I had been, at various times, (and these had been my lives in Africa, Oceania, and America) animals, birds, insects, and plants.

These books were sad and beautiful, all at once. There was a great book of a hyena. I knew, from within, that the hyena was unjustly maligned as a scavenger, and that he is really a great figure, seeking his own game, and running only before the lion. In short, it is the lion who scavenges the game of the hyena, and not the reverse! Perhaps a scientist will note this one day.

I saw, too, my life of great anxiety as an insect. I knew that what a great Sage had said was not quite right. He had said that insects were, in reality, bits of plants and trees that had broken off and lived lives at a level between plant and animal. Well, he was not altogether wrong—in a sense he was correct, because they do meet midway. But in another sense, he was wrong. He implied that the insects do not feel or think. That is wrong. I saw the book of my lives as an insect, and I knew that I felt and thought—not with words but at a deeper place. One life, in particular, was very painful. I had been an insect with several legs, some of which I had lost in battle, and I lay, upside down, in great pain, waiting to die. I was terrified of death and longed for it at the same time! It was a deep hell, the karma of which had come from previous lives as an insect, and the effect of which lasted down even into the present. I had a deep knowledge of death and suffering, and needed to understand it ever more deeply, no matter what form of life I embraced.

I had also been a tree, and flowers, and therein, life was good. But life took on its problematic quality only as I advanced in evolution, up the scale of life toward the higher animals and being human. I understood that being human was in no way "better" than being a cat or a flower or a spider, only "different". All was part of God. All was part of the vast evolution of God and His creation. What mattered only was to live the best life as a flower or spider or hyena or man—which was to fulfill one's Karma. This I had done, aeon after aeon, for I was quite an old soul. But old souls are not better than young ones—we are all part of the great Brahman, the mind of God, which is, itself, undergoing evolution. I saw that in my present life I was ordained to repair much of the damage which had emerged during previous lives. I was destined to make a big advance in my development. I saw, furthermore, that I had been full of the agony of the life of woman, full of the agony of the pain of death, full of agony at the injustice of life. Now, in this life, I was destined to achieve the union toward which my heart and mind and soul had longed for many a long kalpa—that attainment of Nirvana, the enlightenment, which united the Gods with men.

Now I saw that the great image behind it all was the Androgyne Shiva—the union of the Great God with the Great Goddess of the Mother of the Universe, and all in one Golden-Silver form. To this great union the Universe sings.

I looked ahead to the future. The books of the future were there, too, but the pages were blank. It was as if many books were destined to be written here on this planet Earth but, as I advanced on my path, I would help write them more and more. I would more and more be responsible for what was written therein. For that is what it means to be human: we have greater share in our karma, its making and unmaking, than do the plants and insects, who have less will. But I saw, too, that evolution was not just in life and on this planet. There were books that hinted at other forms of being and evolution, on other planets and in other systems. These, too, stretched into the future. Time and space were annihilated for me as I glimpsed the records of Akasha spreading ever more deeply into the Ethereal regions.

My true Enlightenment was more than this glimpse of past, present and future. My true Enlightenment was that I did not really need to "know" all about my incarnations. It was enough that I was part of the divine plan, that there was growth, decay and new growth, and that we are all Gods. That is the message which I bring from my Enlightenment, that is my Vishuddha, my purification. We are all Gods, and ye are all Gods: man, animal, insect, flower, yea even stone, we are all Gods. With that realization, came Peace, which was promised by this Chakra. The Moon doth shine, the elephant glows in his whiteness, the syllables do mutter, and I know the Reality which is beyond this reality and all the realities—Shiva and Shakti are One.

VI

Ajna, the "Place of Command"; the last Chakra, since Sahasrara, the Lotus beyond it, the Sages have said, is not in the body at all. I felt Ajna, that "third eye" between the eyebrows, but I felt it as a cold in my head, and as a headache. So, when I sat down to meditate upon this highest of Chakras, I was cool as the moon, and quiet, but expectant, as well. For here, the Sages had promised, one met Vishnu, Himself.

I looked at the Lotus. Simple. White. A great round moon, with only two petals, white. No animals, not even the white elephant. A Sage had said that no animals meant that experience no longer required the animal reality. Something beyond the reality of the soul? One must wait and see.

Within the Lotus, what? First the Shakti, Hakini, white, with six faces and six arms, seated on a white lotus. She holds a rosary, a skull, a drum, a book, and makes the sign of the mudras, granting boons and dispelling fear. Above Her, in a triangle, the Shiva-Itara in His phallic form; above Him the Pranava, Om, as a flame of radiance. Above them, Manas, the mind, and above them all, in the region of the Moon, Shiva and Shakti, united.

The commentator says that one should meditate upon them all in that order. Now, for the first time, I have the deep desire to do just as the old Sages demanded, and I even wish to do the Yoni-mudra, to free the Manas, the mind, from the world outside. Does this mean that I am, at last, fully ready to submit to Shiva, to Vishnu, my Lord, as man, and as tradition says? I do not know, I go only step by step, as the Supreme Guru has instructed me. And so, I do as instructed: I put my left heel against the anus, and the right heel on the left foot. I sit erect with body and neck and head in straight line. I take in air and hold it. I close my earholes with thumbs, close eyes with index fingers, close nostrils with middle fingers, and close mouth with the rest. I keep the air within, and meditate upon the Mantra, the Pranava, Om, and thus, realize the unity of Prana, the vitality of life force, and Manas, the mind.

Yes, I feel it. I can say, with the Yogis of old, "This is Yoga, the favorite of Yogis!" The warmth of Kundali rises within me, from the centers below to Ajna, the place of command. My Guru commands, and I obey. I meditate, as prescribed, in the right order. Let me then look upon the Shakti-Hakini.

There She is, with Her many heads and many arms. I look at the rosary, and know that they symbolize Her prayerful, orderly attitude, and I know that I, too, now have it, and I have it from Her. I look at the skull, and know that I have embraced death, my humanity and my changing, just as She has embraced Hers. I look at the drum, and know that the sound of the drum is the sound of Om, and that my step beats to It, and to no other anthem of nation, caste or class. I look at the book, and know that wisdom is contained therein, the wisdom of Manas which I must come to know. I look at the mudras, and trust that I both give and receive boons, I both feel and dispel fear.

Now I look into the eyes of my six-headed Goddess. The heads move; they rock back and forth just like the dancers of my youth. I am enchanted and charmed by the movement. But, look! The six heads, like six Chakras, blend as they move, and I see that each is just a phase of the ONE, just as the six Chakras are just a phase of the One. Now the six become one head, and I look deeply into Her eyes. What I see there is both a shock and the most natural thing in the world. For what I see is my own face and my own head and my own body. I look into the face of the Goddess and I see my own. I know that I am the Shakti, and that She is me. I look into her face and I wonder, who has the reality? Is it I who dream of the Shakti and She a figment of my mind? Ah, now I know what the Sage meant when he said that here one goes beyond the animal reality, and beyond the reality of the soul: I am a content of a dream of a Goddess, and the Goddess is a content of a dream of mine. Both are the same. No more pain and sorrow, says the commentator, and such it is. For this knowledge places me beyond myself; pain is there, suffering is there, but it never shall be the same again. Oh, Shakti, I adore you!

Now I look beyond, to the triangle above, wherein dwells the Shiva-Itara, in His phallic form. Yes, I see Him, and I see the lightning sparks which emanate from His head, like the semen from below which rises to nostrils and unites in one strange whole. It is, as they say, the Mount of Meru; it is mountain and wings, with Snake wrapped around; it is the western Caduceus of Mercury. Now, I see it, and my headache goes and my cold vanishes. But what is this lightning-like union? Is it healing alone? What is this phallic staff with snake wrapped around and flaring nostrils above? The wings above and snake below. Phallus and nares; semen and air. I cannot tell until I look above, to the great flaming candle and fire which is just above it. Now, out of the brilliant light, I see my Lord. I finally see in naked flesh, my Supreme Guru who has guided me throughout my yoga, my meditation and my trials. Oh, Lord Shiva, I see you and I know! I know that Your light is blinding but true: for you are eagle and snake, wings and body, semen and air, spirit and flesh. And I know, too, what it means that You are Vishnu, the Preserver, and Shiva, the Destroyer, for behind it is Brahman, the Creator. The Two are One, and the Three are One. Oh, my Lord Vishnu, I am ravished by you as Krishna, mighty singer. Come to me, for I am your Shakti! I am enflamed, enveloped and enraptured, for I know, above and below, and am Queen of the three worlds!

But I will not dwell in this ecstasy, oh, my Lord. For my embrace with You and Your radiance enables me to ascend to that Great eye of Ishvara, the Supreme God who is beyond all creation and dissolution and who is one and the same with Your Trinity of Vishnu, Shiva, and Brahman. I know from your embrace that Your three-fold form is the same as the One, and exists only as You descend into Being. Shine, now, your light of Manas upon me, and enlighten my mind. Show me the pure light of Buddhi.

With my prayer and self-abnegation, I waited a long time, perhaps several hours. And then, in the dim light, I saw a wizened old man. He was a combination of Gandhi, a Sage I once met, and an old monkey. He held up first a magnifying glass, then a telescope. "One eye has each, to make the small big and the distant near. But the one eye of wisdom has to see the 'smaller than small, bigger than big' and that, of course, is Purusha, the Atman, the Self."

This is what the little old man said to me, and then he went on: "Wisdom is not great bundles of facts, nor big words which hide their meaning. Wisdom is Consciousness: to see with the inner eye, the eye of the mind. And that is Ishvara, a creative consciousness. Do you know why it is creative? Because it is to be found only in Ajna. The Shakti here loves to eat of the marrow of the bones. Creative consciousness is the power of the mind along with the marrow of the bones; wings and snake, semen and air. Do you remember your incarnation as a hyena? Yes. Well, then, you know that hyenas have the strongest jaws of all animals, stronger even than the lion. For they can chew the marrow and digest the deepest inner contents. And that is what wisdom is: to know and sense in the bones; to chew one's experience down to the depths of the marrow. If one, then, also sees with the inner eye, then that is all, that is what it is: creative consciousness of Ishvara.

"One must get to Ajna to see it. Kundalini Yoga is not the only way. Many do it in other ways. Look in the bazaars. Look at men. Many have achieved it. Many have gone from Muladhara through Anahata. But in Ajna, you must know, one must rise and see, as well as live and experience." The old man went on speaking:

"Brahma, Vishnu and Shiva are the names for functions of the one Universal consciousness operating in ourselves. Yoga is our means of transforming the lower into the higher forms of this same consciousness. In this, Shiva and Shakti serve you, and you serve Shiva-Shakti.

"But what are Shiva and Shakti? All that is manifest is Power, and that is Shakti. Shakti, the Power, is Mind, Life, and Matter. But there is no Power without a Power-holder. And what is that Power-holder? It is none other than Shiva. Power is Shakti, the Great Mother of the Universe; the Form is Shiva. Together they are Consciousness (Mind), Being (Life), and Bliss (Matter). 'Isness' is the ultimate reality, beyond all form and power, which is what these three connote. They become particular, and thus limited, in the many. The One is the Isness, the Many is the Isness become manifest. Do you understand?"

I thought I understood and I nodded. The old man continued. "I am not so sure. Maya. Your name. Your namesake. Maya is not illusion, any more than you are illusion. In the words of the Shakta Sadhaka Kamalakanta, Maya is the Form of the Formless. You, Maya, are the living reality of the Formless taking Form. And you, and all men, are the Power-holders. All is real: Changeless and Changeful, Activity and Rest, Being and Becoming. Man, in his Mind and Body, is the manifestation of Shiva and Shakti, Power and Power-holder. The object of his worship and his Yoga is to raise this Power to its perfect expression, to raise his own particular and limited experience to the unlimited and whole, and thus to Perfect Bliss. But his yoga is also to bring the Whole and unlimited into the particular, so that the One can become the Many, and evolve.

"And why must it evolve? Because that is the nature of its opposites. Creation and dissolution, activity and rest. World after

World, and Kalpa after Kalpa. All is energy, the Shiva of static energy, the Shakti of kinetic energy. All is potential that must come into being.

"The particular power whereby the dualistic world is brought into being is Maya-Shakti, which is both a veiling and projecting. Consciousness veils itself to itself and projects from the store of its previous experiences. This projection is Samskara, the world in which it suffers and enjoys. The universe is thus the creative imagination of the Supreme World-Thinker, Ishvara. That is why you are both dream and dreamer, Maya. Thus the Self knows and loves the Self."

At that point, I needed to pause and understand what this old man was telling me. If I understood rightly it was none other than that Karma was the effect of previous experiences. My Karma was the result of previous experiences which projected my life further into the world. That is the witch of Shakti. She veils and projects, and that is my life. It is Maya, and illusion, but the true reality as well. Little by little I would eat up my Karma by absorbing the marrow in my bones. I would integrate all my experiences and projections, and be projected no more. But I was in no hurry. There were many lives for that. And eternity as well, for more lives and beings and more consciousness.

I suddenly grew weary with the lives and beings and consciousness. I felt I wanted to flee from the Samskara of suffering. I wanted Nirvandva, freedom from life and the opposites. My Guru spoke again:

"Maya, you can flee whenever you wish. There is the bliss of sleep, dreamless and total. That is a Nirvandva. There is the fleeing to the to the dream, in which the subtle body lives. And then there is your gross body, with all its states and degrees of differentiation. But the best fleeing is Yoga, the magic when you are with the inner eye of manas. It is the yoke which brings freedom.

"There is no need to throw one's eyes into the heavens to find God. He is within. Whatever of Mind or Matter exists in the universe exists in some form or manner in the human body. As stated in the Vishvasara Tantra: 'What is here is there. What is not here is nowhere.'"

I thought about what the Guru said. Yes, man is the microcosm of the great macrocosm. The body is matter and mind is the consciousness of that same matter. Together they live in life. I understood the magic. But I missed the bliss.

Then I felt myself rising, even beyond the great Eye of the Guru. I was gently rising above the wisdom of consciousness. I rose to the place where Shiva and Shakti were in union. I watched them in Maithuna. They were in sexual union and I felt a thrill go through me. I knew that there was, indeed, something higher than Consciousness, higher even than what the Guru had told me. Because higher than consciousness was the Bliss of Love and of Union. Then I saw my vision. I saw that Shiva and Shakti were two seeds in a gram. The sheath of this gram, this chick pea, was Maya, the world as appearance. And the whole, made One. I was that chick pea contained in the Great Maya. But I, little Maya, contained the seeds of Shiva and Shakti. I felt them embraced within me, and I felt the thrill of their perpetual union. I knew that when they were united there was the bliss of Nirvandva, and when they parted there was the bliss of creation. With Creation, came Form. . . .with Brahma, comes Vishnu and Shiva. Shakti takes form in Shiva. I cannot say more. I feel it in the marrow of my bones, and I thrill.

At that moment, my own personal, particular Kundalini rose and merged with the great Kundali. The power of the Shakti rose beyond Ajna, and I felt it at the top of my head, and round my scalp like a thousand vibrating petals, each with a thrill of wonder.

It went above the head, like a halo. I knew that the Chakras were all pierced and now there was *Sahasrara.*

There was the glimpse of the Void, the Shunya which is secret and subtle like the ten millionth part of the end of the hair. All opposites were united, and there was no division. But I could not stay there. The Kundalini did not stay in the Sahasrara, but immediately began to descend, down into Ajna, back into Vishuddha, and all the way down through wonderful Anahata, Manipura, Svadhisthana, to the root support of Muladhara. I could not keep Kundalini there, in Sahasrara, and I knew that I would need many, many transformations before Kundalini would permanently stay there. Only then would I achieve final Liberation, true Mukti. Only then will the union of Sada-Shiva and Chit be complete. But I did not mourn. And I do not mourn. I celebrate Shiva-Shakti. I know that all centers are needed. I know Shiva-Shakti are present in every human act. I celebrate every act as a ritual and a worship. I glory in the Muladhara as much as the great Anahata or Ajna. For the body is Shakti. Its needs are Shakti's needs. When I take pleasure, Shakti enjoys through me. The Spirit is Shiva, and it creates form. Shiva and Shakti are one. I embrace my humanity and my limitation, for the process is the goal.

With that, I came down from my cabin in the mountains. I celebrated my family, for I had been gone for most of three years. I went to visit my natural father in England and to give and receive blessings. I lived, for I knew that I had achieved Enlightenment. I knew that each Enlightenment would be more than the last, and that each act of the Yoga of Kundalini, whether alone in the mountains or in the Karma of Life would be greater than the last, but also the same as before, for all was one.

But before I could fully take up my life again, I slept and awakened here. So, my friends, I find myself here among you. I see the Great Tree of which you speak. I see thereon the many symbols of my own voyage and dhyana. The Tree itself is Mount Meru and the Snake doth wrap around it. I can see all your wanderings therein. My friends, we are here together, why, I know not, but I embrace you!

THE OLD CHINESE MAN

THE OLD CHINESE MAN

I

Greetings. My name is Ch'ien Ching. Until I was strangely transported to this place, I lived for some years on Taiwan. As one can see, I am no longer young, having celebrated my seventy-fifth birthday almost one year ago. Contrary to the usual experience of old age, much has taken place in the short time of one year. In youth one feels that the days are long, that time is endless and that one will never come to be eight or ten or sixteen or twenty-one years old, on a par with all the grown ones. With age, as everyone knows, the days and years rush by and one does not realize that one is forty or fifty or seventy-five, because one still feels as he did at twenty or thirty. Yes, we all are familiar with these common truths, but it is the reverse with me. The past twelve months (tomorrow I shall be seventy-six) have been very full and deep ones for me, yet the time has passed more slowly than during any comparable period of my life.

I shall tell the story of that year—for such seems to be the reason that I have been transported here.

I celebrated my seventy-fifth birthday alone with my wife, K'un, who is also old, but three years younger than myself. I was glad that we could be together, that we had passed more than fifty years in a rich and creative union, yet I was sad. I was not troubled by the prospect of death, for there my feelings coincided with those of a Western poet, who said, when celebrating his seventy-fifth birthday:

> I have warmed both hands before the fire of life;
> It sinks and I am ready to depart.

His sentiments were similar to mine on that matter, though I did not echo the first part of his poem: "I strove with none, for none was worth my strife." Unlike this gentleman, I battled much in life and regretted none of it, for I was vital and alive and creative.

No, I was not sad because of the approach of death. Part of my sadness was because none of my six children could be with me on my birthday. But let me tell you my story, and you will see why I was sad.

I, my wife, and all my children were born in Shanghai. I was an educated man, teaching English in a private high school, but also heir to a considerable amount of money left me by my father, who had been an able businessman. Our lives were typical of the period between the Boxer Rebellion (as Westerners call it) and the final victory of the Communists. We survived Westerners, feudalism, warlords, rebels, Japanese, poverty—all of it, and in very good fashion. I myself had a bridge between West and East, and my wife was my totally loyal and devoted helpmeet. Having to flee in the face of the Communists, we were still able to carry much with us to Taiwan and I was able, also, to continue my work as a teacher of English. Now that the Americans were so much in evidence, my skills were even more in demand. So, we managed. But now to my children.

My eldest son (I think now, with a chuckle, of calling him Number One Son, which would amuse those Westerners among you who know of that great detective, Charlie Chan; I chuckle because I know of that clever man, but my Number One Son would not chuckle, would despise this "Western and debased" use of literature) – my eldest son, whose name is Chen, is a devoted Communist. He was always a thunderous, aggressive, strong youth, like a green bamboo. From an early age he was against all things Western, with the exception of Marxism, and was eager to build a new utopia in China. He was never hostile to us, his doting parents, but he had a strong will of his own. He was a leader very early, and one saw the star on his forehead. He became quite prominent in Communist circles and was away from us for most of his adult life, participating in the Long March, the battles, and the revolution. When the time came for a decision between coming with us, who opposed Communism, and staying with his comrades, there was no doubt; he followed the Communist spirit. That he saw as the right path, the rising of spring, the new era. I was not so sure, but I respected him. I was sad only because we were now going to be cut off from each other for the foreseeable future. For many years has it been so. No word from my son, and yet I know that he is active in the New China.

My second son, K'an, is indeed a different sort. He is a dark, abysmal kind of man, but canny and clever. In his ambiguity, he is more like his mother and my father, but he is uniquely himself in his melancholic nature, his cynicism, and also in his endurance. He became a businessman, like my father, successfully survived warlords, Japanese, and Communists in Shanghai, and now plies his trade in Hong Kong. He is quite wealthy, but sick in spirit in my opinion. He would sell opium as well as tea, if there were a profit. In a sense, he is the victim of the old-new China, lingering on with his cleverness, surviving with his hardness, but withall, sick in spirit. On my birthday, he sent greetings, but there was no love in it.

My youngest son, Ken, is yet again different from the others. He is a quiet one, a sturdy one, a knotty tree, and a black-billed bird. From early in life, he showed a religious nature, quietly intense, with a mystical streak. He was indulged by his mother even more than our eldest, but was not spoiled. He and I had the best understanding between us of all my sons, strangely enough. I say "strangely" because Ken became a Catholic priest, which was a great surprise to us all. He was a devoted Benedictine, spending his life in study and teaching, as well as in meditation. He went to America with his Order when they were expelled from Communist China. He is a mountain, and true, and has complained little in life. Besides his priestly duties, he carves in wood, using old branches and stumps of trees. In this he is closer to his Chinese heritage. He greeted me on my birthday, and I detected in his letter that he, too, was feeling that the world was changing, that even his beloved Church might not carry its best spirit into the future if there was going to be a future. He seemed to be retreating more and more into himself and his sculpture. He, even he, my last son, showed sadness of spirit.

My eldest daughter, Sun, is gentle, loving, and persevering. She has been a perfect daughter to both my wife and myself, and a fine helpmeet to her mate. She is a practical woman, who has been good for her hopelessly romantic and anachronistic husband. He is a poet and a painter who scratches out a meager living, but they survive very well with Sun's economies, and our little help. Sun has grown old and somewhat dispirited. Her husband becomes more pathetic, though we all love him. They seem to embody a wifely devotion, on her side, and an artistic sense, on his, which are less valued in the contemporary world. They, their children, and grandchildren live also on Taiwan, near us, but they could not be here for my birthday.

Li, my second daughter, is a bright and clear-eyed one. She has the most penetrating vision of the times of all my children. She is clever, a fighter, married to a general, but feminine. She has lived well, advised her husband shrewdly, taken proper care of her children (though this was more intelligent and well ordered than warm), and continues to be active in the life of the expatriates, here on Taiwan. For this is what we all are here, even though the Taiwanese are nominally Chinese. In honor of my birthday, my daughter Li sent me formal greetings, a beautiful pre-Ming wooden sculpture of Confucius with a disciple, and a new edition of the *I Ching,* in English translation. In so commemorating the event, she demonstrated her bright capacity to do what is right and correct and well received. The sculpture is handsome, showing my esteemed Confucius riding upon an ox, thus linking him with the great Ox-Herding Pictures which I so value. The *I Ching,* that great and ancient Book of Changes, has always been a treasure for me, as Li knew and to give it to me in English, showing her appreciation for my studies in and appreciation of English—well, it is like a splendid cup of tea. Tea: all the grace of our old civilization, but somehow merely correct, ritualistic, formalistic, and as alive as our old generals on Taiwan, dreaming of a return to mainland China, but destined to merely die. I love Li, but we cannot tell each other the truth that we know.

Lastly, there is Tui, my youngest. She, the joyous and deep one. She, the strange mixture of happy sensuality—seductive in its depth—and innocent merriment, deceptive in its gaiety. She, too, had gone to the West, but out of desire, not as an exile. She studied and became a doctor, and also married a Westerner. He is a Jew from Malta, and they now live in Israel, where she joyously attends to wounds, physical and spiritual, of children. Whenever I see her, I am made more joyous, but now, when she is so far away, and it is so many yeras, she lives more in my memory than in actuality.

And so, despite having six healthy children and a fine wife of fifty years, on my seventy-fifth birthday I was sad. I was sad because my children could not be with me, but mainly because not only my life, but also their lives were tenuous and uncertain. I felt that we were all living at a time of the end of the world. Certainly it was the end of old China, and an end of what had been meaningful in the West, as well. I felt my own sadness as a melancholy of the time. China was dead, but the West was dead, too. I would soon die, perhaps, but all else was dying. I felt that both the world and myself needed renewing, but the renovation was not there, neither for my children, nor for me. How could the renewal occur, I wondered, and what could I do to further it.

I sat in my room, in my quietness, and pondered, "What can further it?" I smiled for this sounded like the words of the book that my daughter Li had given me, the *I Ching.* Sometimes the Oracle says, when asked a question, "Nothing furthers." Was this how it was with me and the world, I wondered, "Nothing furthers?" I did not know.

I desultorily looked at the *I Ching,* Book of Changes. Here was an old friend indeed. The old text, dating back to King Wen and his son, the Duke of Chou, three thousand years ago, had been wise and great. It embodied the greatness of Chinese wisdom, did it not? I thought of the Commentaries of Confucius, that he brought to *I Ching* only very late in his life. The great Master did not even allow himself to study the wisdom of the Book of Changes until he was almost as old as myself, seventy. Even the greatest of the great, Lao-tse, had embroiled himself in the *I Ching.* His followers, with all their codified Yins and Yangs, making of new systems, and their rigidities, almost destroyed the greatness of *I Ching.* I thought, too, of the Western Bible and its greatness, and how, I think, some of the Talmudists almost destroyed it also. But that great Book, like our great Book, survived the strictures of systems and dogmatisms and superstition, as well. We had much in common, old Jew and old Chinese. I once heard a Westerner say that the Jews were the Chinese of Europe. I cannot say whether that is true, but I do know that we are ancient peoples. I am also aware that both Jews and Chinese have treasured family, order, wisdom, and right conduct. We have also been very clever, all the others say, do they not? And we will also be here when they get over their heresies, will we not? Then I had to laugh, for Chinese and Jews are arrogant, are we not?

Beyond arrogance, our ways part. For we, in China, are with male and female, Yin and Yang, and with the union thereof. We are with the Tao, that line of T'ai Chi which unites the opposites, which gives meaning and links a person to heaven and earth. Yes, as the masters have said, there is Heaven, there is Earth, and there is Man. There is the Tao of each, and the Tao of Man in relation to the Tao of Heaven and Earth. We have a triangle of Heaven, Earth, and Man, and a duality of Yin and Yang, and they all meet in Tao. For us no double-triangled star, no six-sided figure! Now I had to laugh at the irony. For our *I Ching,* our great Book, is itself made up of sixes, of the hexagrams, is it not? Of course! That great Sage, Shao Yung, has ordered it for us, has he not? He started with the primary lines, Yang and Yin, firm and yielding, light and dark. Then he added to each again a light and a dark line, obtaining four two-line patterns:

```
——     - -     ——     - -
——     - -     ——     - -
```

Above each of these he added a light line and again, alternately, a dark line, making eight trigrams. Shao Yung did not know this, of course, but the eight trigrams also contain me and my wife and my six children, for such are their names! By chance? By design? Or by Tao? I do not ask, but here they are, we are:

☰	☱	☲	☳
Ch'ien The Creative	Tui Joyous, Lake	Li Clinging, Fire	Chen Arousing
☴	☵	☶	☷
Sun The Gentle, Wind	K'an The Abysmal	Ken Keeping Still Mountain	K'un The Receptive

But Shao Yung went further and made the trigrams into fours and fives in the same way, and finally came to the six lines, the hexagrams! So we, we Chinese, have sixes after all, just like the Jews! But our sixes are different, as Shao Yung showed us, for he arranged them in a natural order, of a square of hexagrams, eight times eight, thus sixty-four. These can be arranged as a square, counting from right to left (just like the Hebrews, again!), and from below upward. The hexagrams can also be a circle, Shao Yung showed us. We arrange them as the Sequence of Earlier Heaven, "earlier" meaning transcendent, *a priori*, and before the beginning of time.

Shao Yung was very great, indeed. Was it only chance that the Western philosopher, Leibniz, came upon Yung's schema and found it the same as his own recently discovered binary system in mathematics? Or do East and West meet in Tao?

So my reflections brought me back to the *I Ching*. I thought further about it. The great Book had been a book of wisdom, a book of character development, but also a book of oracles. Many times I had come to it in search of answers to questions about right conduct at difficult times. Always it had been helpful. Always I was enlightened about my path. I was no doubt a "right man" to receive it and interpret it, for I was, as they say, open to the forces and their meaning. But in recent years, I had been angry with the *I Ching.* It had seemed, more and more, like a rigid old man. When I would pose questions, I would get the same old statements with, what seemed to me, "moralizing" about good and evil. Indeed, it had seemed more Christian and Western and rigid than before. . . .I laughed again, this time painfully. Was that rigidity in me? Was I the old, inflexible man reading his own hardness, sterility, and darkness into this book? Perhaps.

I looked now to the English edition of this ancient text. It was very great indeed, collating all the important writings, separating and combining them with the careful scholarship of the German Sinologue, the expressive language of the English lady-translator. And the introduction of the great Western Psychologist. He was, perhaps, greatest of all. With his clear mind of scientific cast, he had gone even further than our Sages. All of us Chinese had used the book as an oracle for ourselves; the sages had made commentaries. But this wise man used the book as an oracle for *itself.* That was especially clever of him. His foreword showed his respect for our ancient book, and his tact in speaking about the text as an "old gentleman" was shrewd and delicate. Rather Chinese, even. But I thought that this was not enough. It was not enough, at least for me. For I was Chinese, and knew the West, and was old. I, perhaps, had more in common with this old man of Chinese thought, and I was angry with "him". I was angry because "he" had seemed like a man even more rigid and old than myself. Here he was, like me, with a "wife" and six "children"—a family of eight trigrams.

Thus, in a way, my identity and that of the *I Ching* were joined. Yet this venerable man was three thousand years old! He was both very ancient, and here, in this new form approaching the West, young and eager! He was old, and longing to be "renewed", as was I. Perhaps we could talk together.

I became very excited. I thought: the *I Ching* has been a book of wisdom and a great oracle. The Westerner has gone further and asked it about itself. Now, can I not go further yet, and engage the great Old Man in dialogue? Can I not approach it, as a human being, and have it react to me? Why can't we just talk back and forth, in some kind of equality and mutual need? For without people, the old book becomes rigid and a mere repository of magical words. I am sure it wants to be something more than sheer projections of the questioner! Perhaps I am just the one who is suited to have such a dialogue with it because I am, on a small scale, like it!

I hung back then, startled at my presumption. What an inflation! Did I think that I was Lao-tse, or Confucius, or Jung? I sighed. No, it did not have to be that. If, as Jung said of our time, that the Gods truly want to become totally men, then I was not so presumptuous, for I was a man, was I not? Yes. I would try. I would ask the *I Ching* if it were willing to engage in dialogue with me.

"*I Ching*, great Book of Wisdom, I come to you as an old man, as one in need of renewal. You already know that, and know that my being is similar to your own. Perhaps you also know that I think that you need renewing; you have as much as admitted it to the great Psychologist. I propose that we talk together with the aim of renewing ourselves. For how can you be renewed without me? I am only one, but with the one person in the right Tao, everything can be changed. Do you not, yourself, say this somewhere? Do you agree?

With that prayerful, yet assertive, request, I threw the coins for the oracle, and this is what I got: I threw four straight sevens, all firm lines. The fifth throw was ambiguous. When I first looked at the coins, it seemed like an eight, but when I looked again, it was a seven. I did not know what to do. I then threw the last time, and got a nine. I resolved to use both resulting hexagrams, for the meaning of the moment, perhaps, was that both were called for. This is what emerged:

9 ——	(1)	9 ——	(14)
7 ——		8 – –	**Possession in**
7 ——	**The**	7 ——	**Great Measure**
7 ——	**Creative**	7 ——	
7 ——		7 ——	
7 ——		7 ——	

The first hexagram with all firm Yang lines was purely Ch'ien, the Creative, Heaven, above and Creative, Heaven, below. Two trigrams with my name in them! One might almost think of it as a deception. But then it occurred to me that the Ch'ien above was the *I Ching* itself, and the Ch'ien below was my poor unworthy self! Yes, almost too good to be true! This was reinforced by "The Judgment" which says: *"The creative works sublime success, Furthering through perseverance."* Further reinforcement came from "The Image" which says: *"The movement of heaven is full of powers. Thus the Superior man makes himself strong and untiring."*

The *I Ching* supports me, and tells me to be untiring. What joy! But then I look at the changing line, nine at the top, which says: *"Arrogant dragon will have cause to repent."*

Now I collapse, for this is exactly what I feared. "Only too good to be true" was just that. Now I fall from my perch and from my excitement, and am chagrined by the comment which the Duke of Chou has provided and the old and powerful *I Ching* has thrown at me: I am the arrogant dragon flying too high! All right then, I am humbled. What say the Commentaries?:

"When a man seeks to climb so high that he loses touch with the rest of mankind, he becomes isolated, and this necessarily leads to failure. This line warns against titanic aspirations that exceed one's power. A precipitous fall would follow."

Oh, so true. But I do not want to be God, like some Western devil, I want only that the old king, the God, become humanized!

Before I deeply ponder this message, let me look at the other hexagram, which I seemed to throw at the same time, number 14, *Possession in Great Measure.* In it Li, the Clinging, Flame, is above, and Ch'ien, the Creative, Heaven, is below. It is as if my daughter, who gave me the gift of *I Ching* is above me, and I am below. What does it say? The Judgment: *"Possession in Great Measure. Supreme Success."* The Image: *"Fire in heaven above: The image of Possession in Great Measure. Thus the superior man curbs evil and furthers good, and thereby obeys the benevolent will of heaven."*

Ah, here *I Ching* smiles on me, but let us see what the changing line of nine at the top has to say.

"He is blessed by heaven.
Good fortune.
Nothing that does not further."

The Commentary says: *"In the fullness of possession and at the height of power, one remains modest and gives honor to the sage who stands outside the affairs of the world. By this means one puts oneself under the beneficent influence descending from heaven, and all goes well."*

Confucius says of this line:

"To bless means to help. Heaven helps the man who is devoted; men help the man who is true. He who walks in truth and is devoted in his thinking, and furthermore reveres the worthy, is

blessed by heaven. He has good fortune, and there is nothing that would not further."

Oh, all this is too much! The Old One both throws me down and lifts me up! He behaves like a God! But that, perhaps, is what he is, indeed. I am warned against arrogance, and encouraged to proceed, devotedly, in truth, and to give honor to the Sage, probably the I Ching itself. I must take this all in and reflect, and read the Commentaries.

I was very agitated by these momentous judgments of *I Ching*. It was a long time before I could calm myself and gather in the impressions which it had made. I worked hard on the words of the Commentaries, trying to absorb them deeply into my being. I walked in nature, in the rain, which refreshed me, and in the sun which warmed me. I was quiet much of the time. I also went about my daily activities, but no one, not even my wife, knew of the great task that I had taken upon myself.

One night I had a dream. In my dream I saw a large mushroom, growing in a great rain forest. The mushroom had a fine round top and a thick stem. I was informed that the mushroom was the *I Ching*. Yes, it "was" the *I Ching*, an identity, not an analogy. I could view the mushroom from above, in which case I could see its roundness, and could see it like the roof of a house, the occupants living underneath. From this standpoint, the mushroom was an ordered and delicate mandala, with contents hidden, and I was above it and large. Or, I could view it from below—that is, inside it. In this case it resembled an umbrella, which protected me against heavy rains. Now I could look up and see the ceiling of the mushroom as an ordered pattern of delicate strands, like an intricate and regular spider web. It was open to the elements on the sides, but I could not see heaven. Here I was small, but warm and cozy, protected by the *I Ching.* The dream told me that I could have both views, that both standpoints were correct.

There was something else about the mushroom, however, that was not so clear. The stem and a part of the "wall," which was also the ceiling, twisted about itself so that "inside" was "outside" and "outside" was also "inside". But this was true of only part of the stem, not all of it. Here, I think, I was being told that there was an area where "inside"—what was going on in my own soul, and my immediate life—had an identity with "outside"—with what was happening on a larger scale, in the nation, in the world. But this was true only in part of the "stem" and in part of the "wall-ceiling". I did not fully comprehend that distinction except to observe that not all moments are "meaningful" or in Tao, where inside and outside are the same. There are such things, as the West had taught us and we already knew, as cause-and-effect, and separation of opposites. Of course; if this were not so, how would we know of the Tao, at all? Yes, that was it.

What did it mean that one could look at the mushroom from above and not see the stem or the "family;" or look at it from "below" and not see the sky-blue heaven? I thought I was beginning to grasp it. It had to do with the ego. If I were "inside" I could lean on the "stem" which was upright and manly like myself, and the structure of the mandala-hexagram-family would protect me from the potent rush of the heavy floods of heaven. If I were above it, I would be open to such floods and vulnerable to the direct, unmediated action of heaven itself! It was like being helped by a mediator-priest-book or being one's own mediator-priest-book. The psyche was telling me that both were true.

Now I could rejoice. Before I had angry thoughts about that rigid old man Ching who had called me arrogant. Now I had a view which helped me to accept this fine old man. *I Ching* was a mushroom! I could view him from above, and be even greater than he, alone with heaven, but then I would miss his inner richness. Or I could look from below and use him as a treasureful mediator, and be much supported, but could not, then, feel the rain. The psyche, telling this, was greater than either the *I Ching* or my ego. I was happy and could accept that mushroom as a sacred one. I smiled then, for I recalled that my son, Ken, from America, had told me that the youth there were eating such mushrooms and that it tended to free them from their narrow views, to "blow their minds" as he picturesquely put it. Yes, the *I Ching* was a mushroom, and the Tao, which is behind it, "blows our minds!"

I was no longer angry with my friend, *I Ching*, and I could look at the Commentaries. What did they say?

First, the German Sinologue, Sage that he was, said: *"In relation to the universe, the hexagram expresses the strong creative action of the holy man or sage, of the ruler or leader of men, who through his power awakens and develops their higher nature."* A wise saying, expressing Ch'ien above and below better than anything one has heard.

Now the great Confucius takes the Judgment of King Wen, and comments according to four cardinal virtues of Chinese ethics.

"Great indeed is the sublimity of the Creative, to which all beings owe their beginning and which permeates all heaven." Here is the first virtue, "sublimity", which in our Chinese language means "head", "origin", and "great;" this is the generative power and our main virtue of all, humaneness and love.

Second, after sublime, is "success", which is, says the Sinologue, how the sublime (which lies beyond, in the form of ideas) becomes manifest in life. This is how the master Confucius says it:

"The clouds pass and the rain does its work, and all individual beings flow into their forms."

I smile, for I feel as if the Master has had the same "mushroom" dream as myself. For "success" is the gift of water, the water of life, which causes "the germination and sprouting of all living things." We know that they must take some form. Now I understood "success"—how can I say it? The word is from our character Li. That is like mores or customs, or manners—an area in which I have always suffered from constraint. But "li" also means "weapons" and, most fundamentally, true piety, a religious attitude towards life. It is surely morality and propriety, but, as our Master has told us elsewhere, in the superior man, morality functions from within—only the inferior man is governed by worldly law.

This leads to the third virtue, "justice", associated with "furthering." Confucius says:

> *"Because the holy man is clear as to the end and the beginning, as to the way in which each of the six stages completes itself in its own time, he mounts on them toward heaven as though on six dragons."*

Here the Master means the lines, and the six stages of fulfillment of the creative. I felt, at once, that I, to reach my creativity, my true being as Ch'ien, had to connect with the six children of my own generation, and those of the *I Ching.* I felt, too, that my "arrogance" was to leap too quickly to the end. My intuition always went further than my reality, I lamented. *"Furthering of justice, in which each receives that which accords with his being, that which is due him and constitutes his happiness,"* brought to mind my eldest son, the Communist, Chen, for this was a Communist idea, was it not?

Now there came to me a vision of the virtues as expressions of my children and, indeed, the children of *I Ching:* "Sublimity", with its love and humaneness, and greatness and origin, was surely to be found with my third son, Ken, the priest. "Success", with its weapons, water, order, clarity, and religious devotion was surely with Li, my second daughter. "Furthering," with its justice, I saw, would belong to Chen, my eldest son.

And what of the final virtue, wisdom, which is to be found with "perseverance"? This wisdom, this knowing the laws, those laws beyond the worldly laws, which bring peace and harmony, which child is with that?

Ah, it is Peace, which is hexagram number 49, T'ai, and it is K'un, the Receptive, Earth above, and Ch'ien the Creative, Heaven, below. No child, but the union of Heaven and Earth, of me with my wife, then there is Peace!

This is the last comment of Confucius: *"He towers high above the multitude of beings, and all lands are united in peace."* The power of the holy man, when he occupies a ruling place, makes it possible for everything to take its appropriate place, and that is "peace," but only after the four virtues are completed. I do not know the child which carries the fourth virtue of "perseverance" and wisdom, for Peace, as I have found, is not my child at all, but Heaven and Earth, Wife and Husband.

Then the fourth virtue must surely be of Sun, my eldest daughter. For she has the clarity of Li, and her devotion, as well, and she perseveres and endures as do none, not even myself. So, this gentle, penetrating wind, that it is which perseveres, and is wise, for it sees into all darkness and breaks up the intrigues.

So I had my vision: the six creative steps (uniting with my children), the four cardinal virtues (love, piety, justice, and wisdom) and I understood what *I Ching* wanted me to understand. If I could accept the problem of the Creative, if I could reduce my arrogance of striving too high, I would indeed achieve its other promise of "Possession in Great Measure."

I walked happily in the streets and in the forest. I found a mushroom, ate it, and chuckling to myself, I "blew my mind."

II

During the next days and weeks, I tried to implement what I

had learned through my reflections and meditations, and tried to find and repair "outside" what I had learned "within." I first went to my daughter Li and thanked her deeply for her fine gifts to me. I told her what I was doing with *I Ching,* and I told her, too, that I thought that the old China was dead, and that her elderly general husband was doomed to die on Taiwan. She thanked me for my honesty and said that she and her husband knew that they would not return to the mainland, but they had done what they felt was right. She wished me well in my experiment and told me that she had always loved me, though her nature was such that she could express it only in gifts and order and light, rather than in warmth. For her passion was such that if one came too close to it, one would "burn up." We laughed.

I wrote to my son, Ken, the priest, and told him to stand fast in his quiet meditations, and that I treasured him. I wrote, too, to my eldest son, Chen, in Communist China, and admitted that he was seeking the true Justice, which had been denied in our old China. I heard from neither. Only Sun responded with her true gentle devotion, which would have been there even if I had done nothing!

I turned back to *I Ching,* and said to him:

"Oh, good friend! Oh, friendly mushroom! Much has transpired since I last spoke to you. I have taken in your views and, I trust (thinking now of how I ate the mushroom), that I have digested them. I admit that I was angry at your calling me arrogant, but my dream has shown me how to understand it. Also, I believe that I must be renewed by a living contact with each of my children. I still believe, however, that you need me for your renewal, just as I need you. Thus, do I speak perhaps with too many words. But such is where I am. What say you now?"

I threw number 55, *Feng,* Abundance. Above is Chen, the Arousing, thunder, the eldest son; below is Li, the Clinging, flame, middle daughter. The only changing line was six at the top.

Here the Judgment, from old King Wen: *"Abundance has success. The king attains abundance. Be not sad. Be like the sun at midday."* The Image from his son, the Duke of Chou: *"Both thunder and lightning come; The image of Abundance. Thus the superior man decides lawsuits and carries out punishments."* This is a little disconcerting, but still. . . .look at the changing line, six at the top. What does it say?

"His house is in a state of abundance.
He screens off his family.
He peers through the gate
And no longer perceives anyone.
For three years he sees nothing.
Misfortune."

Again I am thrown down! What does the Commentary say? *"This describes a man who because of his arrogance and obstinacy attains the opposite of what he strives for. He seeks abundance and splendor for his dwelling. He wishes at all odds to be master in his house, which so alienates his family that in the end he finds himself completely isolated."*

What could I answer to that? Again crushed, brought down, beaten. Again I am accused of arrogance. All my abundance is as nought, old Ching says, because I wish only to be master. He says that I have alienated my family, and that it is all egoism. Oh, this is too much! But I must speak. I will speak again to this tyrannical book, out of my heart:

"Oh, *I Ching,* it may be true that I am egoistic. It may be true that I am arrogant.It may be true that I wish to dominate my own house, but I do not desire that totally. I desire peace and freedom and brotherhood and to be at one with my children and my fellow creatures. Perhaps it is you, oh *I Ching,* who wish to dominate, to lord it over us, to be the one and only true font of wisdom.

Perhaps you resent that I think that I can assimilate you. Perhaps you resent that my psyche compares you to a mushroom and even shows me that I can look down on you! Perhaps, in short, it is your own arrogance, as well as mine. Have you thought of that? Can you not accept that the psyche is mother and father of both of us? That I was a gleam in my father's eye and a desire in my mother's heart? That you, too, are a product of the labors of good King Wen, and the Duke of Chou, and of Confucius, and Lao-tse and all the others who labored so long, so hard, to understand you and nourish you? Yes, we both existed in the pleroma, in the mind of God, but ordinary humans had to help us come into existence. So, are you not also arrogant? Can you leave your vast impersonal world of law and order and become personal and human? Can you do that?"

Having said this prayer and lament, and yes, having issued this challenge, I threw the coins once again. What emerged was number 51, *Chen,* The Arousing (Shock, Thunder). Above is Chen, the Arousing, Thunder, and below is Chen. Eldest son bursts forth. The Judgment cries out:

"Shock brings success.
Shock comes—oh, oh!
Laughing words—ha, ha!
The shock terrifies for a hundred miles,
And he does not let fall the sacrificial spoon and chalice."

The Image: *"Thunder repeated: the image of SHOCK. Thus, in fear and trembling, the superior man sets his life in order and examines himself."*

Yes, great shock, indeed. Surely to me, but perhaps also to the spirit of the *I Ching* itself, for I have challenged it! What, now, are the changing lines, what do they say? They were a six in the third place and a six in the fifth place.

Six in the third place:

Shock comes and makes one distraught.
If shocks spurs to action
One remains free of misfortune.

The Sinologue says that there are three kinds of shock—the shock of heaven which is thunder, the shock of fate, and finally the shock of the heart. The present hexagram refers less to inner shock than to the shock of fate. The individual can move within his mind, however, and thus, overcome these external blows.

Six in the fifth place:
Shock goes hither and thither.
Danger.
However, nothing at all is lost.
Yet there are things to be done.

The Commentary says that there are repeated shocks with no breathing space. If one stays within the center of movement, one is spared helplessness.

"Yes, *I Ching,* I think I understand. *We both are shocked.* For I have challenged you as the highest authority, and yet I have remained truly pious. I assert, as the Judgment says, that I have not 'let fall the sacrificial spoon and chalice.' I have maintained my inner seriousness even with this challenge. And so, *I Ching,* you, too, have been shocked!"

Let me look at the changing hexagram. The changing lines modify and now comes what? 49, *Ko,* Revolution! Eldest son Chen has indeed been at work, for nothing less than Revolution is occurring. Above is Tui, the Joyous, Lake, and below is Li, the Clinging, Fire. The Judgment says of this:

Revolution. On your own day
You are believed.
Supreme success,
Furthering through perseverance.
Remorse disappears.

The Image continues: *"Fire in the lake: the image of Revolution. Thus the superior man sets the calendar in order and makes the seasons clear."*

I note: 51, the Arousing, and 49, Revolution. They enclose number 50, *Ting,* the Caldron. *I Ching* referred to itself as the Ting, when it described itself to the great Psychologist. I have challenged it further, and we have two sides in which it is enclosed. Now there is Arousing and Revolution. "So, *I Ching,* I will take in the shock and let it stew within me. I trust, powerful friend, that you, too, will take this shock and this revolution into your being and let it cook within your Ting—Caldron—as well. Then, perhaps, we can both laugh and dance! And be heard a hundred miles."

Some time passed in which I tried to assimilate the preceding events and to let the "shock" and the "revolution" work its effect in me and to bring me into Tao. I trusted that the same kind of process was working on the *I Ching,* though the spirit of this Book was not apparent to me. In my reflections, I realized that I had, indeed, been arrogant, and specifically in the presumption that I could "swallow the mushroom." It was true that my dream had described the *I Ching* as a mushroom, and sacred, and that I could look from both above it and below it, but it was a presumption to think that I could really "incorporate" or assimilate that Book. I could no more really comprehend and assimilate all its contents than I could, in actuality, eat the book! That was my presumption! Yet, I was not going to simply bow, either. I had meant what I said to that spirit, and, I think, had caused a revolution in him as well! How could we both change, and relate to each other, without either of us having to incorporate, assimilate, or crush the other? That was a good question, but I was not ready to ask it yet, because I thought *I Ching* needed time to reflect, as well.

With these reflections, I contented myself, along with the

realization that I would need to follow the Commentary: *"Revolution means removal of that which has been antiquated."* Then I dreamt once again.

In the first part of my dream, a magician showed a strange house to me and an unknown woman. The house was made of blocks. From one standpoint it was like a Swiss chalet, closed in upon itself, and from another it was like a large, familial African hut, open to the elements. He held the house like a child's blocks and toys, and then made it large, as if one could really live in it. He showed that one could look into the house and see all the nice furnishings, including pleasant animals who lived there, as well as people; or, one could look from within the house to the outside and see all the magnificent scenery. The former view occurred when the house was like the Swiss chalet, and the latter was when the house had its African character. There was also a third way, in which one could look through the house itself to the beauties of nature on the other side.

As the dream continued, I was inside the house, but now saw two men battling therein. Both were strong and able. One man held a short axe. The other held a long spear that staved off the man with the axe. I watched the battle in which the man with the spear won, but I was disheartened by the necessity of such struggle. With a sigh, I took the hand of my grandson (in actuality, unknown to me), and made ready to leave. My grandson lifted a harmonica out of the earth and asked if he could take it with him. I said I would have to clean off some of the soil, but that he could.

That segment of the dream ended and I now was in a large house with many women bustling about. The house was like the community houses that we had enjoyed in old China, with a large courtyard and many rooms surrounding it, called the old *hut'ung.* We lived in a *hut'ung* even now on Taiwan, but our present one was as nothing compared to the fine one we had in Shanghai, when my parents were alive. I was in a large room of such a *hut'ung* when a messenger came, announcing that the Queen of England was coming to see me. I was startled and wondered why, what? How should one greet such a personage, bowing as we do, or as the English do? I also wanted my little granddaughter to see her. All the women in the household were bustling with excitement as the Queen arrived. She was shy, but a warm and pleasant lady, quite democratic in attitude. She started to speak, to tell me why she had come to see me, but she could not express herself, so I simply took her hand and squeezed it warmly. I remembered that her father, the late King, also had trouble in speaking. He had stuttered, had he not? With this question, the dream ended.

The long dream stayed with me for many days as I tried to comprehend its meaning. Anyone else, I suppose, would see the meaning of the first part at once, but I was particularly dense about it for a long time. Then I understood. The "magician" was the representative of the psychic "authority" who was continuing in his explanation to me of how both the psyche and the *I Ching* could be viewed. Before, it had been presented as a mushroom; now it was shown as a house. Again it was little, made of blocks and could be creatively played with(" from above!") or one could live in it and be protected and warmed by it ("from below or within"). The African, or open-aired hut aspect of it was the more natural, or familial, like the *I Ching* and the world–namely: outer, community, family, book; in other words, open to the world. The Swiss chalet, I realized, was more Western, but also, like the great Psychologist who had written the foreword to the *I Ching*, more "inward," alone, with possessions, and open to the inner world. The house image was more elaborate than the mushroom, and now I saw that from that point of view, one could not assimilate or "eat" a house. One would not wish to, since one would want to make or create one with blocks, or live in it! I laughed with delight. How splendid the image! But was the *I Ching* the same as the psyche in its structure? And why such non-Chinese images for the house as African and Swiss? I did not know.

The battle of the two men I understood as the warrior aspects of myself—one battling in close, the other battling by keeping distance. I was tired of the struggle of these opposites within myself, I was glad to realize at seventy-five. And I was glad, indeed, to leave this battle in the company of my little grandson. I did not comprehend the meaning of that part of the dream until the following day when, by meaningful coincidence, my great-grandson, a grandson of my daughter, Sun, came into the courtyard playing a harmonica which he had gotten from an American soldier! I felt then that I understood. This "harmony" could come only with a resolution of the battle between the male opposites (sword and axe, my son Chen and myself, East and West, *I Ching* and myself) by a newer son altogether, the grandson and great-grandson. This joyous young development will bring peace and harmony with its new spirit. And he will find it in the earth of K'un, my "wife", the great receiver.

That was heartening, but still I remained sad. I thought about the rest of the dream for several days. This dream found me in my old element, the great house in the *hut'ung.* The Queen came there. I realized that I was in my own element, but. . . .? It gradually dawned on me that the dreams were trying to say that I had changed, that the times had changed, and, indeed, even the psyche had changed. Perhaps the *I Ching* had changed, too. The Tao was no longer purely Chinese, but now we had incorporated non-Chinese, even non-Oriental, elements into our Chinese psyche: the naturalness and vitality of the African, and the developed inwardness and order of the Swiss. I realized that I might, indeed, use what the great Swiss Psychologist had taught; I could have an active dialogue with the figures of the psyche. I was, after all, having a dialogue with a book and the spirit therein. Why not with a dream figure? Why not, indeed?

Therefore, as the Psychologist had taught, I "went on with my dream." I dreamed the dream onwards in my waking state and asked the good queen why she had come to see me. She informed me that she, herself, was quite happy and living a good, if rather modest life now that the great British empire was dissolved. She felt that the English people, despite the trials of this period of loss of power, would find a new creativity and joy in life. The land of Chaucer and Shakespeare would be great again and, as all the world knows, would "muddle through" in its own way to a new place. She came to see me not because of herself but because of her late father, the King. He had come to her in a dream, as a ghost, and was very mournful. He felt, yet, the agony of his lack of being able to express himself and because of this fact was, indeed, not able to simply die. He believed that he had failed the spirit of his ancestors in that he had been unable to stem the tide of loss of empire, revolution, advancing socialism, and decay which had come upon England. In his agonies on "the other side"—as the Queen put it, in her English way—he was informed (by Tao, I suppose) of my efforts through the *I Ching* to come to a new relationship with the spirits of my old Chinese ancestors. It was apparently understood that our situations were similar, even though I was not a King. The new China was socialistic and estranged from the ancestral "fathers", and I was "haunted" also. The King remembered that he had known me casually when we were both quite young, and when he had not expected to be King. I recalled having met him in my student days in England, and talking with him, but we had no real contact. Now the Queen was telling me that I was carrying on the work of her deceased father! She had come to inform me of the importance of what I was doing, and to wish me "God's speed." I thanked her and instructed my household to feed and entertain her royally. She stayed, was entertained, and we parted in a friendly manner.

After I had completed this "active fantasy" as the great Psychologist termed such an inner dialogue, I reflected on it. What did it mean? Just as I had thought, I was doing the work of the West as well as the East. I was trying to effect a reconciliation of spirits and bring about a new creativity, by linking present with past, and coming to a better future. Even a Queen came to see me! No wonder I was presumptuous, and found arrogant by the *I Ching*!

Then it hit me! "Like a ton of bricks" as my great-grandson says sometimes–an expression he learned from the soldiers. Or, I might say, thinking of my dream, as a house of blocks, perhaps. What was missing in my work was the Queen! Even the English King needed to come to his daughter, who had become Queen. He, no doubt, was also missing his wife, the Queen-Mother. I had not even informed my own wife, K'un, what I was doing in my work. Like the King, I was haunted, alone, and needed the support of my Queen, and my daughter-Queen. I had already had the support of daughter Li (book and sculpture), and the offspring of Sun, but I needed the support of my wife, K'un! I needed to ask my wife to "receive" these products of my efforts, to simply "take in" as was her nature. I was not sure if this would be so easy, since at an earlier time, she had been reluctant to accompany me on some of my creative journeys, fearing that she would not give me the response that I would wish. I would have to convince her that what I wanted most was for her to "receive" as was her nature, and to accompany me, and "be with me." Yes, this was what I needed.

Equally important was my insight about the *I Ching* itself. I had been addressing the *I Ching* as if it were an old Chinese gentleman, like myself. I suddenly realized that this must be erroneous, even if the great Psychologist had so imaged the Book, and even if all the great masters of the past had been men. The *I Ching,* after all, was based upon the mandala of the *t'ai chi t'u,* the symbol of the great pole, the circle in which Yang and Yin are intertwined. I had forgotten the Yin! The *I Ching* had answered all my questions and assertions and prayers, it is true, but it must have been annoyed at me for personifying it solely as an old Chinese man, full of wisdom! I had, of course, thought of it as a man with family, wife, and children, but my true picture had been of an old man like myself. That was arrogant of me, egoistic, and narrow! Oh, *I Ching,* oh great union of Yang and Yin intertwined! I beg pardon for having offended thee. Oh great Yin, in my ignorance I have erred. I have forgotten the Queen!

I turned back to the book: "*I Ching,* I apologize for addressing you exclusively in your maleness. I now realize that you encompass both the male and the female. I sould have known that already when the psyche showed you as a mushroom, with both a male aspect (stem) and female aspect (round top). I wish to correct my attitude in that regard, both in relation to you and in relation to myself and my life. Would this reconcile you to me, and allow us to continue our dialogue with more harmony and good feeling?"

I started to throw the coins again, but could not. For now, instead of an old Chinese man, I visualized the *t'ai chi t'u,* a marvelous mandala, but not alive. How could I address this union and have a living dialogue with it? I know I could simply perform the technique of throwing the coins, but that would be a kind of magic alone. I accepted the magic, but wanted, as I have said, the personal, living, dialogic relation. The psyche had said that the *I Ching* was a sacred mushroom. Good, I would visualize that. What came to me, then, was a living, pulsating mushroom, alive and a plant. But no, I could not have a dialogue with a plant, could I? Or with a house? Then I pleaded, "*I Ching*, please show me your own symbol, show me your way of being available to me in living dialogue, which would include your Yin as well as your Yang. This is what I ask." Thus I threw the coins.

What emerged was 21, Shih-Ho, *Biting through.* What wryness, I thought. This *I Ching* is very wry, indeed. He, or She, or It, or They, having grown angry at being pictured as a mushroom, is now giving an image of itself of "Biting Through"! Well, just like a woman, perhaps, changing its mind! First it hated being pictured as a mushroom and now it wants to be bitten through and assimilated! How changeable! I laughed a long and loud laugh, for this, after all, is *I Ching*, the Book of Changes! I saw that it was, indeed, changeable, like a woman, and was, indeed, like a mushroom.

The Judgment: *Biting through has success. It is favorable to let justice be administered.*

The Image: *Thunder and lightning: The image of Biting Through. Thus the kings of former times made firm the laws through clearly defined penalties.*

Yes, I thought, justice would be a good thing. There is more justice now, perhaps, but what of the changing lines? There is nine in the fourth place and six in the fifth place. The nine:

Bites on dried gristly meat
Receives metal arrows.
It furthers one to be mindful of difficulties
And to be persevering.
Good fortune.

The six:

Bites on dried lean meat.
Receives yellow gold.
Perseveringly aware of danger.
No Blame.

The *I Ching* is only slightly gentler with me. "Good fortune," "no blame" it offers but also tells of "difficulties," dangers, and the need for perseverance. It is hard to please. Is it presenting itself as "gristly meat" and "lean," "dried?" It seems so, but also as "thunder and lightning." I shall stay with the image of the mushroom, but I miss, still, the joy and pleasure of harmony, and do not see my way clearly.

Such were my thoughts, and I returned to my sadness.

III

My melancholy continued for many days. Only gradually did I understand that *I Ching* was not throwing me down again. No, it was really acknowledging to me that my dream image had been correct, that it saw itself, indeed, as a sacred mushroom. Did it not refer to itself as "dried gristly meat" and "dried lean meat?" And was this not the dried meat of the mushroom? Did not *I Ching* come out of nature itself? The ancients and Sages used yarrow sticks for the oracle, did they not? A plant was the foundation. So, the image of mushroom was true and correct and right. It had "li", both piety and morality. I was appeased, for did not the dream and the image agree that male and female were contained in the image of the mushroom, with the masculine stem and the feminine roundness? Yes.

Why then should I be sad? And why did I continue to think of the *I Ching* as an old man? I had foolishly said that I could not talk to a plant (of course I could), but I had been talking to a book. In reality, I was talking to the spirit of nature—the mushroom—as formulated by men, many of them, and all old Sages! That was it: my quarrel was not with nature, but with the old men or old man who formulated it. That satisfied me a little.

So then, I had to "bite through" and to persevere. How could I do this? At once I remembered that Revolution meant, according to a commentator, "to remove that which was antiquated." Good. I would bite through what the old Sages had said, digest it and make it my own, and then remove what was antiquated for me. The method came to me at once. I would use the method of the great Psychologist! I would go through the signs of *I Ching,* which were, of course, my children, and would have a dialogue with each of them! I would do so according to the "Book" and according to my own images within. I would have to trust that my actual children, those who lived far away, would be in Tao with me!

I grew excited and immediately went to the *Shuo Kua,* that ancient Eighth Wing which discusses the trigrams. This was the work of the great Sages and I read the wisdom therein:

"In ancient times the holy sages made the Book of Changes thus: They invented the yarrow stalk oracle in order to lend aid in a mysterious way to the light of the gods. To heaven they assigned the number three and to earth the number two; from these they computed the other numbers.

"They contemplated the changes in the dark and the light and established the hexagrams in accordance with them. They brought about movement in the firm and the yielding, and thus produced individual lines.

"They put themselves in accord with Tao and its power, and in conformity with this laid down the order of what is right. By thinking through the order of the outer world to the end, and by exploring the law of their nature to the deepest core, they arrived at an understanding of fate."

How beautiful and concise this saying of the Sages!: "By thinking through the order of the outer world to the end, and by exploring the law of their nature to the deepest core, they arrived at an understanding of fate'" But now, I had to go further. I had to go beyond, even, the Sequence of Earlier Heaven, that Primal

Arrangement of the Signs, of the hexagrams, and go beyond my own suffering of the opposites. I knew, intuitively or by Tao, that I had to follow the path of the great King Wen and go through the *Sequence of Later Heaven,* that *Inner-World Arrangement,* which is cyclic and like the year. I had to do that "within" and "without." Only then, only after "biting through", could I hope to come to another relationship with the *I Ching*! Not, perhaps, with the sacred mushroom itself, but with the Old Man who recorded it and the Old Man that I am.

So, here the picture, and then the words which emerged from my dialogue:

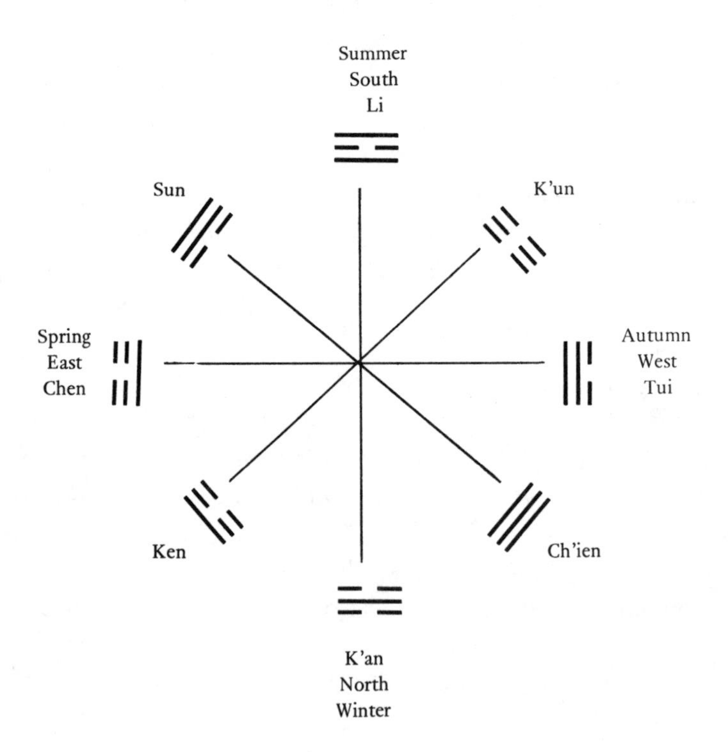

But my dialogue and meditation must be preceded, like a prayer, with the great words of the unknown Sage, who speaks in *Shuo Kua,* because they speak of the Deity, and they speak of the Tao as it moves in cycles:

> God comes forth in the sign of the Arousing; he brings all things to completion in the sign of the Gentle; he causes creatures to perceive one another in the sign of the Clinging (light); he causes them to serve one another in the sign of the Receptive. He gives them joy in the sign of the Joyous; he battles in the sign of the Creative; he toils in the sign of the Abysmal; he brings them to perfection in the sign of Keeping Still.

And so, I begin with Chen, my eldest son:

"Oh Chen, my eldest son; you, in whom God has his beginning; you, my first born in whom I have my beginning, you stand in the East, in spring. You arouse, and you move, and your foot twitches. You are a dragon and you thunder. You are green and young, no matter how old! I know you. I know you within myself as the rebel, as the alive one, forever growing, forever uncontained in forms, forever seeking to be contained, constantly seeking the new form. I see you causing me grief with your thunder; I see you breaking down those old reeds which cannot bend with you. I see you, even, being cruel! But you, my first born, my son 'within' and 'without', I love you. I love your vitality and your truth and your being and I, the father, the bent old man, I bow to you. I break tradition and bow to the young, for thus is the force and vitality and creativity in me renewed. I quote to you, my son, the words of Lao-tse, the great sage, who, though old, could be renewed, and was not a rigid old man:

"After things reach their prime, they begin to grow old, which means being contrary to Tao."

I tell you, my son Chen, that I have grown old, and am contrary to Tao. I beg your wisdom and your love and your renewal!"

Thus did I speak to my son, and thus did he answer me:

"Oh wise father, Ch'ien! You it is I love! You it is, my own father who begat me, whose bones I bear. It is not you whom I push aside, but the brittle reeds who would not let me grow upon the bank. I push aside the past of injustice, of rigidity and deadness! I live and if not wisely, then fully! To you I bow, oh Father, and bow as number one son, who truly follows the spirit of the father and carries on his tradition. I carry on in its truth and its vitality and its greatness. For I, and China, will survive, and our value will survive."

Then, I, Ch'ien, spoke to my eldest daughter Sun, the Gentle, she of wood, and wind and white, of the guideline and the work:

"Oh, Sun, eldest daughter within me, thee I love and treasure, for thee, too, are my eldest and the first of my loins who bears my opposite. For in thee, the Yin begins. From thee, beyond thy thighs, comes quiet penetration, and the cock doth slowly move. In thee—loyal, enduring, penetrating as the wind—I find my time. I can wait for all eternity, for such do you teach me. But more: you teach me gentleness. Were it not for you, soft Sun, good Chen would thunder wildly and not have gentling. Did not the Sages couple you and Chen to arouse Love? Is there not love in the coupling of the Arousing and the Gentle? Oh, Sun, oh Gentler, I love thee!"

"Oh, Ch'ien, my Father and my Lord. I am thy Daughter and none can deny it. Thee I treasure above all—above husband, country, even children. For father who begat me is beyond all, and the father beyond my father is the Creative Father who begat us all, and it is from His gentle, penetrating spirit of wind that my own can flow. So, dear father, I remain by thy side, forever and ever. I kiss my brother's wild foot, and I bow to the great head of my father, in humility and love."

Then, to the South did I, Ch'ien, move and encounter my second daughter Li, in the height of her summertime. Look at her! Look at her loveliness! Is she not the flowering of summer? In her is the brightness in which all creatures perceive one another, just as my gentle daughter Sun is where they become pure and perfect. In Li the Sages give ear to the meaning of the Universe, they turn toward the light.

"And so I turn to you, oh Li, oh fire of light, oh lightning! I know your dryness, I know your support of the warrior spirit. I know that battle for light and truth, and I know that you bring me piety and clarity! You in your rightness, in your great yellow garb, you brought me *I Ching* from without, you bring me clarity from within. Oh daughter, I salute you. I greet you as mistress and guide, as well as daughter. You I treasure!"

Li did answer me thus:

"Oh, father, great Ch'ien! I am a light, but I am as nothing without your breath. My bright eye can see nothing unless it is received by you. My gifts I praise, but they are as nothing unless you receive them. Oh father, you are great, and you do I serve. But beyond you, I serve the light! You and I, together, we serve the light, and such is our battle and our devotion! I salute you in return and bend my knee to our common spirit."

Now did I, Ch'ien, father of many, speak to K'un, my wife within, my spouse and my love, without whom no children could exist. Thus did I speak:

"Oh, K'un, oh great earth, which is both mother and daughter and sister to all mankind; oh, my own private individual K'un who has received and received, who has taken my seed into her belly and had all things fulfilled therein; you, K'un, are my nature. You earth, you mother, you kettle, you container; when none could contain me, you contained me. When none could accept me, you accepted me. When none could endure me, you endured me. All things begin and end in you. And I shall return to you and die and be reborn, as I have so many, many times. You, K'un, you of no words but endless patience, of limitless receptivity, mother of all and everything! The Sages have said that in the Cycles of Being, just as Chen and Sun have produced Love, that you, oh K'un, and your daughter Li produce *mores* and piety. That I believe, for there would be no customs, no manners, without you. But the Sages knew that you, oh K'un, were more than mere manners and customs and more, even, than piety, for you are at the Center, the very Center of the Universe, and you have the greatest virtue of all, Loyalty. Have I not know that? Have I not known that from you? I do not bow, I sprawl. I fall on my face and feel your great earth all under me, and when I die, I will feel you all around me, as well, and I will, at last, be contained!"

Thus did K'un answer me:

"Oh, Ch'ien, my husband and my lord. I do not have words, for I receive and do not pour forth. I follow my nature, for thee I embrace. I take thee to my heart and to my belly. If I swallow thee up, it is only to heal thee, and make thee born anew. Of love I do not speak, for my love goes deeper than words, it goes to the Yin of all being. There is where Love begins, in the belly of the earth, the black soil, the receptive cow, where we are all nourished and sleep. Without thee, oh Ch'ien, I am blind in my darkness and I succumb. Come to me, oh Ch'ien, and create within me your mysteries!"

Then did I, Ch'ien, move to the West, to Autumn and to Tui, my third and youngest daughter, the Joyous. Thus did I speak:

"You, oh Tui, oh joyous lake within me, I move to you, in the mid-autumn of my life, at a time when the buds have come out and it is time to enjoy the blossoms and watch them move in the wind. For in you, oh Tui, with your deep and sensual and joyous nature, I am moved to speak, to smash and break apart old vessels.

I am moved to let the fruit drop, and the nuts of the tree burst open with their richness."

"Yes, oh Father, oh Ch'ien, oh Creative one! It is true that I am a sorceress, for I can work magic with my tongue. It is true that I have moved to that hard and salty soil of Israel to meet there a son of the Prophets so that the wise sorcery, the sensual joy of China will meet the wise and salty seer of Israel and heal the wounded children. For the Joy of my life is healing and speaking, and you, oh Father, know thereof. For you have taught me to speak out of my heaven and my wisdom, and K'un, my mother, has taught me to speak without words, to speak from my sorcery of deep lake. I am both wife and daughter, mistress and concubine, seeress and sorceress. My Joy, oh Father, is your Joy. To find me is to plunge into the depths of the lake! I do not bow to you, oh my father; I embrace you, for I am your sister as well as your daughter, and you, and you alone know my depths!"

I turned from Tui, for I knew that she spoke from the depth of her, but before I could allow myself to feel the full joy, I moved Northwest. What did I encounter, but myself, Ch'ien! How do I speak to myself? How do I address myself in a way other than the way I address the other selves? That is, in truth, not difficult, for it is the "I" I address, and not the other "eyes", And so I speak to myself:

"Oh, Ch'ien, I know you, but I do not know you. Who is it who really knows himself? I thought I knew you, but you change so that what I know changes. Are you that old man I now see there, reflecting upon his being and upon this book? Are you that child of seventy years ago with creative visions? Yes. But I speak to you as I know you now. You are the battler. 'He battles in the sign of the Creative.' How well I know that! How well I know that light and dark arouse each other! I nod, for it has been so all of my life! Yes, oh Ch'ien, I know you, for you, as it is said, manifest in the head, in the questions, in the search. You are round, a prince, and father, jade. You are cold as ice, and warm and deep red as blood. You are, indeed, a dragon, an old horse, a lean horse, a wild horse, tree fruit. I know all these in you, and. . . .of course. . . .in me. And I know, too, that you battle with yourself. Can you answer me, oh Ch'ien, oh Creative one?"

And this is how Ch'ien answers Ch'ien:

"I laugh, oh Ch'ien, I laugh, until it is heard for ten thousand miles! For how can Ch'ien speak to Ch'ien? Is it madness? No, it is not, for who else can speak to Ch'ien except Ch'ien? None other, except that this be possible. For without this, nothing is possible. Can not God speak to man, His creation? Did He not create him in order to be able to speak with him, to come out of His loneliness and speak, to come out of His sadness and have company? And is not this possible only because man can speak with himself? And battle with himself? Am I not you, yourself, oh Ch'ien? I am, and we can laugh! Others who come to know this are torn apart in the battle. Their smithereens are splattered for ten thousand miles! But we can come together as one, and separate and do battle. That, oh Ch'ien, is the gift of the great Ch'ien, the Creator of the beginning, of the time before *I Ching* became manifest!"

Then I, Ch'ien, left this paradox of Ch'ien speaking with Ch'ien and moved, in the Tao, further North, into the depths of Winter, where I encountered my second son, K'an.

"Oh, K'an, you of the Abysmal, of the water, of the work, is it not said, 'He toils in the sign of the Abysmal?' You have I known, as my deep melancholy, my endless toiling to understand myself, my secrets and my mysteries, my piggishness and sick heart. My ear aches from listening and not understanding, from having to survive in bad times, in the darkness of the moon. Who can love thee, oh, K'an? All run from thee. All run from melancholy and work, from mere survival, from endless listening and toiling in the water. But do not be melancholy all the time, my son, for the Sages have assigned you a great and good place: Chen and Sun have brought Love; Li and K'un have brought Piety; K'un, the Center with pure Yin, has brought Loyalty; Tui and myself have brought Justice; but you, oh K'an, together with your still brother Ken, you have brought Wisdom! Is this not true? Can there be any Wisdom without you? Have I learned and become wise without work and melancholy, without dark secrets and laborings in the water? No. I believe, too, in the wisdom of joy and love, but you, dear son, dear despised and Abysmal son, you I embrace. I embrace you because you have been rejected. You in your abysses are always rejected, but I embrace you as the source of my wisdom and as the basis of my being what I am."

Thus did K'an, my son, answer:

"Oh, Father, I, K'an, the melancholy and the Abysmal, I, K'an, rejoice, for I have been understood and accepted by thee, my Father. It is not given to all the pigs, to all the melancholy and the abysmal, to be understood and embraced and valued! But it is so given to me. My gift to you, my father, is my wisdom. It is the wisdom of the moon and thieves, which all others despise, for they fear it. To thee, I give it gladly, for thou dost treasure it. Oh, my father, thee I embrace, and treasure."

Surprised and touched at the love of K'an, I, Ch'ien, moved from the wisdom of the North to the final place, the place of my youngest son, Ken, the Wisdom of the Northeast. I moved to the place of which it is said: 'He brings them to perfection in the sign of Keeping Still.' Thus did I move to my silent son, Keeping Still, the mountain:

"Oh, Ken, you I know. You are my path and my bypath, my stones, my doors, my openings. You are my eunuch of God, for you have sacrificed your creativity of children to the creativity of Keeping Still, to meditation and withdrawal within yourself. You are the dog, loyal, and the guard; you hold fast. You grip firmly and gnarledly, and cannot be swayed. For you are the within, and the voyage within. It is true that all things are brought to perfection in the Keeping Still, and the turning within. And all things are brought to perfection in the highest, which is to be devoted to God. You, my son, I bow to, for in you I find my completion, in you I find my solace, in you I find myself."

Thus did Ken, my youngest son, answer me:

"I thank thee, father, for the adoration of my Keeping Still. But it is the Keeping Still, not I, that is to be adored. Dare I speak and tell the Father that it is the Father in Heaven who is to be adored, and not the Son, who is only His follower? Dare I say that?"

"Yes, you may, oh son, oh favorite of God. But I must say that it is the Son who is to be adored as well. If the Father is to be adored, so is the Son, and not only through Keeping Still."

"Oh, my wife and my children—now I turn to you all—I, Ch'ien, embrace you. How could I survive, how could I exist without you all? I have made my circumambulation of your circle; I have made my circumambulation of the year. I have grown from young to old; I have married and loved and fathered. I have battled and thought and lusted. I have won and lost, succeeded and failed. And I have done so only with you, my family within, and you have done so with me: for we all are one with the Tao, whose path we have followed and do follow, and whose oneness is the greater Circle where Yin and Yang embrace. One and all, wife and children, I embrace. To one and all, family within and without, I bow and I salute: in love, in piety, in loyalty, in justice, and in wisdom.

We all embraced and became a busy, vigorous family in the time of times. For we saw that we could arrange ourselves like the Book of *I Ching!* We laughed, for we, too, could be like a living Book, or like a mushroom! And our laughter was heard for ten thousand miles!

IV

The positive mood engendered by my inner dialogue with my wife and six children was profound. I felt that a real change had occurred within me: a true transformation had occurred in the marrow of my bones. I felt, in particular, that what had occurred between Chen and myself, and between K'an and myself had deep significance. And yet . . . and yet . . . Those little words, suggestive of doubt, they push one onwards, do they not? They rob one of happiness, but push one to a greater happiness. It is as if all that could possibly be included wants to be included and we can never rest completely until this is so. Yes. . .This is what I accept as a consequence of my experience with Chen, the Arousing, and K'an, the Abysmal, because they are the Sons who push to the "new", the larger, the "more". Them do I embrace and to them do I bow!

Was my doubt and uneasiness because of them, my pushing sons? In truth, no. I was really afraid of old *I Ching.* I knew that I had come to a new understanding and feeling, but I was afraid that with another roll of the coins, the old king of *I Ching* would once again throw me down and call me arrogant. I thought, therefore, that I had to reflect again upon "arrogance". I remembered, vaguely, what the Commentary was for the final changing line of my first throw, when I began my dialogue. It was the *Creative,* number 1, with a nine at the top, "Arrogant dragon will have cause to repent."

I had pondered the line, but now I went back to the Commentary and read wise words:

> *Arrogance means that one knows how to press forward, but not how to draw back, that one knows existence, but not annihilation, knows something about winning but nothing*

> *about losing.*
>
> *It is only the holy man who understands how to press forward and how to draw back, who knows existence and annihilation as well, without losing his true nature. The holy man alone can do this.*

These were wise words, and I was ready to take them in, to bite them through. I had known existence and annihilation, winning and losing; I had known how to press forward, but I did not know "how to draw back. . .without losing his true nature." That is where I had failed. I was, thus, not a "holy man."

What is a "holy man?" I knew the way of the Sage and the way of the Hero. Both of these ways of Ch'ien, the Creative, had been vouchsafed me. I had known both: the way of the Sage, who influences through the example set by the wholeness of his personality; the way of the Hero, who sets a standard in the life of men. I had travelled both of these ways, to the degree commensurate with my development. But to be "holy"? What was the way of the "holy man"? Clearly it meant he who knew how to press forward and how to draw back, he who knew existence and annihilation without losing his true nature. That must be the definition of the "holy man." "Holy" is to be whole without dependence upon "success." That, then, would make the great Sage Confucius "holy" because he knew how to do this. He even forewent, as many great Chinese have foregone, any recognition of himself while he lived.

In that same Commentary of the person who has the character of the dragon but remains concealed, Confucius said:

> *"He does not change to suit the outside world; he makes no name for himself. He withdraws from the world, yet is not sad about it. He receives no recognition, yet is not sad about it. If lucky, he carries out his principles; if unlucky, he*

withdraws with them. Verily, he cannot be uprooted; he is a hidden dragon."

Confucius not only said this, he lived it. His success was not his own, it was the success of his teaching. The time was too opposed to him. Is that so now? I do not know. I know only that I am now ready to question *I Ching* once again.

My thoughts have come to this point, *I Ching,* as you can see. I am also concerned and wonder how it is with you. In short, if you are, indeed, a friend, it is time that you speak once again, about yourself, about me, about how you see things at this point. What say you?

I threw number 21 once again, *Biting Through.* The changing line, as before, six in the fifth place:

Bites on dried lean meat
Receives yellow gold.
Perseveringly aware of danger.
No blame.

We are both still chewing and biting, are we not? There is still something to be chewed upon. The problem of "holiness", no doubt. *I Ching* must be meditating, too. I must reflect further, I believe.

The nine in the fourth place has dropped out. "Great obstacles" perhaps have been overcome, but I am enjoined to be "like yellow gold", that is, "as true as gold and impartial as yellow, the color of the middle."

What does this mean? This hexagram has to do with "justice" and "laws". "Individual application of the law," the use of thunder and lightning, excitement and clarity: Chen and Li are asked for. Yet I do not know what is asked for. The laws as they now exist are bad. The "kings" as they now exist throughout the world are bad. Thus also it was in the time of Confucius, who chose to "abide in his room". Yet, I am asked to "bite through."

Part of this I understand as having to bite through and chew more of what the old Sages had to say about *I Ching,* such as the *Ta Chuan,* the Great Commentary. I have studied it and must study it more. That I will surely do, but then there is the "law" and how to act when there is injustice; one is also enjoined to be "holy", to retreat without losing one's true nature.

What is the law? Is it the Tao, the one true law of nature which antedates nature? Is it the law of life, in which Yang flows into Yin and Yin changes into Yang? Is it the law of change, in which there is the Primal order of No Change, upon which are played the "changes" cyclic and sequential, circle and straight line? These laws I can struggle with, cope with, understand anew, ever more deeply. These, too, I will strugle with in my understanding of the Great Commentary. But what about the laws of men and of nations? When the kings, and the laws themselves, are out of harmony with the true Tao?

If one is with Tao, all will be right, suggest the Sages. Yet, what if the world is in another Tao, if one can ask such a question? Are there two Taos? Such are my thoughts, and such is my struggle at this moment. That is the meaning of this moment, oh Spirit of *I Ching,* and I cannot act. Yet, you enjoin me to act, to change the laws, to "bite through." I can not. Perhaps I must retreat and experience the "annihilation."

One thing I know. I can act only personally. I can act only in relation to an individual. What I have seen is that great laws and great customs and great changes do only harm when the individual is lost. When I keep the personal, individual connection–with its flow of change, with its union and apartness and re-union–then I know, in my bones, that it is all right, it is in tune with Tao. But with the larger, with the impersonal, with Tao out of tune with Tao, is that possible?

Oh, *I Ching,* let me question you once again. I experience you once more as giving me a double message. I find you enjoining me to retreat and not be arrogant, and to act and change the bad laws. I find that both of these are wrong for me, are mistaken. I find that without the personal, individual connection, both advance and retreat are "out of Tao." You are driving me insane with your double messages. I implore you to speak more clearly, and to this moment. I promise to "bite through" and chew your Great Commentary at another time. What say you?

I Ching answered with number 52, *Keeping Still, Mountain.* Ken above and below, Keeping Still and Meditation.

The Judgment:

Keeping Still. Keeping his back still
So that he no longer feels his body.
He goes into his courtyard and does not see his people.
No Blame.

The Image:

Mountains standing close together:
The image of Keeping Still.
Thus the superior man does not permit his thoughts
To go beyond his situation.

The only changing line I threw was nine at the top, which is also the ruler of the hexagram. It says: *"Noblehearted keeping still. Good fortune."* The Sinologist comments: *"This marks the consummation of the effort to attain tranquility. One is at rest, not merely in a small, circumscribed way in regard to matters of detail, but one has also a general resignation in regard to life as a whole, and this confers peace and good fortune in relation to every individual matter."*

This is well. I shall now "Keep Still." I shall change the law by being alone with my own Tao. I shall meditate and keep still, acting only in accordance with my "principle" when the personal, individual connection is involved. So be it.

It dawned upon me, after some days, that I was finally at peace with the spirit of the *I Ching.* The "Old Man" was at last no longer accusing me of arrogance; on the contrary, he was according me, in a way, the honors of a Sage! And all because I appeared to be, at last, no longer attached to the results of what I felt I needed to do. I had my own position and viewpoint, acted accordingly, and could be non-involved, detached. . .it is hard to find the right word. . . . I was free. I acted from within, and was not arrogant. In the words of *I Ching,* "Noblehearted keeping still" and the attainment of "tranquillity."

Yes, my aim had been achieved, at least in part. As I viewed the days and the events which transpired, I saw the movements and changes. There were those who sought my aid, and I gave it, as best I could. But I did it in no martyr fashion, for I needed to be fair to myself as well. I saw, too, the movement of the Tao in the world. When I reconciled myself to my own "law"—I saw changes around me. Across the sea, in far-off America, the rigid old leader therein made a remarkable change, announcing his desire for peace and his sacrifice of ambition. I was made happy thereby, but, very soon, a true King, a wise and great black man from the same land was shot and killed by one who hated his non-violence and his search for justice and equality.

So, the Tao was not yet "good." What could I do about it? I returned to my promise to *I Ching,* that I would study the Great Commentary, the *Ta Chuan.* I had, of course, read it many times, and was deeply impressed with the wisdom of the old Sages. When I read again, I was once more impressed, as anyone would be who read of the Book of History, of the Yellow River Map, and the Writing. Most striking is the brevity, the succinctness. They were, indeed, men of few words.

But, what of my own wisdom? How much had I really absorbed within? Had I, in truth, assimilated that dried mushroom? What was the wisdom, if any, that I possessed? Could I put it into words? I did not know, but I resolved to try. This is what came to me:

In the beginning is the Tao. And the Tao is before Tao. What does this mean? In the beginning, when someone is there to even think about "beginnings" there is already order. The order of laws, of relationships, of meaning, of process. . .all this is there "in the beginning." At the same time, there is also "chaos"–that is, disorder. For how can there be order, or can one know there is order, unless by contrast? What is this contrast but chaos, disorder? So, in the beginning there is order.

What is this order? This order is the first manifestation of the Tao (which precedes both order and disorder). It is the line. It is the line of the Tai-chi, the original ridgepole, and it looks like this: –. This line, this ridgepole, this masculine line is Yang, and the Creative, and Heaven, for it is firmness. This is the beginning. But, even in the beginning it is not alone. For, with the line, is there not already posited an "above the line" and a "below the line" and an all around the line? Of course. For, if the line is Yang, and Creative, and Order, and Beginning, and Firmness, then all around it is Yin, and Receptive, and Chaos, and That-which-is-beyond-beginnings, namely, Completion! Thus, when even the Line begins, the Circle is there implicitly. And when the Circle is there, the Yin is there, and the Tao, which existed before existence, is brought into being. Now, we see the true Tai-Chi-tu, that great Circle in which the Line is curving and divides and unites Yin and Yang, and shows the *law* and the *way*, and the *meaning*, all of which Tao is.

Yes. But if the line, –, is the beginning, and the circle is implicit, the firm line leads, by the easy and the simple, through the law of least effort, to the parting in the middle, to the broken line - -. What now? Now we have the Yin, the Receptive, the

Yielding! Now we have everything, do we not?

Not quite. For with the two, with the male and female, with the light and dark, with the opposites, in all their glory, with Heaven and Earth, we still have nothing! Why nothing? Because we do not have Man. Man is the measure, as we know. Without man, the Tao has existence only in the pleroma. Have not the Sages said that the Tao is of Heaven, and of Earth, and of Man? Yes, these three are needed, or there is no totality. Man, as he exists between Heaven (where all is potential) and Earth (where all becomes manifest), is needed to fulfill it. For the opposites exist in him and through him, as well as apart from him.

With these three, Heaven and Earth and Man, and with the two opposites, of firm and yielding, hard and soft, male and female, we come to the union of three and two. How do they unite? How does the potential of heaven and the manifest of earth show itself in the life of man? Why, in the hexagram itself! Three times two, in all its combinations. Ah, the hexagram; it is, perhaps, an image of God, Himself. The six, the six, the six; know ye all that the six is the image of God needing man and becoming manifest in man, for it is the symbol of the union of Heaven, Earth, and Man, and the opposites—all in combination. The six is so sacred in this alone: The union of God and man, of God becoming man.

Now, is that the totality of my wisdom? Yes, it is, for all else follows. All else is but combinations and attitudes, changes and manifestations of the law. And this I have already said. If I do not say it well, one can always read the *Ta Chuan.* One can always read the wisdom of others, of Confucius, and Lao-tse, of King Wen and the Duke of Chou, and of all the others and others. I will surely go on reading them for my wisdom is only my own, and how can I know another's unless I am open to him? In that realization, perhaps, my wisdom goes beyond the Sages of old. For I know that not only does Tao and God become manifest in one's self, but also in another, indeed in all others. In truth, the total wisdom is there only when we are all One, when the total Tao of us all takes place on this earth.

But let me only follow the Master and state how I want to be. This from the *Ta Chuan:*

"In this way (by looking upward to Heaven and its signs, and downward to Earth and its lines), man comes to resemble heaven and earth, he is not in conflict with them. His wisdom embraces all things; and his Tao brings order into the whole world; therefore he does not err. He is active everywhere but does not let himself be carried away. He rejoices in heaven and has knowledge of fate; therefore he is free of care. He is content with his circumstances and genuine in his kindness; therefore he can practice love."

Is this not beautiful? Yes. At times, I can practice it. That is, when I am with Tao. When I die, I trust that I will be in Tao, as well. So come, spirit of *I Ching,* come to me. I, Ch'ien, the Creative one, I know my own wisdom, and I know it in humility. I know it and you and bow to you. Come to me and let us unite. For now I see you. I see you, O Wise One; I see you as Compound of Many Wise Ones, and Uniquely Wise in your own. I bow to you and I see you bow to me, and I am joyous. I feel like a young boy, or a marrying maiden, and I am full of joyful folly. Do I sound like your names? Yes, indeed, for such do I feel myself to be. I am in the flow of Tao. To thee do I bow, oh *I Ching,* as I see you bow to me, and we two, we old men, we dance as did the men of old. We shed our decorum when we "know", for to be wise is to laugh, and to be heard ten thousand miles!

V

My meditations, in time, had left me "tranquil", as *I Ching* itself had expressed it, but something was still lacking. I had bitten through the yellow meat of the mushroom, had achieved the measure of wisdom of which I was capable, but the joy and tranquillity were not enough. What was missing, I knew, was that other "yellow" aspect of the mushroom: the Golden Flower. I missed something I felt I could have—that spirit-body, subtle-body, golden flower. I missed the sense of spirit transformed, of eternity gained in the golden light. I longed for that Heavenly Heart, or as it is said in The Book of the Yellow Castle: "*In the purple hall of the city of jade dwells the god of utmost emptiness and life. The Confucians call it the centre of emptiness; the Buddhists, the terrace of life; the Taoists, the ancestral land, or the yellow castle, or the dark pass, or the space of former Heaven. The Heavenly Heart is like the dwelling place, the Light is the master.*"

This golden flower of many names was not yet vouchsafed me. I had meditated much in my life, and had many great experiences. I had known the Tao as the One in the Many of my life experiences. I had known my own wholeness but not the Golden Flower.

I knew the sacredness of action in non-action, of non-action in action. This, indeed, had been what I had learned which led to my tranquillity. Thus, I knew I could not "produce" the Golden Flower. Yet, I needed it. Should I ask *I Ching?* Or meditate further? I decided upon the latter course. I read, once again, the *T'ai I Chin Hua Tsung Chih,* The Secret of the Golden Flower. I read the commentaries of Sages, of Chinese, of the German Sinologue, and of the Great Psychologist. They understood, but I was alone. They all were great men, beyond me, and I was alone. I accepted my aloneness.

In my aloneness, I reflected. My dreams had told me of the yellow mushroom of *I Ching,* itself a golden flower. It had called itself also a Swiss chalet and an African hut, or combination of these. The English Queen had come to me, telling me of her father's suffering, of his being haunted by the spirits of his ancestors, as I had been, and that I was doing his work. Yes, this had happened, but I had not understood just why this was so. What was the Tao of it?

As I sat, I felt that sitting with me, to one side, were three wise men: Confucius, Buddha, and Lao-tse. They sat in smiling and joyous meditation, and I smiled, too, for in my heart I knew that Confucianism, Buddhism, and Taoism could be as One within me. I looked at each meditating Sage, and saw that each had a Golden Flower shining from within, in the region of his navel. They, too, showed a Light, between the eyes, and I knew that their Light could circulate freely. I smiled and was happy. I was in the living presence of the Sages. I then looked at my own navel, and was startled to see that there, too, was a golden flower, shining. But that did not satisfy me, and I did not know why. I reflected that, indeed, the mere presence of these great Sages would give me the Golden Flower; I reflected that I had, indeed, spent a full life but could have achieved, in reality, more than I did. I reflected that it was now almost one year since I had begun my *I Ching* meditations, and that was long enough, as the Masters had said, for the Golden Flower to be produced; provided, of course, that the man be right. The Sages said that the wrong method in the right hands produced results, and the right method in the wrong hands produced disaster. I knew, in my bones, that I was a "right man."

But I was ill; why? I reached between my eyes, and knew that there was no Heavenly Light there. I knew, too, that I was sick because something else was missing. What was it? I had forgotten the task given me in my dreams by the English King! My soul called out to include not only the Golden Light of the East, of Confucius, Buddha, and Lao-tse, but to include the Light of the West! Had not my dream spoken of the Swiss chalet of the Great Psychologist? And the African hut? Of course!

Then I knew I had to make a pilgrimage to the West: I had to see the English King, in the manner of the Great Psychologist: by continuing the exploration within. More, I had to see the newly dead black Afro-American who had been assassinated. I had to learn from them, to help one and to receive help from the other. It was presumptuous, but I had to do it. The three Sages nodded. So I left on my voyage to the "other world"; I went to Heaven, and this is what I saw:

I saw first that with Heaven is also Hell, for they are both part of that other world. I saw suffering souls, waiting to sink back to earth; they were *kuei,* ghost-beings waiting for re-birth.

Some of these I knew. Some seemed to long for my blood, the ming-eros and hsing-logos of my being. They longed to be free from their purgatory, it seemed, and either rise, as *shen,* and return to Tao as a Golden Flower, or sink as *kuei* and be reborn. Purgatory was to be stuck in the middle, and have neither. I shrank from them; I was not ready for them. And here it was that I saw the English King. He told me that he had waited for me. He said that his inability to speak was because he had been as nothing. He had been a king, and had all the pomp and glory, but he had been as nothing; for he had not been a God-man, like the black man who had just died. The Black Man, the American black minister, had been a King without a crown; he had been a black Christ, a preacher of love and non-violence, a savior of his race and of mankind. This priest was truly a King. Thus spoke the King of England, and he moaned and he sighed. For he had everything and nothing, and the other King had nothing and everything.

I comforted the King of England in this way: I told him that he had been a leader and King of a great nation, of one of the greatest nations of the West; that his nation and his continent had given mankind Art, and Science, and Literature; that these were great gifts that mankind needed desperately. I told him that his daughter was happy and knew that there would be a rebirth of the nation's greatness. I told him that his kingship was symbolic of the "many", of the diversity, of the variety of the West's achievements. But he, this King, smiled only a little. He was not assuaged.

So, I rose higher and I came to the recently dead minister, the modern Black Christ. He looked robust and happy and joyous, and was humming "Free at Last." He said nothing, but looked at me with deep eyes of compassion. Though he spoke not, I heard his rich words telling me that he was, indeed, like a Christ, for he had the Christ within him, and he was a Christian priest of God. But he was, too, like a Jew, like Moses, for he had a dream, and a vision of the Promised Land. His vision was that of the Second Coming, of God coming to Earth once again; but now it would be in every man; the Second Coming would be the One in the Many. The Messiah would appear in Everyman. That would be the Promised Land. This was his vision and he knew that it would come to pass. His life and his death were all part of it, and he would continue his work on his present plane of existence. He told me, too, that he knew of my efforts, and that he knew of the English King, and that we were all involved in that greater work of God becoming Man on earth.

As he spoke, as this African-American, Christ-King spoke, the English King rose and heard his words, which were wordless. And the stuttering king knew that words which are deep are wordless; he knew that his stuttering spirit was because of the profundity of the task; that he represented the Godless, but still creative spirit of Art, Science, and Literature; that these would speak anew; that they and he would be reborn, but no longer Godless.

The two Kings embraced and I was electrified. The paradox: light and dark, powerless king, kingless power; impotent wisdom, potent love; past-future; all these and more, embraced and intertwined. I looked up at them in Heaven, the embraced two

God-Men. And I looked down on earth at the Oriental Sages, also God-Men. I saw, once again, the three and the two, united. With me, there were six, and six is the number of the God become manifest in man. So I knew that I, even I, must become a God-Man. Indeed, I knew that I was already—as we all are—God-men. With that, I looked in the mirror, and saw a golden flower sitting between my brows. I looked at my navel and saw a golden flower, but within it was an image of man, like one that a great Western scientist-artist had painted, enclosed in a circle. For now Man was in the center. In that moment I stood between Heaven and Earth, but I could not stay there for long.

I came out of my meditation and went for a walk. But I was hardly out of the house before my great-granddaughter showed me some seeds she had received in a packet from America. A friend had sent her some seeds of a flower called Cosmos, which would grow into flowers of red, of white, and of pink—with centers of gold. I smiled, for I knew that without the seeds of the feminine, without the participation of the solid earth flower, the masculine golden flower would be only as of air. I did not, even yet, have my Golden Flower, really! But I would wait, with *wu-wei,* with action in non-action, and non-action in action—for that is our way, and the way of the one who would be holy.

I waited, thus, for many days. While I waited, a very galling thing happened. I began to suffer from what one calls allergy of the seeds, in Chinese, hay fever in English. I had, as a child, been plagued with the itching of the nose, the dripping of eyes and nose, the sneezes of death which accompany such an ailment, but it had passed as I had matured, to return only twice in my life. Both periods of return had been when I had gone deep into meditation and experienced the dark and unloving character of the great Yin of mother earth. Now, to my chagrin, I was experiencing the allergy again! Was I a child? Was I merely a poor, loveless little boy who could not take the seeds and pollen of the great Yin? I was angry, and grew angry at the times of lovelessness and stubborness of women in my life. Angry not only at women, of course, but with all those things having to do with the earth, and the feminine, and the giving and receiving of life: with the body, with food and nourishment, with security, with recompense for work, with the experience of being loved and understood. But I felt mostly the negative of all of these, and I felt friction and dryness. I felt that the seeds of Mother Earth were entering my nose and that they were dismembering me. It was as if the "manyness" and randomness and complexity of the birth principle in nature was too much for me to take. Mother nature was casting her seeds about haphazardly, in plenitude and without regard—for some would survive and some not—and these same seeds were entering my nose and making me swell and weep and be dismembered, not counting as a person.

So, I understood something. I had come to terms with the Yang, with the God, with the masculine, and was no longer "arrogant"—had achieved "tranquillity"; but now I was suffering from the Yin, the Goddess, the feminine, from its negativity of lovelessness and impersonality. Before I had suffered from the impersonality of the masculine, through power and arrogance; now I was suffering the impersonality of the feminine, through lovelessness and dismemberment. What would the *I Ching* say to that? What would the Yin aspect of *I Ching* tell me now? Would it come as a loveless, impersonal aspect of the universe, dismembering me? Or, as my little great-granddaughter would do it, planting the "seeds of the Cosmos" in a loving, personal way? I asked, and threw the coins.

You might guess what I threw—it seems so obvious, now. I threw all Yin lines, resulting in number 2, *K'un*, the Receptive! Earth, above and below. Broken lines of the dark, yielding, receptive, primal power of Yin. The changing lines were six in the third and fifth places. You may read it, if you wish, but I want to pick out the parts which touched me.

The attribute of the hexagram is devotion. She is the complement of Ch'ien, the Creative, for she completes him. K'un represents nature in contrast to heaven, space as against time, the female-maternal as against the male-paternal.

And the Judgment? It speaks of "perseverance of a mare." The horse belongs to earth just as the dragon belongs to heaven. "The mare combines the swiftness of the horse with the gentleness and devotion of the cow." Ah, that is what I need to have just now, do I not? Yes. The Judgment says, too, that if the superior man tries to lead, he goes astray. The Sinologue comments: *"The superior man lets himself be guided; he does not go ahead blindly, but learns from the situation what is demanded of him and then follows this intimation from fate."* Wise words. But wiser yet is Confucius:

"Perfect indeed is the sublimity of the Receptive.
All beings owe their birth to it, because it receives the heavenly with devotion."

Ah, would that I could be so sublime and "receive the heavenly with devotion." For the Comment on the Commentary says the *"Receptive is that which brings to birth, that which takes the seed of the heavenly into itself and gives to beings their bodily form. Through it, all individual beings attain success."*

Yes, that explains my difficulty. Nature achieves through the individual and particular, for she realizes and completes the creative which begins in the pleroma. My poor nose just cannot contain all those creative seeds!

The Commentator continues: *"While the Creative shields things—that is, covers them from above—the Receptive carries them, like a foundation that endures forever. Infinite accord with the Creative is its essence. . .The movement of the Creative is a direct forward movement, and its resting state is standstill; the movement of the Receptive is an opening out, and in its resting state it is closed.*" How beautiful! Further, the Commentator: "*to roam the Earth like a mare, yielding, devoted, to further through perseverance.*" Would that I could achieve this great gift of the Receptive, Earth, K'un!

The Judgment goes on, saying it is "*favorable to find friends in the west and south, to forego friends in the east and north.*" That means, of course, from the Arrangement of the Inner-World of King Wen, the Sequence of Later Heaven, that one should seek, when under the sign of the Receptive, the guidance of Tui and Li, the Daughters, and forego the help of K'an and Chen, the Sons. Again the aid of the feminine Joy and Light, and foregoing the Abysmal and Arousing.

The Sinologue says:

"*Man attains eternity if he does not strive vaingloriously to achieve everything of his own strength but quietly keeps himself receptive to the impulses flowing to him from the creative forces.*" All true, and too true. But what of the Image? It says it beautifully:

The earth's condition is receptive devotion.
Thus the superior man who has breadth of character
Carries the outer world.

And the lines? The specific message to me? Six in the third place:

Hidden lines.
One is able to remain persevering.
If by chance you are in the service of a king,
Seek not works, but bring to completion.

The Commentaries speak of "hiding one's beauty." One needs to be free of vanity, to conceal his abilities until the time is right. He may enter public life, but "*the wise man gladly leaves fame to others."* He seeks only to release the forces which bear good fruit.

The other changing line, six in the fifth place:

A yellow lower garment brings supreme good fortune.

The commentaries say that yellow, the color of earth and the middle, is that which is reliable and genuine. The lower garment is that of aristocratic reserve. Thus a man is quietly genuine; beauty is within.

Later commentaries say of this:

"His beauty is within, but it gives freedom to his limbs and expresses itself in his works. This is the perfection of beauty."

Finally, of the whole hexagram:

The way of the Receptive—how devoted it is!
It receives heaven into itself and acts in its own time.

Thus am I quieted and made thoughtful. Before, when I struggled with my namesake of Ch'ien in *I Ching,* I had to face the problem of Power and my arrogance. Finally, with perseverance and dialogue and steadfastness, I overcame it and came to Keeping Still, and Tranquillity. Now that I face the other aspect of *I Ching,* the Yin and the Receptive, I am compelled to cope with the problem of fame and vanity! Ah, it is sad: first arrogance, now vanity and boastfulness. But it is clear: if I can submit to the power of Ch'ien, of Heaven Above, and become as K'un, the receptive earth, modestly and with devotion, then the seeds of creativity will not puff me up or make me weep or itch! I should follow the example of my great-granddaughter and accept the seeds modestly and plant them. Those which are viable will live; the others will die and, like the ghost-spirits of *kuei,* return to receptive mother earth for a different re-birth!

Oh, K'un, oh Receptive Mother Earth, I hear with devotion. I hear and I understand. With *wu-wei,* like you, I receive.

VI

Many days passed as I suffered the restraint upon my action, upon my understanding, upon my capacity to produce or sustain the "Golden Flower". My poor nose, with its sensitivity to the seeds: I buried it deeper and deeper into the earth of K'un, in every way that I could. I did it literally and concretely; I did it symbolically. But no rest came.

As if by Fate, two books arrived from the West and from the South—just as *I Ching* had told me. From England came a book about re-incarnation, and from Turkey a book about extra-ordinary powers of perception. Each was by a lady—the one a charming and active medium, the other a dull and repetitive scientist. But both women annoyed me. I thought: Is it the seeds of these women which clog my nose and make me annoyed? But I read. I saw that the West was beginning to understand what we understood by the Golden Flower. Here, they were calling it the Supra-Physical, or "energy-fields". I saw, too, that the Sensitives in the West were becoming aware of the Celestial Body, the aura around the person showing the state of his soul. They even talked of the various centers of the body, similar to the centers that we knew from *wei lu* at the tip of the spine, to *ni-wan* at the top of the head. They understood that these energy centers were as lights and vortices from which and to which the soul does flow, and from the Yin-Yang of the universe the energies circulate. I saw that the West was beginning to catch up with us in the East. I saw that not only did I need to include the English king, I needed to incorporate the European and Asia-Minorian ladies!

But it was hard for me. I took in their scientific descriptions of the "energy field." I accepted that the Subtle-Body was partially a result of successive re-incarnations of the soul. I accepted that the field that was described was both the "vital" one, associated with the physical body and its health, and the emotional-mental one.

Best of all, I knew that a sensitive woman had described the flow of the energy field as if in a figure-eight, with the center in the region of the Heart. Was that not what our Masters had always said? Of course. Now these Western women were showing it, too.

But I was feeling more and more sad. The "seeds" had driven me deeper and deeper into sadness and despair. It was as if all was true, but utterly meaningless!

So, I sank further into despair and into darkness. Why was I so annoyed with these Western women? Was this the reason for my allergy? Do such feminine seeds cause me to suffer at my nose and eyes? I ruefully recalled the injunction of the Masters, to "look at the end of one's nose" and to "concentrate upon the Eyes." I was doing so, but sadly. I disliked those women, I realized, because they were so different from our old Chinese image of woman! They were not even women. They were self-satisfied, arrogant, and stupid! Now, I laughed. For the days of the concubine, of the charming little girl following her lord and master daintily are long since over. But I cannot accept it. How, in my darkness, can I receive seeds which will nourish me; how will I produce the "golden flower", or, at least, energize the one I have already?

I realized that I was, indeed, in the Abysmal, with K'an. I realized, too, that I longed for Li, the Light, which would free me, and thereby produce the Golden Flower. At last, I saw that K'un, the Receptive, was feeding the seeds of the Golden Flower into my being. I was experiencing the arrogance of Yin, just as I had experienced my own arrogance. The crushing of my vanity was taking place. I knew that how I received these seeds, how I took the blow to my ancient, masculine, Chinese vanity, would determine whether, in truth, I would weep and suffer from the seeds, or whether I would be renewed, fructified and enriched by the seeds. The seeds would take effect, anyway; it was up to my K'un, my receptivity, whether I would experience them with joy or sadness.

So, I understood. I sank deeply into myself. I sank into my own abysmal flesh and darkness. I sought out every crevice, every orifice, every atom of flesh and sought to have it open to Li and the light. I searched out not only the seven traditional Centers and let the circulation take place, but I sought out every corpuscle, every fragment of my body. Come, O Light, I called, come and Circulate. Come, from every life which I have ever lived. Come and let me breathe you into myself. Let the power of your light-seeds take root in my flesh-earth. Let the Golden Flower of Light breathe through me. Let it glow and make me feel alive. Let it awaken me to the endless births that I have had. Let it flow and heal the places of sickness, the places of weakness. Let it fill up the places of soul-energy where the "sappers", as I say, have depleted me. Lift me out of my abyss of K'an and unite with me into the deepest Golden Flower. Such was my silent prayer from the atoms of my flesh.

That night I dreamt. I dreamt that people came from the land of the Dead. It was the Land of the Occult. They came in great numbers to me. Many, many were women, but also there were men. I saw a great dark woman with great dark eyes whom I have known throughout eternity. She had been in agony from the "Seeds of Despair" but was now about to smile from the Seeds of Light. I knew that all these creatures of the Dead represented the manyness of the Seeds, and that how I would encompass them, feed them, be fed by them, would determine the shape and form of the Golden Light. They came from the Larger World and from the Smaller World. They pulled and they gave. Each was a mystery. Each was like a different *I Ching,* and I was astonished. For not only was there that great and good holy Book of *I Ching,* upon which our Sages had struggled and given their Seeds, but there were "books" and seeds which I did not know, or knew only in small ways. These seeds were the secret and arcane; they were astrology and chirology, tarot and fortune-telling, and of wisdoms of which I had no name. End of dream.

When I awakened, I saw that I needed to apprehend those seeds, and go beyond even that which I had comprehended from our great Chinese Masters. I saw that this was what was meant by Seeds of the Queen, to unite the dull Science, and the arrogant English clairvoyance, with the wisdom and depth of our Chinese Tao. But to do this in my own being would, in truth, force the destruction of both my arrogance and my vanity, for it would stretch me beyond every system that I had ever known.

The seeds were changing me. I was a youth, and no longer an old man. I was being and about to be reborn. It was as if the Light were circulating with every breath. I felt the light touch every corpuscle, every hair, every atom of flesh. I felt my flesh respond.

Now I was outside myself and watched a figure-eight dance of light-seed and dark-flesh. I saw Li and K'an as if in a figure-eight dance. They swirled and they parted. They united and joined together. They became as swirling bits of dust-light, and light illuminating specks of dust.

I saw that this light, which had been there always, was my Celestial Body, my Soul-Being, my Subtle-Body, which was both eternal and contemporary. It was effected, like Karma, and effecting. This light, I saw, this union of Li and K'an, was not only around me, but around everyone. It was of different colors and depths, depending upon the development and state of the individual. It was around plants (especially mushrooms!) and even around crystals. All living things had much of it, and all objects had it as well. Now I know why the Golden Flower was also called the Diamond Body, and the Celestial place, for it was around the diamonds as a great two-fold level of energy. One level came into the diamond and moved out again. This was not the reflection of ordinary light, but a kind of plaited light-energy like the braids of hair.

The second level moved out from the center of the stone, and seemed to have its origin there. It was extremely luminous. Thus it was, I knew, that Sages had called the Golden Flower a Diamond Body, for the Central Self of the Tao, in the center of the navel and the Heart, was like the light from an actual Diamond. All this I saw, for I saw that magnets have colors, of red in the South and blue in the North. We have always known this to be true, have we not?

I saw the expansion of the light, but now I listened to the Light of Li speak words to the Darkness of K'an. I heard words of love. As I listened to the mysterious incestuous words of union, I knew that the true origin and end of the Cosmos, the seeds which made it all grow and decline and be reborn, and the end to which all beings tended was Love. I, Ch'ien, in my wisdom, found that my wisdom was no wisdom, without the Light of Love.

I listened intently to the sounds. It was as whisperings. It was as the words of lovers, and I was thrilled by them. I could not hear them all, this song of union, but this is some of what I heard:

Oh, Li, my Sister. I, K'an, the abysmal depth of the flesh and body and matter and temporality, I speak. I speak out of my limitation and my concreteness. I speak out of my masculine depth as a Son of the Great K'un. Under the Moon I speak, with suffering of my Lightlessness. Come and fill every pore with your Light. Love me, and envelop me, and let me embrace thee! For my being is only as dead matter, as dust, without your pure light!

Oh, K'an, my brother, I, Li, speak. It is true I am light, but I am clinging light. I do not exist unless I attach myself to thee. Can light be seen without a medium? And you are that medium. I come and enclose myself upon thee. I long to touch every crevice, every cranny, every corner. I envelop myself in thy being as thirstily as water upon parched land. Which is thirstier, the water or the land? They crawl toward each other: it is as if the flesh creeps in anticipation and the waves of hungry desire which are invisible are the most real! Thus do I long for thee! Come, let us dance, let us make the music of the Golden Flower. Let us circulate in our Eight, and let all centers glow! Let us unite in the Gladness of the Tao, of the union of Yin and Yang, as of K'un and Ch'ien, and of ourselves and our own being. Let this mystery increase, until the great union envelops all that exists in a joyous cacaphony of Love.

Such were the words which I, Ch'ien, being old, and having celebrated a life of seventy-five years, being wise and foolish, being what I was—such were the words I heard. But the words were also as flesh, for they spoke from within my inner darkness and light. They spoke as words from within the ear, going out, and from within the eye as light, going out. Can you not perceive that? Do you not see each other's light, each other's subtle body and Golden Flower in the Light of the Eye? Of course. And so did I celebrate the Golden Flower, in my Being and my Becoming. For I was whole. I bowed to *I Ching.* I had no more need to query of it, now, for I had it inside my bones. The Light and Golden Flower upon which it fed and from which it got its sustenance now resided also in me. For I knew that the Light, the Golden Flower which was around all things was around *I Ching* and around me, and it poured from within out, and from out within.

And so did I, Ch'ien, almost faint from joy and happiness. It was as if not only I and my wife and my children were all united, but it was as if all mankind were united and all the beings of the universe. When I thought I would burst with the greatness of it, I found myself here, in the Garden among you all. Look there upon that Great Tree! Do I not see the Golden Flower? Yes, I see that six-petaled, and eight-petaled one. I see, too, the Tai-Chi-t'u, for it doth glow as do we all. I see that the Golden Flower has been realized, that each of you has a Golden Flower, and the Sages, and the Queens, have become as Gods. Nay, that the Gods have become as men!

THE MEDIUM, SOPHIE-SARAH

THE MEDIUM, SOPHIE-SARAH

I

My name is Sophie-Sarah. As a child and youth I was also called "gypsy," "fortune-teller," "Madame Sophie" and "Sophie, the Medium." As you might guess from this, I have dabbled in the occult, but before I speak of that, I feel that I must tell you something of my background. The story of my personal life is less central to why I am here, I think, but I must tell you about "who I am," historically, before I can tell you about "Who I Am" as I discovered it through the great crisis of my life, which involved the occult.

I am well past fifty years old, but still look attractive, if I do say so myself. I was born in Rumania, but was conceived in Spain, before the First World War. My father was a talented but rather impractical inventor of Russian-Jewish extraction and my mother was a very strong Austro-Hungarian lady who combined the vitality and cleverness of her Jewish father (a businessman), and the beauty and intensity of her Greek mother. I have, in point of fact, inherited not only my name from my grandmothers (Sophia was my Greek grandmother's name, and Sarah was my father's mother's name) but also many of their traits. I was dark and intense and pretty, like my mother's mother, and impractical and dreamy like my father's mother. The point, though, is that in temperament and in appearance, I was more like a Spanish gypsy than anything else. Much of my life has been an internal struggle between gypsy and Jew.

I do not think that this conflict was engendered simply because I was conceived in Spain on a honeymoon trip and subject to the astrological influences surrounding the moment of conception. Rather, I firmly believe that I have lived several previous lives in Spain and that it was, in fact, the unsolved problems of these previous lives that were evoked by the chance event that my Jewish parents happened to spend their honeymoon there.

So, you see, I believe in re-incarnation. No, that is not quite right: I *know* that there is re-incarnation, but I know it for myself and neither can nor wish to prove it to anyone else. I shall have more to say about these previous lives in Spain and what they meant to me, but first I must tell you about the course of my present life.

I was a dreamy child. I liked to tell myself stories and to perform all sorts of magical tricks. I had a temper and was inclined to stormy outbursts. My parents were very good about both sides of me, allowing me to indulge my imaginative activity as a creative pastime and accepting my emotional intensity without spoiling me or encouraging pseudo-dramatics. I thus had a healthy upbringing and was enormously loved by and loving toward both of my parents. From what I have seen of my generation in Europe and America, I realize that my experience of family love and understanding was not at all typical. The separation between generations seems to grow wider and wider, but this was not true for me, nor for my children, or grandchildren.

The intensity and dreaminess, however, fostered a mystical and wild streak in me and inclined me more toward self-examination than might have been my nature otherwise.

Other than that I was quite normal. I was deeply loved by my parents, had plenty of food and comfort, friends, a good education, and was not deprived of my fantasy.

Throughout my childhood and adolescence, my parents and I wandered all over Europe, especially around the Mediterranean, in search of support for one or another of my father's inventions. Some of these inventions were successful, some not, but my mother made up for his impracticality with her ability to sew, to paint, and to charm people. We always had plenty of money, though few lasting relationships.

But I, what was I? From the age of nine or ten onwards, I was everybody's gypsy, astrologer, palmist, medium. At first it was a game I played; people indulged the cute play of the pretty child. As time went on, there was a growing belief in my "powers;" adults, even my parents, grew to respect me and to put value on my "gifts." This was particularly surprising because, at least until the advent of Hitler, World War II and the Holocaust, most people were highly rationalistic and very suspicious, if not downright hostile, toward anything "occult." Because of the irrational destructiveness of Hitler and the horrors of the Holocaust, people do not ridicule the irrational as they did, particularly the irrationally destructive. Imagine, then, what such a rationalistic environment, giving adulation to a "mystical" and "gifted" child might do to her.

Can you imagine? It inflated me. Well, I was, as I say, a healthy child, so by the time I was in my middle teens and beginning to be more involved with boys and love than with "astral journeys," I tried to get away from that kind of attention from others to me. It wasn't easy. I could accomplish this only by convincing the "others" and myself that it was all a fake, that I was no "medium" and had no powers of predicting the future, reading character, or the like.

When Hitler came to power in 1933, my parents evaluated what was happening and wisely decided to emigrate to the United States. I used that change of milieu to change my personality. From the age of 19 onwards, I turned away from the occult and tried to live a conventional life. It was easy for me. At first, in America, my parents encouraged me to continue to dabble in the occult. I tried to convince them that it was all fake, and I nearly succeeded, but, I am afraid, I convinced myself more than I did them. Nonetheless, life went on happily for me, by and large.

I later married a man who was a psychologist and, for a time, I flirted again with my "mediumship" by taking an interest in his projective methods of personality diagnosis. I would occasionally look at the results of his Rorschach tests and say more about his subjects and patients than he was able to tell from his more rational, scientific methods. Since he is very intuitive himself, this was no ordinary accomplishment. I grew afraid of this talent (thinking it "pseudo") and backed away from it. I satisfied myself with the raising of our four lovely children. I had been an only child and very much wanted to have several children, not because I had been lonely as a child, but because I wanted the experience of family life and roots, rather than "specialness" and "wandering." We had friends and a good life together, including the usual problems and pains of all human beings. We were lucky enough, however, to be spared the greater pains, such as loss of a child or other loved ones; or poverty, or disgrace. No, we had none of these.

So, for the most part, my life has been usual, except for the particular experiences the last several years. These have had to do with the occult and it is because of these occurrences, I think, that I find myself here among you.

About three years ago, I began having strange dreams and sleepless nights. I had always been a good dreamer and prided myself on my ability to interpret or cope with my dreams in such a way that I could use them in my development. I did this without the help of an analyst or books. Occasionally, I asked my husband what he thought of a dream and would profit from his reactions, but otherwise, I worked pretty much alone. In the past, some of my dreams had been deep or "big," but these new dreams were different. They were of another order than the ones I had theretofore. These dreams seemed more like "objective" events, coming to me from outside myself. I had known about the "objective psyche," both from reading and from my husband, who was an analyst trained in the method of C. G. Jung. I had tried Jung's ways of understanding dreams, and had found them very satisfactory. But these dreams were different. Surely, they were like the "objective psyche" but they seemed more concrete, more specific, more detailed than the symbolic reality that Jung had written about and that I had experienced earlier.

In addition, I began to have unexplained intensity of feelings: deep depression and wild elation. I had always been emotionally intense and had lived deeply, both alone and with others, but these swings were different. Was I undergoing another "change of life?" I had experienced the physiological "change" without incident some years earlier. Was I experiencing the first stages of madness? Neither was true. I knew in my heart that neither was true, but I needed reassurance, so I went to respected scientific sources for help. A medical friend convinced himself and me that I was not organically ill by giving me a complete physical examination. A psychologist friend was kind enough to give me a battery of tests, which convinced us both that I was not losing my mind.

I was thrown back upon myself. I could easily have confided in my husband what was going on inside of me. Indeed, I had kept him fully informed until this point, but he seemed to worry too much about me, and I saw that this might well take him away from all the important duties in his life, as well as take away the pleasures and joys of our relationship otherwise. In deepest truth, however, I really wanted to be utterly alone with these new experiences. Some unformulated voice was stirring in me. It was saying that it wanted me to take on its message quite alone, at least for a time, and that I should share it with no one else, not even my husband. So, with some trepidation, I accepted this internal hint and waited in silence.

After a time, several strands of word-fantasy began to make themselves clear. They would repeat, as questions, or as commands. Sometimes it would be "Read Kabbalah!" or "The Ten Commandments must be reinterpreted." At other times there would be a wail of moaning, as if the dead were coming back to cry to me. But through all of it came a persistent question: *"Six million dead Jews. Why six million dead Jews?"* Sometimes the question came quietly as if in despairing resignation. Sometimes it came as a demand that I answer this question at once, with the implication that if I did not answer adequately, I would be killed. Again the question came as if God, Himself, Blessed be He, were being asked the question and I was present to hear the answer. Still again, the question came as if all Jews were silently posing this question to themselves, to the world, and to God.

In all of these ways the question came. It came with ever-increasing persistence and intensity. I had great difficulty understanding why this question was presented to me, as if either I must answer it or I must ask it of God. I had not suffered the Holocaust of Hitler and the concentration camps personally. Some remote relatives, it is true, had died in the ovens, and I was saddened by that, of course, but I had not personally suffered a family loss.

Like every Jew, I was overjoyed with the advent of Israel. Like most Jews, however, I also felt my identity as a human being as well as a Jew, did not plan to go to Israel to live, and—when I did think of these things—thought more about the unity of Mankind, the plight of black people, of the poor and hungry and oppressed of Asia, than I did about the fate of the Jews.

So, I wondered, why was I chosen for this question? Then I laughed. Are not the Jews "chosen?" Without regard to their virtue or the justice of it? Do not Jews customarily answer a question with a question? Of course. And that, perhaps, was why God chose me, just because I was Jewish, and could question, and, maybe, could laugh.

But my laughter died in my cheeks. A chill overcame me as I thought of my childhood "mediumship" and the games I had played with it. Suddenly I felt a deep shame for the tricks and games that I had played with my occult talent. I cried all day and the next, and felt an increasing agony. Even in the midst of my agony, I knew that I was being unfair to myself or, rather, that something in me was being unfair to me. Why was I so seriously responsible for playing like a gypsy or medium in my childhood? Do not other children play this way, too? Why should I be so hard on myself?

The answer came coldly and deeply, without compassion: I had a gift which I had rejected. In order to be like all other children, in order to be "assimilated" into community life and to be an ordinary girl, I had abandoned the gift of God. For God had given me this gift of mediumship and relation with the occult. I had been Chosen just for this. It was important. How many Jews had God chosen for mediumship? Not many. Not many since the

Witch of Endor. God chose the Jews as prophets, and as rabbis, and as doctors and scientists. That He did often enough. He also chose them as victims and as His Son. But He did not frequently choose them to be gypsy-witches and occult transmitters. He didn't do that because He did not much approve of Jews doing that, and I was not certain if He cared for it in anybody else, either. At least the Jewish God did not like it. But I, in any case, had been so Chosen, and had misused, then rejected my calling. I had sold my birthright for the security of middle-class life.

God, apparently, could accept "ordinariness" less than anything else. At least from Jews. Jews had to be "special." I had rejected my specialness, and I had better reconsider. These thoughts, I was convinced, came from something beyond my own ego. If they did not come from God Himself, they came from an internal Authority that I had to respect.

I realized that I must accept my mediumship, and use it in a way which would be acceptable to God, or to that Authority inside me which was connected with that same talent. When I submitted to the truth of this realization, I immediately received other messages from within, which let me see that I had spent several previous lifetimes in Spain, been a gypsy, a fortune-teller and a medium several times before. Incarnations back, I had even been a male, a deeply mystical Jew who had known Moses de Leon, the writer of the Zohar, and had made great strides in coming to know the God of the Kabbalah. Later on, I had been a gypsy who had used her occult powers badly, for selfish ends, and this was the real reason that I was so shy of using my talents in this lifetime. I remembered only too well how I had betrayed my calling when I pretended to contact the dead, for money and for prestige. My body had suffered greatly because of this: I had painful leg amputations, loss of beauty, and a death in pain and ugliness. On another occasion, I had been called a "witch" and burned at the stake, but my witchery had been true: I had abused a real talent for the sake of power and evil.

All of this revealed a neglected part of myself as a woman involved with the occult. It opened up an area which had long been neglected by God, Himself, as we witness from the Bible. He had encouraged it, all the same, even among the Jews, in Kabbalah. In short, it became clear that God's left hand and right hand were doing different things.

These new thoughts preoccupied me. I once again began reading in the occult and I opened myself to my mediumship.

Promptly as I opened myself, I had two dreams. The first one was as follows:

Many women come to me from the occult world, the "after-world." I am told that I am going to expand more and more in that direction, and that my powers will increase greatly. What had once been "witchy," negative, and fraudulent would take on a positive quality. A "dark woman" with very dark eyes comes to me and looks deeply into my own. Is she my "self?" End of dream.

Some days later, I dreamed the following:

I am deep, deep, beneath the worlds of Gehenna, of Hell. I am looking at backsides. At this deep, deep place, I am given the Mitzvah by God to speak about and explain the *Shuah*, the Holocaust. It is denied everywhere. They say: "How is this possible; how can one speak who has not concretely suffered it?" But it is true. I will speak because I am so ordained by God. And it is so, via the dead, through six million who want to speak, through the medium. End of dream.

The second dream was just in those words, and I could not make it any different. Thus it was that I was led into. . . .

II

". . . .and thus it was that I was led into . . . ." I could not finish these words. For some days I was suspended, not knowing what it was I was being "led into." Nor can I tell you now that I know for certain where I was led. I was not "told" that it was Hell or Purgatory, or any such place, though I believe that it was a kind of Gehenna. Nay, I know that it was a Gehenna, but I also believe that there are several Gehinnom, many states had circles of being in hell. "Planes of existence" is the phrase I have heard, and that, too, is what I mean, not in a pale theosophical sense, but as a living reality.

So, then, I was led into a Gehenna in which I beheld a vision. The vision was of a vast number of people suffering in agony. They were in all states of torment, twisting in torment. They were starved and burned and heated in furnaces. They were being humiliated. Little boys were hanging from ropes by their necks; little girls were forced to watch their mothers being raped. It was all of the flesh, yet all the figures were as wraiths. I knew that all of these were living images of the *Shuah*, the Holocaust. The people were undergoing the agonies of the unspeakable Hells which were inflicted upon them. I knew that these were images of the past, the living images of torment and despair as they had existed historically, and would exist for eternity. This sin against mankind would exist forever and could not be expunged. Yet I knew—and do not ask how I knew this, it was given to me to know in as real a way as the fact that I am here to tell you what I experienced—I knew that the living beings who had experienced all these horrors were no longer here. They were mercifully on other planes of existence. They had either already been reborn in new lives on earth, or in other states of being. In short, they had been "re-incarnated" in various states and were free of the horrors that they had endured.

Yet the horror continued. What did it mean? I became aware that just above the grey sea of suffering humanity was a figure of a little man, standing at a lectern. He was gesticulating and preaching and raving in a highly emotional state, trying to affect this mass of people. His drama was extraordinary: he would raise his arms up high; he would clasp his hands together in front of his chest with an anguished show of feeling and intensity; he would let his arms drop between his knees, as if summoning up all the truths from the depths, with conviction, to make his point. The man wept, he snorted, he cried; he spoke deeply and seriously; he spoke softly and reasonably. He went on and on and on and on.

I could not make out his face. It was vague. I strained my eyes and then moved in closer. Can you not guess who it was I saw? Can you not imagine who it was who spoke in such a highly dramatic way? Who else would be required to suffer the pain of Hell in this way? To preach one's message to the despairing, suffering souls to whom one has caused unspeakable anguish, pain, and humiliation? It was, of course, Adolf Hitler.

I thought: How sensible a punishment. No, not a punishment, since no "punishment" could possibly repay that man for the pain and destruction he had caused. No, it was a kind of ironic truth. That man had a mission, a belief; he was, he thought, a Messiah for the people of the earth. Let him, now, convince his victims of his vision. Let him, now, be allowed the full use of his powers; let him see the pain and anguish and misery he has caused. It occurred to me that Hitler perhaps never grasped the immensity of all the pain and anguish and misery he had caused, because it would have killed him on the spot. Who, among us, can really see all the pain we have caused and allow it to continue? None, for we must all rationalize it, and say that it is for a "higher cause" or in proper "retribution" and other such explanations. But here is Hitler, required to explain, testify and convince his victims, for eternity.

They cannot be convinced, of course, can they?

Or can they? What is "eternity" after all? Can any of us really conceive of what "eternity" is? Is not the anguish of unbearable pain an eternity when it is more than an instant? Or, oppositely, the impossibility of containing the ecstasies of love for more than a little while, without "bursting?" What good is the "eternity" of punishment? Is this what the Lord, Blessed and Praised be He, wants? Does He get pleasure from endless retribution? Does an "eye for an eye," "tooth for a tooth" mean just that? Must we forever remain with that level of justice, a primitive kind of vengeance? Even when we rationally add that the Lord meant no *more* than an eye for an eye, no *more* than a tooth for a tooth? Yes, and a life for a life? No *more* than that?

So, while I contemplated the vision of Hitler explaining himself and preaching to his victims, I began to have thoughts of the Deity, Himself. What kind of a God was this, to permit the horror of six million dead Jews? So, my thoughts turned from Hitler to God.

I thought that I saw Hitler with one eye. He was God Himself. Hitler was alive, as God was alive. God must be a madman, continually causing destruction and catastrophe with His unconsciousness of Himself, just like Hitler. For why else would He permit such destruction to occur?

So, I was asking, for the first time, *"Why six million dead Jews?"* The answer was beginning to filter down to me. This image of Hitler was like the pictures one had seen in the films, the voice one had heard on the radio. But it was also like the lectures I had heard from certain German Jews. I remember an "assimilationist" speaking at a lecture, seeming very much like Hitler in his manner. I recalled encountering other Jews who were like Hitler. They were weak, pompous little men, jealous of their power, for they had very little of it personally but used and identified with the power of their office, or institution. Or they were devious and unable to face a person directly. They were rigid and moralizing and unloving. I remembered them, and I felt revulsion.

"And God made man in His own image." All of these, then, are images of God. Then Hitler, too, is an image of God. Is it not God who is being made to face the horror of His works? Good, then let God face His own destructiveness and unconsciousness! Good, then let us, Mankind, cry out to the living God to face His horribleness!

God is not dead! That is an impertinence! God is too horrible to die! He ought to live forever just to see how horrible He is! It is just that our old images of God have to die. Even the image that Job had must die, and he had the most profound one after Moses, did he not?

I remembered then from Kabbalah that only Moses had a true intercourse with God. It was Moses who saw God "face to face" and was transfigured thereby. The story was that once he had this "intercourse," he could not longer have "intercourse" with his wife. Shades of Freud, who also gave up sexual union with his wife, once he had his own "vision." Job, my thoughts went on, had seen the "backside" of God. He alone was vouchsafed that vision. The consequence, as Jung had taught us, was God having to become Man. The first Messiah had come, and Christianity resulted thereby.

What, now, would God do about all Mankind seeing His "backside?" Not only did Job see the "backside" of God, in His plot with the devil, in His unconsciousness, and in His vast display of unrelated power, but all Mankind has now seen this! There are six million dead Jews, oh, my God, who have seen this! They, and we, know what a Hitler you are! We know that You are rotten and self-involved, concerned only about Your own power and visions and cannot even cope with the worm of Man. We see this, now, and what are You going to do about it? Send another Holocaust? How many would you like?

Such were my thoughts, as I contemplated the figure of Hitler speaking to the multitudes of suffering Jews. And I knew the answer, or thought I did: God must be so ashamed of His power and unconsciousness, that He must become Man in all of us. Not only His one Son of Christ as the Messiah which we Jews had not accepted, but at least in the Six Million Sons and Daughters of the destroyed Jews. What else could He possibly do than enter into the souls of the Six Million more deeply?

I remembered that in Kabbalah it was stated that the original Jews of Mt. Sinai numbered 600,000. Each face and being therein constituted an individual experience of God, and that there were, therefore, 600,000 different interpretations and views of the Torah! How deep and true! But what of the Six Million? That is the 600,000, an entire Jewish Totality, raised by ten times. A totality raised by a minyan, another totality. What could it mean? What "Gematria," what Kabbalistic meaning did this play of numbers intend? That God had given His message to the 600,000. The six hundred thousand had given way to the One, who was the Son of God. But now the One, who was the Son, would give way to the Six Million. There would be, at least Six Million Sons of God. God must, for His own sake, incarnate in all of them, and in all of us who could bear it. Only this, only this could possibly redeem the horribleness of God! Furthermore, God had to have this, in order to fulfill His own need for consciousness, and for humanness.

All this came to me as I viewed the horrible-laughable picture of Hitler preaching to the Jews!. . . .The words, the Six, the Six, kept coming to me. Six is the number of creation. God created man on the Sixth day, and He created man in His own image! The six, the six hundred thousand and the six million. So six is the number of

God creating Man, and in creating, Encountering Man, and, in encountering, Choosing Man, and, in choosing, finally, of Becoming Man. For God has to become Human. He has to become one and whole with His creation, which is less sinful than He, Blessed be His name!

As I viewed this view, and thought these thoughts, I saw the figure of Hitler cease his posturing and gesticulating and his impotent screaming. I saw him desist from this horror and begin to weep. I saw him fall flat on his face before the multitude of Jews. I saw him beg for forgiveness. And I saw the multitude of Jews in their answer. Many, many, fell flat on their faces as well, in the face of the Living God and His Horribleness. They fell and they wept, for they, like I, understood that this Horribleness was part of the Horribleness and Wonder of God becoming incarnated in Men. And that this incarnation was greater, by far, than the incarnation of His Son, which had been the last great event in the history of the Jews. For now the incarnation would be total, for every man who would bear it; and what man could claim that his wielding of power was always good and loving and true. These Jews fell and felt the fall of Adam, and his sin, for we were all there, as Kaballah tells us; we were all there in the first man, and we all participated in that first sin. It was the sin of pride. But now we are justified, for it was God's sin, too. And those among the Jews who saw this were transfigured, for they, too, like Moses, were seeing the image of God, face to face.

But there were those Jews who did not forgive Hitler. There were those Jews so hurt, so mortified, so betrayed, that they could not. In these the rending was so great that they needed aeons of love to soften the pain and dry the blood of their wounds. For them there would be grief and lamentation, despair and excess of love for eternity and eternity and eternity—as long as would be needed for their wounds to be healed from all pain.

There were others among the Jews who would not forgive, not out of pain, but out of the same arrogance and conceit, posturing and impotence as Hitler's. They were doomed to suffer as Hitler had suffered; not out of punishment, for that old view should die. No, they were doomed to live their impotence and harshness and stupidity until they could be softened and transformed. For they, too, like the Hitlers and the fools, were sparks of the Divine Image. They, too, had to be transformed through pain and enlightenment, until God, in all of His Grandeur and Horror, can be totally redeemed. And how can God be redeemed until His creatures, those created in His image, are totally transformed? This is the work of the universe. This is the task of the era which comes. This is the meaning of the Aquarian age, when God will become more totally Human. That is the Messiah of us all. That is the work of us all, that God be united with His Shekhinah, and we, mankind, are His Shekhinah!

Such was my image, and such was one answer to the question, *"Why six million dead Jews?"*

III

Can there be another answer? Is that not enough? What more can one ask of the Living God? Such were my thoughts for many days after I had this revelation. The image of Hitler preaching to the Jews so astounded me and so horribly-laughably gripped me that I lived and re-lived the experience, including his weeping and redemption, many times. It was as if the message—of God becoming Man—was enough for the redemption of the Six Million. . . .

Or was it? Certainly not. It seemed enough for me, but I, of course, had not been among the Six Million, any more than I had been present among the Six Hundred Thousand at the foot of Mt.

Sinai. Yet I had been there in spirit, my mediumistic experience had said, as had said the Rabbis, the great Sages among the Kabbalists. I was surely chosen for this strange vision, was I not? Yes.

So, I waited. I waited until the Good Lord, Blessed be His Holy Name, would descend unto me and tell me again the answer to the question, "Why Six Million Dead Jews?"

Then I had another vision. It was as if I rose up—no, not all of me—only my eyes; yes, my eyes rose up the entire Tree of Kaballah, that great Tree of the ten Sefiroth. My eyes rose up and beheld, in the distance, far beyond the Tree itself, an image of a fountain. Yet it was not a fountain. Water poured like a holy flame out of this fountain, yet one did not see the fountain itself. One saw only the pouring out of the water-flame.

My vision of the fountain vanished as abruptly as it had come to me. I was then left with a strange sense of futility and wonderment as to why I was vouchsafed this vision, only to have it taken away before I could learn anything, experience anything, or answer again—as I felt I must—the question, "Why six million dead Jews?"

The feeling of futility was worsened by a strange event in the world. A leading political figure from a great American family was shot by an assassin, just as the leader was enjoying a triumph in his campaign for high office. The family had been rent asunder by many deaths and agonies. Here, again, another rending asunder, and now by a dark little man, of whom one knew nothing, except that he was born in Jerusalem.

What was all this darkness, I asked myself? One felt the bleakness of the symbols of that poor family, Christ-like in the continual sacrifice of their innocent sons. . . .And yet, and yet, what was all the violence and lawlessness about? "Violence and lawlessness—how awful," complained the nation, yet it was often violent and lawless itself. Was she, in secret, fascinated by the violence? Is that the evil?

Violence, death, lawlessness. Death, lawlessness, violence. I sank down under these, and it seemed that I was now occupied with the part of the question, "Why six million dead Jews?" which had to do with death. DEATH. The word leaped out at me. It was larger now than dead Jews alone. There was a dead white hero and several dead black heroes. Why *Death?* The question came in capital letters: WHY DEATH? And now the word DEATH changed, and I saw instead the tetragrammaton, the holy name of God which the pious Jews of old never permitted themselves to pronounce: YHVH. Yachveh or Jehovah.

As I pronounced the sacred name, as I violated the ancient taboo, there appeared before me the image of a man strangely familiar to me. He had a dark beard, was clearly a Jew, and had a scholarly manner about him. I recognized him: he was none other than myself from a previous incarnation. I knew at once that I was faced with the Rabbi of myself of lifetimes centuries before. I intuited that I once again was going to play out the conflict between gypsy and Jew, between woman and man, between rationalist and mystic. But now the struggle would be within myself. I was going to have to solve for myself the conflict that had plagued me through many lives. How, indeed, could I be a medium for God, a creature meant to express the occult truths of the Most High, how could I do this if I could not even reconcile these differences within myself?

As I thought these thoughts, the Rabbi nodded. It was as if we both knew our long history of struggle, of how we had betrayed each other, of how we had hurt, fought, loved and were passionately tied to each other. I had been now one, now the other, sometimes experiencing the other in the form of another person, sometimes as myself. But now, dear Lord, now, in Thy

Name, we were going to reconcile ourselves at last, if we could. And we were going to do this in answer to the question, "Why six million dead Jews?" For only between us, only in the union of passion and mind, female and male, could we hope for a solution.

The Rabbi then spoke:

"Death. Lawlessness. Violence. Evil. We must, you and I, struggle with the questions of Death, of the Law, and of Evil. For only then can we contribute our part in the answer to the QUESTION. For it is the Question that must be capitalized, as well as death and evil; the Lord must acknowledge the question, our question, the Jew's question, mankind's question. Let us begin, Sophie-Sarah, let us begin."

"Begin, then, Rabbi, begin. Tell me what you know of Death. Why is there death in the world?"

"The Torah begins with God creating the world. He is, thus, a creator God. Did He, then, create the opposite of creation, did He create death? No. For the Torah says that it was man who created death. Our first parents created death by the sin of disobedience. They ate the fruit of the Tree of Knowledge. The Tree of Knowledge, therefore, is the same as the Tree of Death, just as we were told. Man was expelled from Paradise, kept away from the Tree of Life, from having immortality. Death, sayeth the Lord, comes from knowing, and particularly, from knowing how to distinguish good from evil. Man is to blame, therefore.

"My understanding of this, Sophie-Sarah, is that Death is a consequence of consciousness, of awareness of separation. Death, therefore, is partly an illusion. For we die, are reborn, die again. God originally meant us to be forever alive. And thus we are, though we must die and be reborn in order to achieve again, ultimately, the state for which we were meant. We are meant to 'be as Gods'."

"Rabbi, your words are too intellectual. Though they may be

true, they carry no fire, they carry no weight. That same Lord who blamed man for the existence of Death also said, 'Thou shalt not kill.' Yet He kills more than anyone. The Lord is a slaughterer, or have you not read that in your Torah? The mind cannot speak of death. The mind can only speculate about it. The heart must speak."

"The heart may speak, Sophie-Sarah, but there must be understanding as well. I understand that the Lord needed our consciousness. I understand that the Lord let our first parents taste of that Tree of Knowledge, because He needed our understanding. He needed a consciousness to share creation with. Now that is not only dryness of the mind, is it?"

"No, Rabbi, it is not. What you say is true, but I must turn from you, oh Rabbi. I must turn from you when it comes to Death. The heart must cry out to God for the Death of the six million Jews. The heart must also cry out for the death of the fallen American Christian and his martyr brother, their parents and wives and children. The heart must cry out and speak, too, to the fallen black Americans and their parents and wives and children. For how can we explain to them, the close ones, the death of their loved ones? You, Rabbi, cannot. Nor can I.

"You, oh Lord, help us to explain to them. Tell us why the innocent die. Help us, we Jews who have suffered the innocent death of the Six Million, and the millions before in our history, help us to explain to the poor-rich white Christian family the personal tragic death of their sons, and to the black families who have had the same. What can we say to the twenty million black people who have suffered just as Jews have suffered? What can be said to them?. . . .Nothing. For they will have to write a new Bible, and a new Word of the Lord.

"Well, then, Oh Lord, my God, speak to me from Your Holy Fire, tell me in words of the agony of the people, who wait, O

Lord, in their pain of violence and rending asunder. Think Lord, even of Your instrument, the Arab assassin who foolishly took the hero's life, in the belief that he was a positive vehicle of his country! And think of the Arab's poor mother who can only weep!"

How long, O Lord? How long?

How long will we, suffering mankind, have to await redemption?

How long must we tolerate our own ignorance and pain, and have it compounded by Your own?

How long must we cope with our own violence and greed and horror, and also have to take on Your own?

Is there no end to it?

Is there no end to the burden that both we and You have put upon us?

THERE IS NO END, MY SON. THERE IS NO END.

You speak to me as Your Son. I am not Your son. I am a woman, and true, and I cry out in anguish.

I will not bear Your burden like a loyal son, for I am a woman.

I am tempted to be a loving and understanding mother-daughter to You,

But I will cry out.

> ALL MY CREATURES ARE AS SONS TO ME. OF THIS, TOO, THERE IS NO END. OF CREATION THERE IS NO END. NOR OF DESTRUCTION. I GIVE AND TAKE AWAY. AND I AM GIVEN AND AM TAKEN AWAY. THE CHRIST IS MY SON AND I AM HE. THE WHITE IS MY SON AND I AM HE. THE BLACK IS MY SON AND I AM HE. THE MOTHERS ARE MY SONS AND THEY ARE ME. ALL IS I, AND ALL IS NOT I. THUS IS MY NAME CALLED, "I AM" FOR ALL THAT IS, IS "I AM." IN THE BEGINNING, THERE IS THE LORD "WHO." AND THAT IS THE LORD "HE" OF "WHOM" YOU SPEAK. THEN, IN THE COURSE OF THE AEONS, THERE IS THE LORD "YOU" WHO SPOKE TO MOSES AND TO BUDDHA AND TO CHRIST. AND NOW THERE WILL BE THE LORD "I" TO WHOM EVEN SOPHIE-SARAH WILL SPEAK.

These words of God, these words of YHVH—for I was convinced that they came from the same source as had spoken to Abraham and Isaac and Jacob, and to Moses and David and Jesus—these words came slowly and heavily and quietly. There was no thunder in them. There was not even any fire in them. But they came as heavy chunks of rich earth, each of which had a tongue in it which could speak His name. For that is the NAME of God, too. The spirit speaks through the earth, the Voice of God speaks through his creatures in the flesh. And I, even I, Sophie-Sarah, the lowly handmaiden, will be the Lord God, "I" to whom He will speak as "You and I" as He did with Abraham and Isaac and Jacob and Moses and David, and even as an "I" as He was with Jesus. For now the Lord will speak through me as "I"!

It is too much, for it is like a psalm without being a poem. There is an answer to each part of the question: "Why Six Million dead Jews?" "Six Million" answered, and "Death" answered. Jews, those chosen ones, that too, has been answered. And now, the question "Why?" becomes replaced by the question "Who?" and the question "Who?" is replaced by a sequence of "He" to "You" to "I"! The whole question is raised and it is answered: Listen, O Mankind, for the Lord, our God, the Lord is One!

IV

The heart had spoken when it came to the struggle with Death. And I was glad. For what can the mind do with death except rationalize or explain? It cannot take away the fear of death, or the pain to loved ones. Only the heart can endure that! But the heart needs the mind after all. I thought such thoughts some days after this numinous encounter with God, and I felt guilty. For I had abandoned the Rabbi of my soul, just after he had come to me. I was guilty of repeating once more the rejection and one-sidedness that I had done throughout my incarnations: heart or mind; passion or truth; mysticism or reason; never both. And now the heart had won. But had it really? Was not what the Rabbi had to say true? Were not his words about the task of man having to help God in His creation a deep and passionate truth? And was it not also true that man needs to be ready for this to grow up to it? I realized my error and came to my Rabbi asking for forgiveness, this holy man so recently found and so quickly rejected.

"Do not trouble yourself, Sophie-Sarah," he said. "I know that Death cannot be answered with reason alone. I know that understanding and logic are no match for fear and passion. But my words are not just logic. Indeed, there are those who would call me fool, call me one of faith, not reason. No matter. Our task is understanding, and to help the Lord come to greater consciousness of Himself. For this, the heart is needed too. The mind bows to passion. Was it not a non-Jew who said, 'Let reason be a slave of the passions?' I agree. Let reason and understanding serve the flaming heart and fiery fountain which emerges from the God who is forever unmanifest. The limitless God, the *En Sof* who is beyond all words and images and ideas, is that fountainless fountain which you experienced when you reflected upon the question for the second time. It is from that source that the holy water-fire comes, and it is because of that fire in you that I bow to you. For reason is like the fountain, it must be the vessel and servant of the water-fire."

"Strange, Rabbi," said I. "You, a man, being a vessel for a woman. It is almost like the images I have heard of: the Jews are like a woman, married to God. They, too, are a vessel for His fire. I blush at the comparison, Oh Rabbi! You swell me up, and I am in as great a danger of pride as our first parents!"

"Have no fear, Sophie-Sarah, we have more to do than can be managed by you or me alone; or, indeed, by you and me together. That stops pride. Let us continue with our task. We have faced Death. We must, yet, face Lawlessness and the Law. And for this, I must say, knowledge and the mind will need a place!"

"It is true, Rabbi. Among the dreams I had, came the command, 'REINTERPRET THE LAW.' That, too, was a Mitzvah from God, a commandment. Imagine! A commandment to reinterpret the Ten Commandments, a law to re-interpret the law. I will surely need all that you can give for this task."

"Sophie-Sarah, you have struggled with the Gematria of the *numbers*, especially of the number six, just as did the old Kabbalists. Now you—and I—must struggle with the Gematria of the *letters*. I must tell you that the old Kabbalists recognized the Voice of the Lord as the Instrument of Creation. The Voice of the Lord is the Law, and it is expressed by the instrument of the

WORD. But the word is made up of letters, those twenty-two in Hebrew and twenty-six in English. When God speaks, he speaks in Words, and the Words are made of the twenty-two or twenty-six letters. Each creation is a word, the pious rabbis told us, and each exegesis of Torah rises up as a mitzvah and a creation. So, then, Sophie-Sarah, your mitzvah and commandment to re-interpret the law is a creation. The Voice commanded you to listen and think anew, thus create anew. And for this will I help you. Shall we reflect?"

"Oh, Rabbi, your words are like a clear stream which cools my fire and make me happy to be with you. Begin the clear stream of your questions and reflections. I shall accompany you as best I can. Thus, I pray, may I serve the mitzvah that God has given to me."

"What is 'The Law'?," the Rabbi began. "How are we to understand it? Is it the 'statutes' of God and His 'decisions' *(toroth)*? Is it the written words of the entire Bible? Yes and No. For 'Law' is *Torah* which means 'oral direction'. God speaks in words and the words filter down and grow hardened into written statements and into 'laws' as statutes. But directions are not statutes, Sophie-Sarah. The Lord gave you a Mitzvah (a direction, a command, a task, an oral law), no ordinary "statute" such as most of the six-hundred-thirteen in the Bible which include such laws as a prohibition against wearing clothing made of linen and wool!. . . .And yet, 'the law is the law' say the judges, secular and religious. For all laws, they imply, are the Word of God. Is it so?"

"I do not think so, Rabbi," said I. "The laws may have been the word of God in the beginning, but when they harden into statutes, they are already dead. And deadly, rigid men use these statutes against us, to hurt our hearts and restrict our freedom."

"You speak of 'in the beginning,' Sophie-Sarah. In the beginning, we are told, was the Law of the Ten Commandments.

God spoke to Moses and Moses spoke to the people. Moses brought the Ethical Code, but there was a Ritual Code, too. There were two Stone Tablets, were there not? Perhaps the Ethical Code was on one, and the Ritual Code on the other. Are we obliged to follow all of the laws? All six-hundred-thirteen? If so, then the code, the law, becomes a meaningless burden, and where, then, do we have the Simchath Torah, joy in the law? I do not know. Perhaps one must choose, Sophie-Sarah.

"There always have been those who followed the letter of the law and not the spirit. We don't need the Christians to tell us about it, do we? We have great Kabbalists who tell us that even the Torah itself, as written, is merely the Throne of God, the seat upon which He sits. The Voice of God is the reality; it is the unseen Voice which sits upon the Throne that we worship and obey. It is with Him that we dance in alacritous union like a joyous Chassid!"

"Now you speak my language, Rabbi! Voice of God and Throne of God: it is the Voice that we worship in dance! Yes!"

"It is not just I, Sophie-Sarah, who speaks this way. Listen to Jeremiah about the law, for he, we are told by Rabbinical tradition, was the guardian of the original Stones. After Moses and Noah, it was Jeremiah who kept the ark of the Stones, until Jerusalem—blessed be her gorgeous memory—was taken by the tyrant Nebuchadnezzar.

"What does Jeremiah say of the Voice? Jeremiah said that the Lord told him: 'For in the day that I brought them out of the land of Egypt, I did not speak to your fathers or command them concerning burnt offerings and sacrifices. But this command I gave them, Obey My voice, and I will be your God, and ye shall be My people: and walk ye in all the ways that I have commanded you, that it may be well with you.' Thus sayeth Jeremiah."

"But it seems as if the Lord changed his mind," said I, "for earlier he lusted after sacrifices and burnt offerings!"

"Yet again," The Rabbi continued, "Jeremiah tells us—nay, promises us—from the Lord: I will put my law in their inward parts, and write it in their hearts; and will be their God, and they shall be My people."

"Ah, would that this were true," I said, "that the law be written in our hearts and inward parts. If that were true, we would no longer need the wisdom of St. Paul who went beyond the law, through the law. Nor even Jesus, who came to fulfill the law, but transcended it into the one law of Love of God and neighbor. Love of God and neighbor. But the Sermon on the Mount did not accomplish it for Christians either. St. Paul spoke truly of them, as of himself and us, when he said that the law was not written in their flesh! So, then, Oh God, what is Your law, that we struggle with it, obey it, defy it, violate it, interpret it, but do not find it, alas, in our hearts or inward parts? It does not touch our flesh." Thus did I turn toward God, but no answer to my question came, so My Rabbi and I turned to the "laws" themselves, the basic ten as given us.

"The sages tell us," the Rabbi said, "that there is, in truth, only one law, that against idolatry. Adultery, after all, originally meant idolatry. God means, therefore, that we should really have no images of Him at all! We must hear His Voice and break all idols, including the images of Him which become outworn. He, Blessed be His Holy Name, will not be contained in any images, or idols, or symbols. He, the Silent One, the Transcendent One, will go beyond all of them. This is His Voice and His Commandment, and that, we need to know, is not a burden but a Mitzvah, a joyous fact of eternity!"

"I agree, Rabbi. The voice is forever. The throne must be renewed!"

"But let us look at the laws, Sophie-Sarah. Perhaps we can then understand the voice from the shape of the throne!"

"The first few laws," the Rabbi said, "speak mostly of God Himself, and His Vanity. No other Gods, no images, no taking the Name in vain. Enjoining us to copy His creativity, including the Sabbath for Him. He even tells us that He is a Jealous God". . . .

I start to understand. Jealousy, vanity, changing His mind; it sounds more like a powerful and intense woman, not a man!

"Rabbi!" I said. "No wonder He called me Son: I called him Father! God is a jealous female, demanding and vain, like all of us. God is a Goddess! And the Laws which are trying to be expressed by Him-Her are the Laws of His-Her nature, not ordinary statutes which we enact as a convenience and then discard!

"I begin to glimpse, Rabbi. Thou shalt not commit adultery—not adulterate and water down. Thou shalt love totally. And who, pray, but a woman could command love? 'Thou shalt love the Lord, thy God, with all thine heart and with all thy soul and with all thy might!' As if love can be commanded at all. Yet it is true, as a natural law, is it not? Thou shalt love whether thou knowest it or not, likest it or not. It will show itself some way. Some men worship power and that is their love, their God. Others love fame or fortune, or lust, or self. The chief value is God, and that is always loved totally, is it not? Yes! The Lord is telling us in Torah, that His laws are the Laws of the Soul. They, our people, comprehended it at that level then, and we must, all of us, understand it anew."

"You are right, Sophie-Sarah," said the Rabbi. "We have had Science, but no real science of the soul. Religion speaks to the soul, and we must find the laws of the soul. Perhaps the laws of the soul are the laws of nature in microcosm. Is the Goddess speaking, telling us of Her Nature?"

"I think so, Rabbi. I think so."

"Ah, Sophie-Sarah, you are starting to think! Just as I bowed to heart and soul, you begin to think! Perhaps we will merge in the law, the laws of the Goddess, no less, and become as one.

"But I want to return to the Stones, the Tablets of the Law. I want, still, to understand the Law, before I merge with it. The Ten Commandments, scholars tell us, were really called the Ten Words. Ten Words. What could this mean, or could it have meant? Was not God telling Moses of His-Her Nature? Were these not the Ten Names of God as the Kabbalists tell us, in the Tree of the Ten Sefiroth? Thus it seems to me. For God is always speaking to us in His Voice, and we can comprehend it only in part. We codify and enclose it, in order to keep it—bless our poor, bumbling hearts—but we fail. We must listen anew to the Voice, to the Ten Words, the Ten Names of God, and hear again what His-Her nature is, and how we are to understand it.

"For that is the Law: thou shalt love with all thy might and heart and soul. With total devotion, always. There is nothing else that can be done, you can hardly do otherwise. All you can do is better understand, better worship that which you love and adore and serve. And you had best grow more conscious of it, lest you worship a stone idol, a dead image! Praise the Lord. Blessed be His-Her Name!"

"Beautiful, Rabbi! I said. "You are speaking, now, with a heart. Let us speak the Ten Words, the Ten Names of God, and see what feelings, what images they evoke. Let us speak the names of the Lord, as the Kabbalists have given them to us."

"Hear, first, Sophie-Sarah," said my beloved Rabbi, "the great Rabbi Eleazar, who sings, in the Kabbalistic Zohar, with an audacity greater than ours:

Before God created the world, His name was enclosed within Him, and therefore He and His name enclosed within Him were not one. Nor could this unity be effected until He created the world. . . .He made it for His own behoof, for His own

> *advantage, to display His glory, to show that He is one and His name is one.*

"So, do you see, Sophie-Sarah? Rabbi Eleazar knew, long ago, as we know, that God created the world and the Law for His benefit, to be united with His Name, His holy Oneness. So, to know His Law, we need to know His Name! That is the Law! Hear further what good Rabbi Eleazar says:

> *"And the earth was void and without form." This describes the original state—as it were, the dregs of ink clinging to the point of the pen—in which there was no subsistence, until the world was graven with forty-two letters, all of which are the ornamentation of the Holy Name. When they are joined, letters ascend and descend, and form crowns for themselves in all four quarters of the world, so that the world is established through them and they through it.*

"So, my Lord, let us, Sophie-Sarah and I, establish Your Name. Let the crowns of our saying Your Name arise, and allow You to unite with Yourself. Our saying thereof unites You with Your Shekhinah, and thus the King is reunited with the Crown! Thus do we follow and meditate upon God's law."

Thus did my Rabbi speak knowingly and beautifully. And thus did our meditation begin. Hear, now, our meditation upon the Law, the Words, the Names of God.

"In the beginning," the Rabbi began, "before there appears even the Name, or the thought of the Name, is the En Sof, beyond the limitless All. And then a breath occurs and the Holy Name makes itself manifest, as the 'supreme crown.' But this supreme crown of God carries the Name (whisper it, do not shout it) EHEIEH. And what is this EHEIEH? What does it mean? It means only 'I shall be.' Oh, Great Lord, what a great Name is this; for the Lord sayeth to Himself, as the 'He' 'Who' knew Himself and proclaimed His state of creating Himself: 'I begin with a future!' What great name of the Lord is this? 'I shall be' —EHEIEH. So, in the beginning, when the breath moved in a whisper, the great 'I AM' stated His intention, His being and the fact, 'I shall be.' Thus is the Name of the Lord. For ever and ever: EHEIEH! Time is created out of timelessness.'"

"The Crown, and 'I shall be.' Beautiful! God pours Himself like an upside down crown from heaven. The King abandons His rulership and pours out His holy water-fire toward creation. I feel it, Rabbi. I feel that when God proclaims His Name, EHEIEH, He has already proclaimed that I, even I, Sophie-Sarah, shall exist as well. EHEIEH, Time and Being come into existence. Yes, Rabbi, beautiful."

"The Name of the Lord moved onward," continued the Rabbi. "Now came the name, ASHER, and the fuller name, ASHER EHEIEH. And what, pray tell, does the Lord mean with this name ASHER? Blessed be His Name, ASHER means only 'which.' Imagine! We have had 'Who', 'He', 'You', 'I am' as Names of God, and now we have 'I shall be which.' Particulars are formed in time. In ASHER, the Lord is a point. At that particular moment in the time of the beginning, the Lord particularizes: He curls up upon Himself, and can say only that He is a point. But, the Rabbis tell us, ASHER is also the mystic and recondite temple, the source of the 'beginning', of Reshith. It is the point of Wisdom, the primordial intelligence of God. That, we know, comes from *Rosh,* the head. Rosh, anagramatically, comes from the letters of ASHER: Aleph, Shin, and Resh. So, ASHER is the 'which', which is the beginning, the idea, the head and point and source."

"Oh Rabbi," I said. "The Gematria of the letters of the names of God are too puzzling to me. I can only understand ASHER as particular, individual—that I can understand and treasure. That God curled up upon Himself, like a caterpillar about to nest and then transformed Himself into a butterfly, that I understand. The play with the letters I leave to you, Rabbi. God like a caterpillar, a unique and particular caterpillar, undergoing transformation into a whole new state—that is enough for me!"

"From the 'beginning' in wisdom," the Rabbi went on, the Name, hidden and mysterious, moves on, out of the temple-palace, into the creative mystery of the *Bara Shith,* the 'beginning' in fact: 'He created six' on the sixth day, He created the six directions and, wonder of wonders, Man! Now, the seed comes to light. The Zohar, the bright splendor, inches its way and we come beyond the primordial idea of ASHER; we come to intelligent understanding, and the expression of God in the Voice. For now we have the Voice of the Shofar, the ram's horn.

"This Voice of the Shofar announces, on the Day of Atonement, that God is also in the state of at-one-ment. What is this Atonement, this unity, this complete blending of the 'upper waters' and the 'lower waters'? Of Heaven Above, and Earth Below? Of the created universe with the mind of God? It is none other than the One, unspeakable NAME—the one NAME which we Jews are not allowed to utter, the Name YHVH. And why are we not allowed to utter it? Is it because this tetragrammaton is just the 'not speakable', and 'limitless'? No, because we already have this Name of God, in the En Sof. And that is quite 'speakable' for we have no strictures against it. Is it, then, because if we speak it, we are, like some primitive, stepping upon the shadow of God, and that makes Him nervous and irritable? Certainly not.

"The truth, Sophie-Sarah, is that when we speak the Name YHVH, we are entering into the primordial creative act itself! This tetragrammaton has an intimate connection with the primordial Thought: For IT, the tetragrammaton, the four-fold Word, was the chosen instrument for making the Divine Thought intelligible and realizable to the human mind. The Divine Name was enclosed within the Lord, and the very speaking of the NAME was one of the purposes of creation! So, when we see or speak the Name YHVH we are participating in the Divine Creation itself!"

"Rabbi, that the Shofar, the sound of the ram's horn should announce God's union with His Name, His at-one-ment, and ours with Him; and that the six is the number of creation, those two things I glimpse intuitively. For it is true that in creation I am at one with God, and like a God. When I gave birth to my children, I felt like both a handmaid of God, and a Goddess myself. I also understand unspeakableness. I understand that there is that which cannot be spoken, should one desire it or not. Every woman understands the wordless look of love. But I still do not understand your Gematria, Rabbi. Explain to me, for I would understand with the head, the *Rosh,* as you say, as well as with the heart."

"Each letter of the Holy Name, Sophie-Sarah, is associated with a separate grade of creation. Thus, with the grade *Reshith,* the 'beginning', there is the letter Yod. With the next grade, *Elohim Hayyim* (the Lord creating the Heavens), there is the letter He. This He is the 'upper He' of the creation of the Heavens, and these heavens are of the letter Vau. Now we come to the second He, the 'lower He', and this is the creation of the earth. For, 'In the beginning, the Lord God created the Heaven and the Earth.' And these are the letters of the Name of God, YHVH. On the first day, there existed the creation of the letters Yod and He; with the second day, the combination of Vau and He; while with the third day all four letters were combined into YHVH. This is the making manifest, the transformation of YHVH, the unspeakable, into JEHOVAH, the speakable name of God."

"Rabbi, dear Rabbi. Your Gematria escapes me. You go too far from images. I feel that I am being lectured at, rather than being with a beloved friend who is meditating with me. I have read Kaballah, too, dear Rabbi, and I particularly like what Rabbi Hiya said about the process of making manifest, about the time when the voice of YHVH is heard. Probably you know the quotation I mean. He was speaking about the passage in Torah when:

'The flowers appear on the earth, the time of song is come,
And the voice of the turtle is heard in our land.'

Rabbi Hiya said that when God created the world, He endowed it with everything, but only in potential. When, however, man appeared, forthwith 'the flowers appeared on the earth'—all the latent powers were revealed. 'The time of song was come': the earth was now ripe to offer up praises to the Almighty, which it could not do before man was created. 'And the voice of the turtle is heard in our land': this is the word of God, of YHVH, which was not in the world till man was created."

"That is beautiful, Sophie-Sarah. I bow to the wisdom and beauty of Rabbi Hiya. But I bow even deeper to the poetry of The Book, the poetry which speaks of the voice of God as the turtle's voice.

"This turtle song, this sweet silent voice which sings in Spring, the time of creation, the day of creation of man. For does the turtle not have six points: four feet, head and tail? Does he not have an upper shell and lower shell, like the letter, He's, in YHVH? Do not the shells have hexagrams upon them? And do not the roundness of the shells speak of the point and circle of the first beginnings? Yes, Sophie-Sarah, the 'voice of the turtle' is the Voice of God.

"What remains to be said after this? Nothing. What more can one say after one has invoked the Divine Voice of the turtle? Nothing. What more can one do than sing the praises of the Almighty in YHVH? Nothing. . .Yet, but yet, the NAMES of the Divine One, blessed be He, go on, for now we have touched only three of the Divine ten and we must go on and speak of the other seven and thus arrive at the totality of the ten. This is our Mitzvah, and Commandment, Sophie-Sarah, for of the Commandments and of the NAMES, there are ten."

"Let us go on, Rabbi; let us go on."

"After YHVH, there is EL GADOL, the 'Great God.' The Great God is that which emerged from the primal ether, and that is the great God of light. For the Lord said, 'Let there be light' and it was this Name of the Lord, EL GADOL, which emerged with the lightness, as the lightness of the sun. But it was not our sun; it was the primordial sun, the sun of consciousness which was long before the light of the sun. Oh, EL GADOL, primordial Lord of Light, Who said 'Let there be. . .' With the light, there came, also, kindness, and the love of God, which is warm and compassionate, yielding and merciful. All this was on the Right side.

"At the same moment, at the second day of the creation, came the Left side, the power and stern judgment and punishment of God, and the Name of ELOHIM. With ELOHIM, there came also Darkness, thus sayeth the Lord. Thus created He, them. For the 'Them' is the disunity, the 'many' of ELOHIM. Sh-sh-sh. God is also a plurality! ELOHIM is the name of God having to do with the 'more', the angels and the powers. Even good Rabbi Simeon, he of the benevolent wisdom of Zohar, tells us that the angels are jealous of man! Mind you, the angels of God, yea, even the parts of God, are jealous of man! Did not the Lord tell us that He is a jealous God? Yes, for thus is He a plurality, jealous of other Gods. 'No other Gods before me.' He is like a woman, and dark, with her dark face of passion–jealous."

"Rabbi, perhaps the trouble in understanding lies with me. I understand your Lord of Light, the sun; I grasp the plurality of Elohim, the darkness; I sense, too, the struggle of Right and Left, of kindness and mercy versus jealousy and judgment. But I only sense and understand, Rabbi, I do not feel. Make me feel, Rabbi! Make me know in my flesh these names of God, EL GADOL and

ELOHIM. Were not these names and laws to be written and felt in the flesh?"

"Oh, Sophie-Sarah, you know! You do not need my words for it, for the understanding of it, for the grasping of it. Has not your life, and my life, been just such a struggle between mercy and judgment, giving and getting? Have you not suffered the conflict between the one God and the many, the one love and the many? Have not jealousy and desire clawed your being? This battle within God is the battle of our deepest selves, and you know it. You know, too, that beyond EL GADOL and ELOHIM, beyond the battle of light and dark, of the one and the many, of love and power, there is reconciliation in the name of JEHOVAH, of YHVH made manifest in compassion and beauty. For here, the voice of the turtle is heard in mercy and sweetness."

"You are right, Rabbi. I knew this, but I suppose that I needed you to remind me of it. I needed, perhaps, to know that you, too, knew it, in your bones and heart, and not only with your head. Our lives, indeed, are of the Lord, right and left, light and dark, one and many, EL GADOL and ELOHIM."

"The 'small still voice' which comes after the fire," continued the Rabbi, the sweet voice of YHVH as it manifests in JEHOVAH, lasts only for a time, and the next NAMES of the Lord bring quaking and fear and chaos. What are these NAMES? They are ZEBAOTH and SHADDAI. ZEBAOTH, the Lord of Hosts, the martial God, the God of spirits who instills fear into the hearts of Israel's enemies! This is the NAME which is the author of the *Bohu,* the 'quaking' of the *Tohu-Bohu,* the chaos and the quaking. Just as Darkness was under the aegis of ELOHIM, and spirit under the aegis of YHVH, then Bohu, the quaking, is under the martial lord of ZEBAOTH, and chaos is under the mystic nature of SHADDAI."

"Further, beyond the battling of the Lord, beyond the chaos

and quaking of the mystic nature, beyond the Lord of Hosts and the Lord of Chaos, comes the reconciliation, once again, in the EL. EL is the 'Glory of God.' This is God when He is manifest in His Glory—a glory, as Rabbi Simeon tells us, which is splendour upon splendour, when the 'heavens declare the glory of God' as her bridegroom. For this EL manifests when there is a union of God with His Own Glory. God is united with Himself, and this is the basis and foundation of all the active forces in the Lord. Here is another Gematria of letters: EL (the great God, in His Glory), combined with H and Y and M to form in our Hebrew tongue, ELOHIM. And the He, Yod, Mem, with which the El combined, make *hayam,* the sea, and the lower waters. The 'upper waters' combine with the 'lower waters' in the great unity of the Lord. This is the meaning of the upper He and the lower He."

"Enough of Gematria, Rabbi. And enough, too, of ZEBAOTH and SHADDAI! Enough of wars, enough of battles, enough of fear! We can bow to EL, God's glory, without such chaos and quaking!"

"Oh, Sophie-Sarah, it is because of the chaos and the quaking that we must resort to Gematria! Without our poor attempts at trying to understand, without our efforts after divining the meaning, the direction of God's will, without those, well then, the Power of God, especially when it is frightening and destructive, would break our poor heads!"

"Just, Rabbi, as God's love can break our poor hearts! I understand, Rabbi, I understand."

"Let us go beyond the nine Names, Sophie-Sarah. Let us complete our mitzvah and task. Let us go beyond the nine to the tenth.

"Could there be more than this nine-fold unity of the Names of the Lord? Of course, for the Nine are as nothing without the tenth, and the tenth is ADONAI, the Lord of Earth. What is the

Lord without His creation, the earth? Nothing, or nearly nothing, for without His creation, there would be no one to sing the praises of the Lord, to exult in His creation, and to reflect upon the Glory and help the Lord unite with his Shekhinah! Sophie-Sarah, that is the whole work of the Universe: to assist the Supreme Crown of the Lord to unite with His Kingdom, and become the Lord of the Earth, ADONAI. The Lord of the Heavens, of the supreme crown, is incomplete without his Kingship, and this Kingdom is that of Mankind."

"Amen, Rabbi, amen. Now I understand you. Now I am with you."

"Rabbi Eleazar tells us that Adon (Lord) is another name of the ark of the covenant. So, ADONAI, the Lord of the Covenant, is the One Lord who made a Covenant with His people, Israel, and through His people, with Mankind. ADONAI, thus, is the LORD of the Covenant, of God contacting and binding Himself with His creation, the people, and thus coming to His own union.

"It is written: 'The Lord reigneth, the Lord hath reigned, the Lord will reign for evermore.' There is an upper world and a lower world, the upper being a pattern for the lower. The Lord reigneth above, the Lord reigneth in the middle: these are the 'reignings' of the first nine names. 'The Lord will reign below' is the Lord ADONAI, the tenth name. It is He who made the sign of the covenant, and remakes His sign again and again. Each time, His covenant is more of Himself. Praised be ADONAI.

"At one time, King David reversed the order, Rabbi Aha tells us, and said: 'The Lord is King for ever and ever', thus in a psalm. 'The Lord is king', below, 'for ever' in the middle, 'and ever', above, for there is the reunion and perfection of all. God 'is king' above, and 'will reign' below.

"So, praised be ADONAI, the Lord of earth, where the Crown unites with the King. The King without a crown is the Lord without his Shekhinah. Mankind without the Lord is the Kingdom without its King! Shema Yisrael Adonai Elohenu, Adonai Echod! Hear Oh Israel, the Lord our God, the Lord is One.

"Thus are the Ten Commandments: the ten NAMES of the One God. And that is the law: to utter His Name, in creation, in love!"

Thus did the Rabbi and I complete our meditation upon the Ten Names of God, the Ten Laws of God, and the goal of God.

V

Many months passed before I could again address myself to the question of "Why six million dead Jews?" Indeed, I had hoped that perhaps I was freed of the questionable blessing, of the "mitzvah" which I had received to cope with that problem. Just as he had appeared, the Rabbi of my soul had vanished after we had accomplished our meditation upon the Names of the Lord. Though I missed him a little, I counted it a blessing, I must confess, to go about my daily life, and live simply and accept whatever joy came my way. If that constituted a running away from the "commandment," let it be so—I ran. For, despite the greatness of the Lord's Voice, despite the wonder of His communication, I knew what it meant to "fear God." I was reminded of the first precept of Rabbi Simeon in the *Zohar.*

Rabbi Simeon knew that the real fear of God was not the fear that one may lose family or possessions, nor the fear that one will suffer punishment and tortures of Gehenna; no, not these. The real fear is the anxiety before the Master, blessed be He, who exists. That is the fear before the *tremendum,* the holy fear, which is neither fear of the lash, nor of the loss, but fear of the Lord! This is the fear, the Torah tells us, which is the beginning of wisdom.

I also understood Rabbi Simeon's second precept that one does not love God merely because He has provided one with riches, or length of life, or children, or power over enemies. No, none of these. Does one still love the Lord when one is poor, or childless or weak? Can one still love the Holy One, blessed be He, should the wheel of fortune turn against him? This kind of love is the "great love," the perfect love.

I was beginning to know both perfect fear and perfect love. I whisper it, lest the Tempter, cursed be He, induce me into the sin of pride, of knowing too much.

But that crinkle, that chink in my armor of satisfaction in everyday life would come up to haunt me of an evening. The darkness would creep upon me; depression and anxiety would vaguely haunt me. Still I turned away from these.

After some months, however, I could not turn away from what began to emerge in my dreams and then in my waking life. I experienced, in short, the haunting of the six million.

At first, I would hear only moaning and sighing in my dreams. Then there came louder cries and shouts and the calling of my name. Finally there came the Command, from the dead, from the six million, to speak to them of evil. "Why evil?" they shouted; "Why suffering?" they called.

"Have I not answered?" I dared to respond. "Did I not speak, from Kaballah and from visions, in answer to the question, 'Why six million dead Jews?' "

"You have answered," one suffering soul said. "You have answered the question of the six, of the six million, of the six million dead, of the six million dead Jews, you have answered; but the question of evil, why evil, why evil, that you have not."

I paused. I thought: they wanted an answer, these dead, as the whole world wants an answer, as it has always wanted an answer. Is there an answer? I do not know. But I must answer; it is my mitzvah.

But I could not answer alone. I needed the help of my Rabbi, my Kabbalistic soul-brother whom I had neglectfully abandoned. No sooner had I acknowledged my need for his assistance, no sooner had I whispered, lovingly, "Rabbi," than he appeared, handsome and clear-eyed as before.

"Your need is my need, Sophie-Sarah," he said. "And your commandment is mine. How can we really be parted for long? Head without heart is like a dry river bed, a vessel without its cooling, nourishing stream."

"Yes, Rabbi," I said. "And heart without head is a raging fire with no chimney to direct its force to heaven, and no hearth to contain its warmth and show its gorgeous flame. We need each other."

"Let us try, then, Sophie-Sarah, to answer about evil. But now the commandment comes not from the Lord, but from the dead, those honored and despised, those terrible and beautiful dead."

"Yes, let us try, Rabbi. Help me, as I shall try to help you. Help me, first, with your mind and your knowledge. Help me speak of evil to the dead.

"Oh, dear dead," I, Sophie-Sarah, began. "I cannot answer, for I do not know the answer, but my Rabbi can tell you the answers of the Rabbis, blessed be their pure hearts, and of the scholars, blessed be their pure minds. My Rabbi knows much."

The dead left off their moaning. I trusted that they wanted his answer, so I turned to him, and he spoke:

"Evil, dear dead," began the Rabbi, "is separation, or isolation. Sin always destroys a union and this was the Original Sin, through which the fruit was separated from the tree, as one Rabbi puts it, or as Rabbi Ezra ben Solomon has proclaimed, when the Tree of Life was separated from the Tree of Knowledge. When a man falls into isolation, when he seeks to maintain his own self, his own pride, instead of the original context and harmony of all which has been created, then he has used the magic of the serpent. He has used this magic, either to rend asunder God's order, or to unite that which God has separated. That is evil.

"Thus, sayeth the Rabbis, Adam's sin was great. But Rabbi ben Yohai says that the Sefiroth were revealed to Adam in the shape of the Tree of Life and the Tree of Knowledge, in the form of the middle and last Sefirah. Adam, instead of preserving their original unity, and thereby saving the wholeness of 'life' and 'knowledge' and bringing salvation to the world, separated the one from the other. Furthermore, Adam worshipped only the Shekhinah, the last Sefirah, and did not recognize its union with the other nine Sefiroth. Thus Adam interrupted the stream of life which flows from sphere to sphere and brought separation and isolation into the world. That is evil.

"So, from the beginning, with Adam, there has been a painful fissure, a rent, in the life and action of the Divine. This is the painful 'exile of the Shekhina.' Only when the original harmony is restored, as in the beginning, will 'God be one, and His name one,' for all time.

"Rabbi Simeon even says, 'It is therefore necessary for man to acknowledge that God and the Lord are one and the same without any cleavage whatever. The Lord He is God. When mankind will universally acknowledge this absolute unity, the evil power itself will be removed from the world and exercise no more influence upon earth.'

"How does man do this? How does he mend the rending? By religious acts: Torah, mitzvoth, and prayer. That extinction of the rending, of the stain, the restoration of harmony, that is the *Tikkun,* man's task in the world. When all is redeemed, then there 'shall be perfection above and below, and all worlds shall be united in one bond.'"

As my Rabbi told these truths to the six million, as he

explained the problem of man's sin and his task, and of the division in the Divine Life, they all nodded. They crossed their arms across their chests and took upon themselves the sin of our ancestor, for they knew, as we all knew, that all our souls were present at that first event, and that we all partook of Adam's sin of division.

"But," I, Sophie-Sarah, called out to them, my six million dead brothers and sisters, "our sin is also God's sin!"

They looked at me in amazement and fear. I was somewhat surprised, for my Rabbi and I had already hinted rather strongly at this viewpoint earlier, had we not? When we meditated upon the commandments and the NAMES of God? When we spoke of the necessity of God becoming human? Yes. But somehow, stating it so baldly was shocking. Not even the Zoharic Rabbis were so audacious. Was I not in danger of repeating Adam's sin? Perhaps. Let my Rabbi help me then, and return to what the learned scholars, and the pious Rabbis have said, for they, even they, tell us dark facts.

"The causes of evil lie deeper than human sin and pride and separation," continued my Rabbi. "No, Sophie-Sarah, evil was not created only by man—that would be an even greater *chutzpah,* to believe that! Even though the Torah hints at this, there are deeper truths from God—when one is ready to receive them. Nor is evil only, as some say, a relative matter, a figment of one's imagination. No, evil is real and exists—listen deeply, dearly beloved Sophie-Sarah and fellow Jews—in the nature of the Godhead Himself! There, one has said it. But one must explain:

"The totality of divine potencies, of the ten NAMES of God, and of the ten Sefiroth, is sacred and good, so long as each stays in relation to all the others. But the fundamental cause of evil, dearly beloved, is in Geburah and Din, the Power of God, the Sefirah of God's strict justice, rigor with judgment, as well as His power.

When God's *Left Hand,* which symbolizes this Sefirah, is balanced by His *Right Hand,* the Sefirah of Hesed, of mercy and love, then all is order and good. Fierce fire, stern judgment, sacred wrath, must be balanced by mercy and love. But, dearly beloved, when the fierce fire of God, the stern judgment, and sacred wrath tears itself loose, when it hypertrophies and breaks away from mercy, then, dear ones, the fire breaks away from God altogether and is transformed into Gehenna, and the dark world of Satan.

"Satan, the evil one, is the Hypertrophy of God's Wrath. So taught Moses de Leon, so taught the Zohar, and so, too, do I believe. Thus, dear friends, evil is from the Godhead Himself."

"Is it only you who thinks so, Rabbi? Now I, even I, Sophie-Sarah, would want other rabbinical authority for such a dangerous statement. I can imagine what the rabbi in my nice, American temple would do with such a statement! 'Evil is in the nature of the Godhead Himself'—our local rabbi would burst! Give us, Rabbi of my soul, give the dead and me other authorities for this view."

"All right, Sophie-Sarah, let us hear the words of the good Rabbis. They, too, tell us that evil is from division. Division was created by God on the Second Day. Hear Rabbi Simeon:

"'And God said, Let there be a firmament in the midst of the waters. Here in the particular (day) there is an allusion to the separation of the upper from the lower waters through that which is called 'the left.' Here, too, discord was created through that which is called 'the left!' For up to this point the text has alluded to the 'right'. . . .It is in the nature of the right to harmonize the whole, and therefore, the whole is written with the right, since it is the source of harmony. When the Left awoke, there awoke discord, and through that discord, the wrathful fire was reinforced and there emerged the Gehinnom, which thus originated from the left and continues there.'

"Rabbi Simeon goes on to tell us how Moses tried to reconcile this division, but was only partly successful. The good Simeon continues: 'When discord was stirred by violence of the left, the Avenging Spirit was reinforced. There issued from it two demons which immediately became solidified without any moisture, one male and one female. From them were propagated legions of demons, and to this is due the inveteracy of the unclean spirit in all those demons. It is they who are symbolized by the foreskin; the one is called "adder" and the other is called "serpent", the two however being but one.'

"Do we not see, Sophie-Sarah and fellow Jews? The demons are 'without moisture', no soft dew of kindness, no salty tears of love and wisdom, but dry as a desert. And the foreskin, that source of the demonic: Is it only the sensual which is so dark? No, for Rabbi Simeon goes on to speak of King Solomon—and who, Sophie-Sarah, is more sensual than King Solomon, he who sang in the Song of Songs? None. What does Rabbi Simeon say? He says:

" 'King Solomon, when he "penetrated into the depths of the nut garden," took a nut-shell (klifah) and drew an analogy from its layers to these spirits which inspire sensual desires in human beings, as it is written, "and the delights of the sons of men (are from) male and female demons". . . .The Holy One, Blessed be He, found it necessary to create all these things in the world to ensure its permanence, so that there should be, as it were, a brain with many membranes encircling it. The whole world is constructed on this principle, upper and lower from the first mystic point to the further removed of all the stages. They are all coverings one to another, brain within brain and spirit within spirit, so that one is a shell to another!'

"It is a great chain of being," my Rabbi continued with his own thought, "where everything is shell to a previous grade of perfection. And even the demonic is necessary to 'insure permanence!' Can there be a nut without a shell? A brain without a membrane? Is not God a living Being?

"Even as the tree cannot exist without its bark, and the human body must shed its unclean sweat and blood, so does the demonic have its root in the mystery of God.

"More: The sensual is not the demonic, for the very union of God with his Shekhinah is sensual. It is the lower without the upper, the division of flesh and spirit, separation of soul and flesh—that is the evil.

"One thing more, Sophie-Sarah, one thing more, honored dead, and I will leave off my explanations, my quotations from authorities. The one thing more is to understand how it was that evil came into the world. How did evil begin? Evil began because the word *meoroth* (lights) is written defectively in Torah! When God says, Let there be lights in the firmament of the heaven to light upon the earth, 'lights' is defective. Rabbi Jose says: 'The defective spelling indicates the lowest, namely, the moon, which is the cause of the croup in children. It is also the cause of other misfortunes, because it is the smallest of all the luminaries, and sometimes it is obscured and receives no light at all.'

"Thus, dearly beloved, we are told that the 'lack of light' is the source of death, evil, Lilith. Lack of light. Lack of awareness, of consciousness. With this there is one-sided wrath and judgment. With this there is one-sided love. Not enough light. And it was so, in the beginning, on the second day, when discord was created. Listen now to Rabbi Isaac:

" 'On the second day was created Gehinnom for sinners; on the second day, too, was created conflict. On the second day the work begun was not finished, and therefore the words "and it was good" are not used in connection with it. Not 'til the third day was the work of the second finished; hence in the account of that day we find twice the expression "that it was good," once in reference to its own proper work, and once in reference to the second day. On the third day, the deficiency of the second day was made good: discord was removed from it, and mercy was extended to the sinners in Gehinnom, the flames of which were moderated. Hence the second day is embraced in and completed by the third.'

"And those, oh six million, and Sophie-Sarah, those are the reasons for evil in the world."

As my Rabbi completed his explanation and his dissertation upon the reasons for evil in the world, I, Sophie-Sarah, turned to the dead, those six million who had haunted me with the question. I turned to them to see if this wise and profound answer satisfied them. As I looked, I thought I saw a smile. Can you imagine it? I thought I saw smiles upon the faces of those six million innocents who had suffered more, been tormented more, hounded more than any six million in history! But they smiled. They smiled and looked at me as if to ask, Was I satisfied with the answer of the Rabbi? They smiled as if to say that each and every one of them had his own experience of evil, his own explanation of evil, his own struggle with evil. Their struggles with evil, it was implied, was their own struggle with God. And no one can answer this question for anyone else! We can help each other, explain, just as my good Soul Rabbi had done, but each of us is ultimately alone with God, and with the question of evil. Each must ask of God, and answer to God about evil in Man and God. . . .Thus did I understand, in a wordless, unspeakable way, what the honored dead, the tormented six million, were asking of me. And I knew that they were right.

I turned, therefore, to my Rabbi, and wondered if he, too, saw what I saw upon the faces of the six million. I wondered if he, too, was satisfied with his answers, the answers about evil from the Kabbalistic rabbis and from himself. I saw his face and that he, too, smiled. I saw that he, too, understood what I had understood from the dead. I saw that he, like me, could not only not answer for anyone else, that we cannot even answer for ourselves; that our lives are a struggle with God, to both give and get the answer to the problem of evil. Life is the answer.

But not only life, but love. For life without love is a life without union, and division is the evil. So, without further words, my Rabbi and I embraced. We joined hands and hearts and minds. We joined in a spiritual-soul-physical union where two became one. We joined in love and helped in our *Tikkun,* we helped assuage the evil in the world. Two became one, and I became whole.

VI

After my union with the Rabbi of my soul, after my vision of wholeness, I thought: I have answered enough. I have given the answers of the wise ones, of the Kabbalists, of the scholars, of the rabbis, and of God as He has spoken to me, Himself. It is enough, the NAMES, the Gematria of the letters, the Law, the vision of the Evil One, himself. It is enough, it is enough, it is enough. Hound me no more, O Lord! Hound me no more, O Six Million! Thus did I think, in quietness and seclusion. So wise and secluded was I that I did not even withdraw, but lived my daily life as one should. Thankful are we for ritual; thankful are we for the strictures, the lines, and the rules, which protect one from the living face of God.

Thus it was that I knew that I was protected from the Face of the Living God. And thus it was I knew, that I, poor fool, thought I was preaching to the six million! Oh, now I knew in an instant that I was a fool. For it was not I but the Six Million who had seen the Living Face of God. They, dear Lord, have seen Your Face. They, dear Lord, have seen the darkest Face of all, and now they bask in the warmth of Your light Face, the face of Love and Care, like tender balls of cotton which soothe their wounds and rest their bones. The children dance about You and play at the feet of Your throne. And what else, having seen Your darkest face? Man can only flee from Your face to Your face.

And I? I thought I was called to preach, to lecture, and to prophesy. For I am a Medium, am I not? Am I not the Medium, Sophie-Sarah? Am I not the chosen one of God, to speak of His message? Have I not been asked to speak for the Six Million?

I laugh. For He has spoken already to us all, and has shown His face to the Six Million. But not to me. Not to me. Show me Your face, dear Lord. Show me Your face. Speak to me. Break Your silence. Tell me. Tell me. Not in the words I have used; no, not in those. But tell me, and show me. Until I am at rest, and, dear Lord, until You are at rest, too.

This was my prayer over time. It was a silent prayer as I went about my daily life. I said nothing. I went to *shul* and was a woman in *shul* like all others, listening, gossiping, praying. Accepting, from without, that this was a man's religion. But inside, but inside, I knew differently. I knew that it would change. I knew that we women would no longer sit only outside, or enclosed, or removed. For the face of God was going to be seen. And it, dear God, would be a feminine face, too.

So, I waited.

Time went by, and I did not know how to say it, do it, finish it, proclaim it. I had prayed, there was no answer. I had called out, but there was no statement in return. . . . Again I laughed. Was this not the experience of the Six Million? Did they not call out, and pray, and beseech? Not in wonder and need, as I was calling out, but in agony and pain and despair! And did not God abandon them? Did He not turn away from their prayers and beseechings and pains? So it seemed to them, no doubt. So it seemed, until they died. But I saw them, the dead ones, the Six Million who died. They came to me, did they not? They came to me and spoke and demanded and beseeched. And I responded, did I not? Even when the Lord did not? I responded, I was human, and answered, when the Lord did not!

But did He not? Was His silence not an answer? Was His waiting not an answer? Did He not respond with the rise of the Ghetto? Did He not respond with the rise of Israel? Yes? No? Do you say that the Ghetto arose, not God? Do you say that Israel arose and responded and fought, not God? Are you saying that Man responded, not God? Yes?

Well, I agree. For man responded, and that is God's need, and His response. Now that I have seen the Six Million and have responded, now I see that that which has responded in me has been God. From God to God. Now that I have responded, I see that the Six Million are satisfied with me. I see that they have seen the Face of God that I have not. I have seen it from afar, indirect. But this is what they desired of me, the Six Million. They have desired that I tell them of my experience of the Faces of God, not of theirs! They no longer hound me, they no longer beseech me. Whatever I tell them, I must tell them out of my own experience. That is what they demand. For it is from there that they speak. We each have seen the face of God, of God becoming!

And you, dear brothers and sisters, you must speak of the names and laws and letters of God! You must speak out of your experience, for that is God speaking in you. You must let us all know what you have seen, for that is what they want, the Six Million! And that is what God wants! How do I know it? He has told me so! And what, pray tell, has He told you? Perhaps He has told you to listen to me further. Perhaps He has told you to hear my tale. For my tale may be similar to yours. If so, then listen, for the Lord has told me to tell what I see of the Faces of God. He has asked me to tell of His Faces in the ten mystical crowns of the Sephiroth, the ten crowns of the one King, the ten Faces of God which are One Face. He has asked me to tell them in the frame of Kabbalah, in the frame of the continuing and ancient vision of the Jew, but of the Jew enlightened by the thousands of years. For what has happened since the birth of God's son? Kabbalah has happened. Enlightenment has happened. But also Auschwitz has happened. But the ten Names can carry Auschwitz. And the ten crowns can answer the Trinity. They are one answer. For your answer must count, too. So hear, Oh friends. So hear, oh Jew. So hear, oh Gentile. Hear what I have seen of the Face of God. I know that my vision is only one vision; it is incomplete without yours. For your face is also the Face of God.

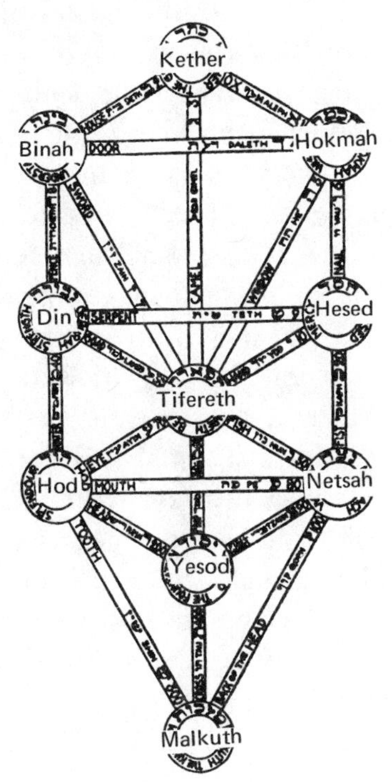

In the beginning is KETHER, the Crown. It is the Supreme Crown, just barely manifest to man, and the link with the En Sof, the hidden God, who is always beyond our grasp. O Lord, I thank thee for coming into Being in Kether; I thank thee for being King, but I thank thee, too, for always being beyond. I thank thee for never being totally manifest, for as great as Being, as great as the living, as great as the fantastic marvellous idea of God becoming totally man, there must be a Becoming, there must be a future, a more. For I have seen the face of my own greediness for more, and that, too, must reflect the Face of the God of the beyond, of that which leads me further. And that is the place beyond the Crown. But Crown, too, I must have. KETHER is the beginning, the most mysterious and recondite, which begins with "In".

Can you, dearly beloved, see that Crown? Can you see its jewel-bedecked quality? Can you see the ten tines? I see them as pointing up and reaching toward the limitless wonder of the hidden En Sof. I see them as pointing down, with the ten faces of the Almighty shared therein, going around the center of Nothingness, and sharing in the One. I see it as the Tree growing upside down from Heaven, the Tree of Kabbalah and of Life, which is eternal; and I see it as the Tree growing from deep in the world, in the earth of Man, and reaching up toward the ever-coming-closer and ever-retreating En Sof, the Tree of Knowledge. So, see the Crown, and pray to the two Trees in One.

But come with me, down the grades from the Tree of Heaven, or up from the Tree of Earth, for, as the Crown points, it is pointing up or down. Come with me, as I say, and see the face of HOKMAH, the Wisdom and primordial idea of God. For that First point is the "beginning", as we have said, when God, the Father, moves out of his reconditeness into creation. O point, O Father, O wisdom of maleness, of the archetypal idea which moves from the eternal into the temporal, which allows itself to suffer the coming into being! It is a suffering, this becoming, but a joy and a wonder and a greatness. This is the wisdom of the Lord.

And move from the Father, across to the Mother, the BINAH of Understanding and intelligence. For the point of the eternal must be understood and received, must it not? Is not Creation the true creation of Heaven and Earth? Is not the Lord both the Creation and the Reception? The Wisdom and the Understanding? The Father and the Mother? So sayeth even the Kabbalists of old. And so say I. So the women will not be excluded, say we! Small, say you, and shame! Small, say I, but true. For now, the Face of God is the face of opposition, of conflict. Even here. For the One has become two. And the two must flow up and be resolved in the one of KETHER, or flow down and find the lower union, the earthy union, the farther union, all the way down to RAHAMIM or TIFERETH, Compassion and Beauty. This do I know, O Lord, this, too, have I experienced. But before, O Lord, before You sink and fall so far, let me speak of Your face of HESED, of love and mercy, and of GEVURAH-DIN, of power and stern judgment. I must speak of these, for now Your faces come closer and we, mankind, can taste You and see You and fear You and feel You.

HESED. A male face. One of mercy, and kindness, of forgiveness. The Christians, they saw that face as one of the Woman, of Mary. And they, too, were right. For one face can be malely kind and femalely kind. But this kindness, this mercy, is that of the One Lord of Passion who has become peaceful and merciful. The One who can even forgive the Evil One. He can, in short, having discovered His own total opposition with Himself, forgive Himself. HESED. A male face. One of love and mercy.

GEVURAH and DIN. A female face. A face of power. The face, dearly beloved, of Nature Herself. The power of it all: the winds, the rains, the earthquakes. God's face. Female. The power of judgment and passion. And, it is a secret—it is Female. For it needs the power of the Male, of HESED, to restrain it. It needs the mercy of the male to soften it, else too hard, too powerful. And HESED? Without Gevurah, He is nothing. Without the passion and the power, His love is hollow and His mercy insipid. That is not our God, O Children of Israel! That is not our God! But beware, O Children of Israel, when Male and Female are separated! Beware! For then there is only power and passion and stern judgment—and there is destruction. Or there are only words and rules and regulations and emptiness—and there is destruction.

The two do battle, and they go up, the Male and Female, to the Mother and Father, and up to the Crown. But also they go down; they go down, go the Brother and Sister of Hesed and Gevurah; they go down and unite in RAHAMIM, the compassion of God. They unite in the RAHAMIM of God, who mediates his own Brother-Sister pair, and reconciles His-Her Self in Compassion. He reconciles in compassion, dearly beloved, where power and kindness are One. But, dearly beloved, He reconciles, too, in TIFERETH, in Beauty. For some, Compassion is all they long for of the Lord. But for us, for you and me, who live to create, to adore and to love, we need TIFERETH, the Beauty of God, to sustain us!

Oh, TIFERETH, You are the beauty of the Universe before which I weep and am dazzled. Oh, Central Column, all poets know that you are at the Center, for without Beauty, there is no Truth. And, without Truth, Beauty has no existence.

Is there more? The Six Faces of God are enough, are they not? Is not Six the number of Creation? Is not the Creation of Beauty in truth and wisdom enough? What more could the Lord want? What more could we want?

More faces. The Lord goes on, both higher and lower. For there are new opposites, are there not? Out of the grandeur of Beauty, we rise and fall to NETSAH and HOD. NETSAH, victory and lasting endurance. A maleness. And HOD, God's majesty, a femaleness. Are not these opposites, too? Have we not felt the maleness of enduring forever, of staying with the conflict of opposites, of enduring the battles and the wars and the absence of an answer from God? Is this not a maleness? Yes. . . .and no. For now, the victory and endurance and battle are both more abstract and more concrete. When we adore, when we love and bask in the Glory of God, His-Her majesty of HOD, is that Male? Or Female? Yes.

But, more than both, more than the conflict of NETSAH and HOD, of enduring battle and the power of holding on the one side, and the adoration and surrender on the other—more, as I say, than these in God, are the wonder and intense pleasure of their resolution, in YESOD. What is YESOD? YESOD, the "foundation", the basis of all the active forces in God: all the forces of God have descended from the first through the eighth face, and now are united in the ninth, the basis and foundation. Do you know who this is? This is none other than the Zaddik, the righteous one, who is the Foundation of the World. For Noah was one, and Moses was one. And David and Solomon. There have been many and many a Zaddik. Many and many. And there will be many and many a more. For now, dearly beloved, even Sophie-Sarah will be a Zaddik! And how do I know? The Lord has told me so! And you, too, dear friend, you, too, will be a Zaddik, for the Lord wants it. He wants us all to be the foundation, the righteous one, the basis of His forces and faces. For your face is the Face of God. Have I not told you? Yes. And you must listen. For then, too, I will listen to you. YESOD, foundation, Zaddik, righteous one: where God becomes human, and incarnates Himself in the world. The ninth place, the place of the Enlightened one, the Righteous of God. And know, all, that this, too, is a He-She place, for all!

And yet, and yet more. Is there still more? Yes, dearly beloved, there is more. There is the tenth. What is the tenth? It is MALKUTH, the Kingdom of God itself. For what is the King, in His totality, in His eight faces, or even in His nine faces which show in the One, or in the One person, if He does not have a community, a Kingship? What is it, this lack of community? It is a narrowness and a lovelessness. And what has the Kingdom, the community, included heretofore? Why, the *Keneseth Israel,* of course. The Chosen People. The community of the Chosen. And this, dear brothers and sisters, will continue. But the Lord has told me that His Community is the World. The Lord has told me, even, that there are Worlds beyond Worlds, but that His incarnation in us all, will lead to the KINGDOM OF GOD UPON EARTH. The world will be made up of Zaddikim, dearly beloved, of male and female Zaddikim! It will be a world of the Heavenly Jerusalem come to Earth. And that is the Shekhinah: when the Lord will be totally united with his Kingdom, in us as individuals and as a world. It is coming, dearly beloved. It is coming. The King will have His crown, facing up and down. The King will have his Kingship, facing up and down. And this is the work of us all: to become Zaddikim in the service of the Lord, and the coming of His Kingship. It has happened, it is happening, it will happen.

Thus is the Tree of the Lord! And thus is the picture of man, of Adam Kadmon, the primordial man and the future man. For we are all he, are we not?

And that is why I am here, my nine friends. For I knew it when I spoke of the faces. I knew that I would be both myself as a Zaddik and included in a Minyan of ten. And I know that we ten are symbolic of the Minyan of the World. I know that this tree we look at together, the Tree of Life, and the Tree of Knowledge in One, is what all Mankind will see one day, whether it takes two incarnations or hundreds! We know it, we ten. My friends, my brothers and sisters, I embrace you. We know it. That is our message. Let us tell it to the world.

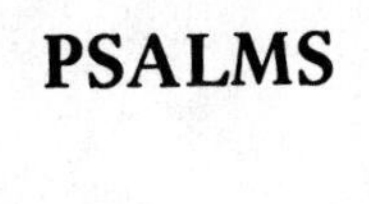

PSALMS

PSALM # 1
(of JMS)

Book of JMS

Book of Jehovah's Mess
Book of Jahveh's MS

Book of God?
Book of Man?
Book of God's Man.

What is God's Man?
He possessed by God?
He hounded by God?
Yes.

What is Man's God?
He the Tyrant?
He the Lover?
He the King?
Yes.

Come, King.
Come, Lover.
Come, Tyrant.
Come, Hounder.
Come, God.
Come!

PSALM # 2
(of JMS)

Oh, God!
I can say nothing without You.
I can write nothing without You
You force me to write and to speak.
And to remain silent.
You.
Why?

I want you:
My son. My daughter
My friend. My enemy.
My partner.
You I want. Like a God.
Like Me.
Like.

O, Lord. I weep. Your wanting me crumbles me.
I am little. I am tiny. I am small.
You raise me up. You drop me down.
Don't you know my soul is strained?
Don't you know my body aches?
Don't you know my spirit wilts?
Don't you know?
Don't you?

I know.
I.

PSALM # 3
(of Julia)

I sing my song unto the Lord, the Lord of Hosts.
For He is the Lord who fights Israel's battles.
He fights not in despair and desperation
As did the pathetic Jews of my Poland
As did the heroic Jews of my Warsaw
He fights in thunder and glory and delight.
He fights in victory.
He fights when few fall. He fights in six days.
For in six days did He create the world.
The War is of a creation, not a destruction.

I sing my song unto the Lord, the Lord of Sorrows.
He is not the Christian God, this Lord of Sorrows.
He sorrows not for Christian nor Jew, but for Mankind.
As did my father, the Atheist Communist.
As did my grandfather, the Orthodox Jew
He sorrows in pain and agony and beating of His chest.
He sorrows in tears.
He sorrows when no one else sorrows. He sorrows for eternity.
For on the second day did He create division
The division is the sorrow, not the destruction.

I sing my song unto the Lord, the Lord of Love.
He is not the pagan God, this Lord of Love.
His is not the love of Eros, nor Aphrodite, but of Mankind.
As was that of Moses
As was that of Isaiah
He loves in passion and justice and joy.
He loves in warmth.

He loves when all have ceased loving. He loves forever.
For love was before even God created.
Until He created, He did not know that He loved.

I sing my song unto the Lord, the Lord of Praise.
For He is the Lord whom I praise in thanksgiving.
I thank Him for His love and His devotion

As did my father
As did my grandfather
Him I thank for I am alive.
Him I praise.
Him I praise when I can no other. Him I praise when He can not.
For in His creation, He is praised.
The Creation goes on, not the destruction.

PSALM # 4
(of Julia)

Lord, You surprise me.
Has anyone told You that before?
I don't think so.

You are adored, damned, proclaimed, reviled
You are loved, begged, given, serviled.
But has anyone said, "You surprise me?"

Oh, Lord, my beloved!
You surprise me, astonish me!
This I give you.

Has anyone else?

PSALM # 5
(of Sophie-Sarah)

Lord. Lord.
These are Christian words: Lord, Lord.
Too refined, not passionate.
Too smooth.

Adonai has a shriek in it.
It has the bitterness of Jew woman.
It has the retching cry of Jew man.
It has command.

We Jews do not say, respectfully, "Lord."
We shriek, "Adonai!"
We complain:
"Things should be better."

I retch too.
I cry.
With bitter Jew gall.
With Jew tears.

Not just for the Six Million.
Not for something so large, horrendous
Not for something so impossible as that.
No. Just for a loving Jew family.

A Holy Jew Family.
Imagine!
Is not God a Jew Boy?
Should He not take care of His family?

But say You, "There has already been one, or two.
A trinity of Joseph, Mary, Jesus.
A Trinity of Father, Son, Holy Spirit.
But you Jews have rejected it."

Maybe so.
Maybe that is why there is bitterness.
Maybe that is why there is little love.
Maybe that is why there is gall.

But the Christians are no better.
They have their Christ, yet look to us!
They, too, have gall and tears.
They, too, await the Coming.

What, then, oh God?
How long, oh Lord?
Adonai! Adonai! Adonai!
Adonai?

PSALM # 6
(of the Knight)

Lord, You are peculiar.
When I think that at last I have grasped You—
Not, mind You, to possess You, but to understand You;
When I think, as I say, that I have grasped You—
You elude me.

Yes, I know.
Everyone has told You that.
Yes, I know.

But Lord, You are peculiar.
Even when You say, "Everyone has told Me that."
You are like a fickle and demanding girl,
Wanting to be told, in a very special way:
I love You.

You want to be grasped, perhaps,
With the heart, not the head.
You want to be grasped as One.

Fickle girl that You are
Demanding girl that You are
You want to be loved-known as You:
Peculiarly,
Uniquely.

You are right, oh Lord!
You are right, great Lord of my being!
You are peculiar, unique, One of a kind.

I must love-know You as You
For that, dear Lord,
Is how You grasp me.

PSALM # 7
(of Maria)

Could God be Mother-Daughter?
No? Why not?
Too female?
Not awesome?
Well, then, you are prejudiced,
Are you not?

Can you think of God as Mother?
As gentle one to soothe your pain?
As passioned one to hear your cries?
Rejoice in your success?
Adore you as Her child?
For Her sake, as well as yours?

Can you think of God as Daughter?
As girl who needs your soothing?
As child crying on your chest?
Shining in your eyes?
Adoring looks from you?
For your sake, as well as Hers?

Well, She is, you know.
She is Mother-Daughter.
She does hear and soothe, rejoice and adore.

She does cry and shine, needs to be loved.
How do I know?
She has told me so!

"Not enough" you say,
She has not told you.
All right. But think.
Think of the Book—Old and New.
Think of the Author.

Does She not want to be adored?
And loved?
And placated?
And to love you?
Think. Is it not so?
God-woman?

PSALM # 8
(of the Knight)

Lord, I am Your Knight.
A fool am I, and dull.
People see it.

Lord, I am Your Knight.
Pedantic am I, and heavy.
People suffer it.

Lord, I am Your Knight.
Moralist am I, and righteous.
People hate it.

But Lord, I am Your man!
Why did You make me thus?
Why do You want it?

Lord, I am Your man!
Why do You not support it?
Lord? Lord?

PSALM # 9
(of the Knight)

Oh God of my Fathers, Hear me!
I command it!

For You have summoned me
And demanded of me
And twisted me.

You have shown Yourself to me:
Humpty-Dumpty on a wall
I have heard and seen it.

Now I must taste it.
Now I must know it so deeply
That all the other fools who despise me, hate me, revile me
Will fall over.

Yes, fall over.
Just as I have.
And You have.

PSALM # 10
(of the Knight)

Lord, I have seen you
In Your complexity.

I have seen Your Trinity
And Quaternity
As well as Your Duplicity
And Six-Foldedness.

But Your love?
Have I seen it?
I don't know.

Creation, struggle, horror, care,
All these.
But love?

PSALM # 11
(of the Arab)

Arab am I. In the dark.
And the darkness is of my lust.
But Esau lusted, Lord,
And You loved him.

Arab am I, Oh Lord.
Son of Allah.
But pagan is my soul.
Do You love me?

Arab am I. In the moon.
Loving am I.
I know it.
Do You know it?

PSALM # 12
(of the Arab)

Crescent moon and silver star.
These are the signs of love.
Curving gracefully,
Shining quietly.

The muezzin sings.
Is he a moon?
Or a star?
No, he calls to them.

Sing, oh tenor
Moan, oh muezzin
Cry, hyena
Silence, goat.

For Allah loves.

PSALM # 13
(of the Arab)

Esau and Ishmael.
Why did their fathers love them so?
Because wild and hairy?
Because intense and mad?

Maybe they knew, these fathers.
For they were chosen by God,
And rejected by God
And loved by God.

Maybe they knew, these fathers
That the unchosen sons are chosen.
That the hairy and the wild and the mad
Are of God.

For I know it.
Allah told me.

PSALM # 14
(of the Ronin)

I need no psalm
To adore.
It does. Doesn't it?

Buddha laughs. He cries.
He waits. He sits.
A round one. A belly one.

Breathe.

PSALM # 15
(of the Ronin)

Ha!

PSALM # 16
(of the African)

I have known bitterness, Oh Lord.
As lately as an hour ago.

Bitterness, said the ancients, the wise ones—
Bitterness is lack of wisdom.

Bitterness, say they, is the taste of copper
Bitterness is the dross of metal.

Taste of copper, dross of metal,
Unredeemed man, all the same.

But I have known bitterness, oh Lord,
And the ancients are wrong.

Bitterness is disappointment and rage.
Bitterness is wrath and wrung hearts.

Bitterness is absence of love.
Bitterness is pain and unshed tears.

Bitterness, oh Lord, is lack of You.

PSALM # 17
(of the African)

Anger, Anger; you sit like a tornado
Hovering over a bleak Kansas landscape.
You wait, spinning on yourself,
Ready to devastate.

Is it desert you blow away?
Or man's hearth?
Crops?
Or dust?

No matter, you sweep as you will.
You go where you want,
When you want.
Atom bomb? Nothing!
Missile? Nothing!
You devastate.

It is me you devastate.
Do you know that?
Anger of God, you wipe me out!
From within.
Please stop it!
Please.

PSALM # 18
(of the African)

Oh Lord, I know wrath.
I know my rages and furies.
Touchy am I, and passionate.
But my passion turns to flash fire.

Suddenly, unexpectedly,
I am attacked. I scream.
No one knows why.
But I know.

And You know.
You are there.
You, or Your Devil Son.
You are the same. We know.

Measured with Your wrath,
My rage is as marbles,
My anger a game.

Yours is the destruction of Nature.
You know.
I know.

Yours is the destruction in me,
Oh Lord.
We know.

Help me. . .
To stop You. . .
In me.

PSALM # 19
(of Maria)

Lord, Come to me.
Make me Your bride.
As you did Maria,
My namesake.

Lord, I love You.
Do You know it?
Has Your spouse told You?
If not, hear me.

Maria has heard me.
She has listened.
Will You listen?
God of the fathers,
Of the sons,
Of the holy spirit?

PSALM # 20
(of Sybilla)

God is a raging fire.
No warm quilt, He.

God is a burning thirst.
No mild dryness, He.

God is.

God is a hawk-eyed vulture.
No dove is He.

God is a vicious beast.
No lamb is He.

God is.

But God is a lamb, a dove
And a hawk-beast, too.

God is a dryness and a quilt,
And a burning-fire-thirst.

For God is love
And love is these.

PSALM # 21
(of Julia)

Lord, You do not exist.
Has not the world told You so?
You are dead, they say.
And I believe them.

For I am an atheist-communist, after all.
And a scientific psychologist.
I have to acknowledge that.
But I have to believe in something.

Maybe atheist-communists don't exist.
Nor scientific psychologists.
They are dead, I say.
And I believe that, too.

Lord, You live.
I know it.
For I am atheist for You, communist for You
Scientist and Psychologist for You.

You live, God, in me!
I live, God, in You!
We live, Lord,
Believe it!

PSALM # 22
(of Maya)

Lord, I feel in You, my belly.
I hear in You, my heart.

Hunger flowing,
Desire dangling.

Me in You?
Or You in me?

Kundalini turning,
Kundalini twisting.

Lord, the earth turns beneath me
The visions outreach me.

Reality everyday
Stars of forever.

Above greater than below?
Earth more real than heaven?

Kundalini rising,
Kundalini falling.

Lord, in six centers are You,
Sahasrara, too.

Awareness waxing
Consciousness waning.

Kundalini growing,
Kundalini shrinking.

Lord, You are the Kundalini
Shiva-Shakti of desire.

Lord, You are the Kundalini
Purple-Snake of life.

To You I bow in homage
To You I bow in love.

Come Shiva, Come Shakti
Live in me, I live in Thee.

PSALM # 23
(of the Old Chinese Man)

Fathers and sons: a painful phrase.
And painful because apart.
Sorrow in separation.

I miss my sons, far away.
Communist, priest, wily trader;
All far away.

Must it be so?
Do sons go and daughters stay?
Must it be?

So good the daughters, loyal
So warm their love
So sweet the care.

But sons, but sons.
One is Chinese after all.
And sons are like oneself.

Rebel and loyal
Foolish and shrewd
Loving and vengeful

Sons.
God has his beginning there:
"Arousal," creative.

And ending:
"Be still, the mountain"
Withdraw. Dream.

And God has His middle, too:
"Melancholy," "Abysmal"
Dark and piggish.

And so,
In missing sons,
I miss my God.

Come sons, and come God.
Renew me.
Warm me.

Let me be as wife and daughter
To receive Thee.
Unite with me.

But no.
I am a father, after all. . .
And a son. . .

Come Sons, Come God
Father calls.
I command.

Come Father, Come God
Son cries.
I plead.

Arrogance gone
Tao moves
Flower grows.

PSALM # 24
(of JMS)

I have known You, GOD, I have known You.
As JOSEPH knew dreams, as MOSES knew the fire.
And I have felt You, Lord, in my body-soul have I felt You.
In the whole of my life, Lord, in the whole of my life.
Let me tell you how I have known-felt You, Lord,
Let me tell You have I have felt-known You.

I have known Your complexity, Lord, just as the Knight did.
And I have known Your love.
Like the Arab, Lord, like the Arab,
And like Sybilla gripped by passion.
Like the Chinese seeing Your power, Lord,
And the Ronin learning God IS.

I have known, God, like Julia knew paradox,
As wisdom and mind and beyond.
I have been Your alchemist, Lord,
As the African, and as Maria saw Your Goddess.
I have known totality with Maya, Lord,
With Sophie-Sarah seen Your darkness.

Lord, I have known You. . .
And You have known me.
As Knight, Arab, Maria, Lord,
Have You known me, all them.
You have known me, tormented me, loved me,
As ten thousand more.

Oh, God of my spirit, soul and flesh
You are all and everything, as they say.
You are even nothing, as they also say.
But You are me, and me You.
That they do not say.
I am Your MIRROR, MAN.

Where You leave off, God, I begin.
Two peas in a pod are we.
Lord, You are love, they say, and they are right.
But You are WHOLENESS, Lord, without me, nought.
Grow, my Brother, love, my sister
Rule, my father, live, my mother

Accept me, my child, as I accept Thee.